ALFRED BENZON SYMPOSIUM III

Ion Homeostasis
of the Brain

ION HOMEOSTASIS
OF THE BRAIN

The regulation of hydrogen and potassium ion concentrations
in cerebral intra- and extracellular fluids

Proceedings of the Alfred Benzon Symposium III
Copenhagen & Lund, 20-23 May 1970
held at the premises of the Royal Danish Academy
of Sciences and Letters and at
the University Hospital of Lund, Sweden

EDITED BY

B. K. SIESJÖ
S. C. SØRENSEN

Published by

MUNKSGAARD, Copenhagen

In North and South America:
ACADEMIC PRESS, New York

SCANDINAVIAN UNIVERSITY BOOKS

DENMARK MUNKSGAARD *Copenhagen*
NORWAY UNIVERSITETSFORLAGET *Oslo, Bergen, Tromsø*
SWEDEN LÄROMEDELSFÖRLAGEN *Stockholm, Gothenburg, Lund*

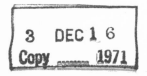

Published simultaneously in the U.S.A. by Academic Press Inc.

Printed in Denmark by Andelsbogtrykkeriet, Odense
ISBN 87 16 00 280 6

CONTENTS

Welcome by the Foundation

The Alfred Benzon Foundation was founded in 1952 by Dr. Bøje Benzon in commemoration of his father, who was an outstanding pharmacist in Copenhagen.

The aim of the Foundation is to support the medical, the pharmaceutical, and the basic biological sciences. The trustees of the Foundation have tried to fulfil this aim in various ways, but have in recent years concentrated on two major activities.

First, an annual lecture was instituted. At the lecture the speaker receives the Alfred Benzon Prize in recognition of his contributions to science. Until now, five distinguished scientists from other countries have graciously accepted our invitation and have been our honoured guests.

Secondly, it was decided to support a series of symposia on topics of current interest, chiefly within the basic biological sciences underlying the disciplines of medicine and pharmacy. The first symposium (in 1968) dealt with "The Role of Nucleotides for the Function and Conformation of Enzymes". The second symposium, which was held in 1969, carried the title "Capillary Permeability. The Transfer of Molecules and Ions between Capillary Blood and Tissue".

The present symposium on the regulation of hydrogen and potassium ion concentrations in cerebral intra- and extracellular fluids was suggested to us by Dr. B. K. Siesjö and Dr. S. C. Sørensen. We in the Foundation are indebted to these scientists for their initiative as well as for their enthusiastic collaboration in planning the Symposium.

Because of the anatomical complexity of the system, the problem of ion homeostasis in the brain is a very difficult one. Major steps towards a better understanding of the underlying mechanisms have, however, been made in recent years and have evolved parallel with an increasing knowledge of active and passive transport of ions in other, structurally less complicated, biological systems. The problems of cerebral potassium and hydrogen ion homeostasis have also attracted growing interest among clinicians, since they appear to be of great importance to practical medicine. To the trustees of the Foundation the selected topic, therefore, appeared very promising. Considering the aim of the Foundation, we found it most rewarding that Dr. Siesjö and Dr. Sørensen planned the Symposium in such a way that an interdisciplinary exchange between physiological research and clinical observation was possible.

It is a great pleasure to see that so many of the invited guests have been able to come and I wish you all a hearty welcome to the Symposium. We are very grateful to you for coming, and we do hope that the organization of the meeting is sufficiently efficient to repay in part our great debt of gratitude to all participants.

The Symposium starts in Copenhagen, Denmark, and proceeds to Lund, Sweden, on the other side of the narrow strait called the Øresund.

The Foundation hails this opportunity to support Nordic collaboration and extends its sincere thanks to the president of the Royal Danish Academy of Sciences and Letters and to the Rector of the University of Lund for giving us access to the distinguished premises of their respective institutions.

Jørn Hess Thaysen.

The Relations of Blood, Brain and Cerebrospinal Fluid

Hugh Davson & Keasley Welch

INTRODUCTION

The modern view of relations between blood, on the one hand, and brain and cerebrospinal fluid, on the other, may be illustrated by Fig. 1. According to this, the cerebrospinal fluid and brain extracellular space may be regarded as two compartments in parallel, supplied by separate sources of blood, namely that in the choroid plexuses and the direct blood supply to the tissue, largely derived from branches of the large pial arteries. This "parallel" relationship between the cerebrospinal fluid and extracellular fluid is in marked contrast to the "series" connexion suggested by Goldmann, v. Monakow and, most forcibly, by Stern & Gautier (1921–1923). According to the series relationship, communication between blood and brain took place through the cerebrospinal fluid as an intermediate. The theory of Stern & Gautier, although no longer entertained, is worth retaining in the record of the development of our views on the nature of the blood-brain barrier, since the theory was the result of a number of semi-quantitative studies on the system which were the first of their kind, the great bulk of the work in this field being, before this, little more than a study of intravital staining. In addition to providing semiquantitative results on the passage of a number of well-defined solutes from blood to the cerebrospinal fluid and brain, the work of Stern & Gautier was of great value in its emphasis on the relations between cerebrospinal fluid and brain. On the basis of their theory, exchanges between brain and cerebrospinal fluid were unrestricted, and the theory only failed because it ascribed an exclusive role to these exchanges, as opposed to the more limited role envisaged by the modern theory as illustrated by Fig. 1.

University College, Gower Street, London W. C. 1, England.

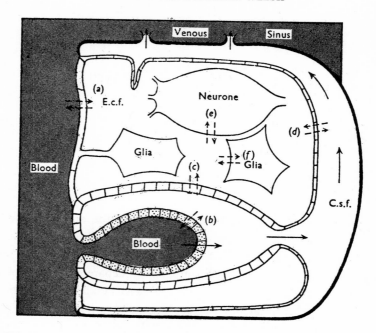

Fig. 1. Schema, illustrating relations between the various compartments of the brain. (Davson & Bradbury. *Symposia of the Society of Experimental Biology.*)

An important step forward in the quantitative description of the relation between the three compartments was made by Wallace & Brodie (1939, 1940); these authors injected Br⁻, I⁻, and CNS⁻ into the blood and estimated their concentrations in both cerebral tissue and cerebrospinal fluid after different periods, comparing these values with the concentrations of Cl⁻ in the same samples. If the Br⁻, for example, came into rapid equilibrium with the tissue fluid of the brain, we should expect to find the ratio of Cl⁻ to Br⁻ the same in both plasma and tissue after a short period; if, on the other hand, diffusion equilibrium were slow of achievement, the ratio Cl⁻/Br⁻ would be higher in the tissue than in the plasma. Studies of these ratios showed that they were invariably greater than unity even after many hours; i. e., they showed that Br⁻ penetrated slowly into the tissue spaces. The striking finding, however, was that the ratio in the tissue was always the same as that in the cerebrospinal fluid, and this seemed to indicate, as Stern & Gautier had suggested, that the cerebrospinal fluid was acting as an intermediary for the supply of the anions to the brain. Their later study, on the other hand, led them to reverse this relationship, and they suggested that the brain might well be the source of the material reaching the cerebrospinal fluid, i.e., the brain might be forming the cerebrospinal fluid, at least in part.

KINETIC STUDIES

The work of Wallace & Brodie, who studied both blood-brain and blood-c.s.f. barriers, was extended by Rudolph & Olsen (1956) and Olsen & Rudolph (1955) to Na^+ and Br^-, and to a number of other solutes by Davson (1955). It was shown that with ^{24}Na the kinetics of uptake by cerebrospinal fluid and extracellular fluid of brain were remarkably similar, as illustrated by Fig. 2, where the curve represents the uptake by c.s.f. and the plotted points refer to brain. This congruence was interpreted as the result of separate transport across the blood-c.s.f. barrier in the choroid plexuses and across the blood-brain barrier, presumably the capillaries of the central nervous parenchyma. Studies with more lipid-soluble solutes, such as thioureas and ethyl alcohol, revealed that equilibration of the brain could occur much more rapidly than equilibration between blood and cerebrospinal fluid, as illustrated by Fig. 3, and the approximate equality of the rate of equilibration in the case of ^{24}Na revealed by Fig. 2, was therefore regarded as a special case. It was emphasized that the rate of equilibration of a lipid-soluble substance with the cerebrospinal fluid would be helped by exchanges between brain and cerebrospinal fluid since, as Fig. 3 shows for ethyl thiourea, exchanges between brain and cerebrospinal fluid will favour net flux into the cerebrospinal fluid (Davson 1956). The virtual absence of net exchanges of ^{24}Na between the brain and cerebrospinal fluid, deducible from the similar rates of equilibration with plasma, suggested that the rate of formation of cerebrospinal fluid might be measurable by the rate of turnover of ^{24}Na in the cerebrospinal fluid; thus it was argued that ^{24}Na would enter the cerebrospinal fluid in the freshly secreted fluid at approximately the concentration in that of a dialysate of plasma; in the absence of net gains from the brain, the rate of equilibration would then be given by rate of formation of the fluid. The turnover constant for ^{24}Na, deduced from Fig. 2, was 0.0041 min^{-1} and would correspond to a replacement of 0.41 per cent of the volume per minute. The rabbit's cerebrospinal fluid has an average volume of 2.5 ml, so that this would correspond with a rate of secretion of 10.2 $\mu l/min$. This is sufficiently close to the measured rate, namely

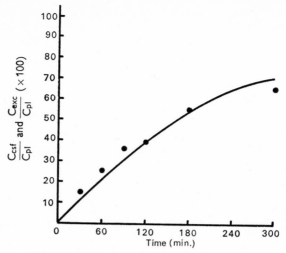

Fig. 2. Penetration of ^{24}Na into cerebrospinal fluid (curve) and brain extra-cellular fluid (points) when a constant concentration (C_{pl}) of the isotope was maintained in the plasma. The "chloride-space" was used as a measure of extracellular space. Ordinate: Concentration in C.S.F. (C_{csf}) or extracellular fluid (C_{exc}). Abscissa: Time in min after establishing plasma concentration. (Davson. *J. Physiol.*)

10.1 μl/min (Bradbury & Davson 1964) to suggest that the main influx of sodium into the cerebrospinal fluid is by way of the primary secretion of the choroid plexuses. More recent studies of Pollay & Curl (1967) suggest that there is some net influx of secretion, and therefore of sodium, from the brain into the cerebrospinal fluid; if this is correct, the rate of secretion by the choroid plexuses is correspondingly less.

BLOOD-BRAIN BARRIER

The main question as to the nature of the exchanges between cerebrospinal fluid and brain tissue was investigated from the earliest times; thus the true basis for the concept of a blood-brain barrier rests not only on the demonstration that trypan blue fails to stain the brain when given intravenously, but also on the demonstration that it *does* stain the brain when injected into the cerebrospinal fluid. Thus it has been argued that failure to stain the brain after intravenous injection is simply due to the fact that there is no extracellular space in brain into which this molecule can diffuse, so that

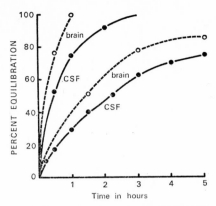

Fig. 3. Penetration of ethyl thiourea (upper curves) and thiourea (lower curves) in brain-water and cerebrospinal fluid. (Davson, Kleeman & Levin. *Drugs and Membranes.*)

the existence of blood-brain barrier has been called into question (see e.g. Davson & Spaziani 1959, and Davson, Kleeman & Levin 1963 for a refutation of this suggestion). The demonstration that the brain can take up trypan blue when presented by way of the cerebrospinal fluid, but cannot take it up when presented by way of the blood, is unequivocal evidence for a restraint on the passage of trypan blue from blood to extracellular fluid of the brain, i.e., for the concept of the blood-brain barrier. Stern & Gautier's studies showed that passage of various solutes, such as iodide, thiocyanate, ferricyanide, and so on, was easy from cerebrospinal fluid to brain, but very restricted from blood to brain. The quantitative studies of Bakay (1960) on ^{24}Na and those on a large group of solutes by Davson (1955 b) indicated that exchanges between cerebrospinal fluid and brain were, indeed, relatively unrestricted compared with those of the same substances between blood and brain, and this suggestion was given quantitative verification by the now classical study of Rall, Oppelt & Patlak (1962), who measured the diffusion of inulin from the perfused ventricles of the dog into the adjacent nervous tissue. The kinetics of the process indicated that there was no measurable barrier to diffusion between the two compartments, and the ultrastructural basis for this conclusion was provided by the electron-microscopical studies of Brightman (1965), who injected ferritin into the ventricles of rats and examined the brains from 10 to 200 minutes later; the particles escaped into the brain along an intercellular route by moving through the spaces between ependymal cells. The junctions between ependymal cells were consistent with this observation; thus at the apical ends of the cells the usual junction was a fascia adhaerens rather than a zonula adhaerens, so that complete occlusion of the spaces between ependymal cells is excluded by these observations.

COMPOSITION OF CEREBROSPINAL AND BRAIN EXTRACELLULAR FLUIDS

Wallace & Brodie's studies on the rates of exchange of bromide and other anions resulted in the suggestion that the extracellular fluid of the brain was comparable in composition with that of the cerebrospinal fluid, so that the cerebrospinal fluid could be considered as a representative sample of the medium surrounding the central neurones. The composition of the cerebrospinal fluid is different from that of the blood plasma or of a filtrate of blood plasma, so that if this suggestion is correct, we must conclude that the central neurones are surrounded by a medium that is different from the medium surrounding other cells, e.g. those of skeletal muscle, since it is reasonably well established that the extracellular fluid surrounding these is similar to a dialysate of blood plasma. If this suggestion is correct, then we must conclude that the composition of the extracellular fluid of the brain is controlled by active transport processes, or, if not, that it is the cerebrospinal fluid that controls its composition. Thus the cerebrospinal fluid could be secreted with its characteristic composition, with low K^+, high Mg^{++}, high Cl^-, low HCO_3^-, low glucose, and so on, and by virtue of the rapidity with which exchanges occurred between the cerebrospinal fluid and the central nervous parenchyma, the cerebrospinal fluid could impose its own composition on that of the extracellular fluid of the parenchyma. It was suggested that, on this basis, the composition of the cerebrospinal fluid should change as it passed from the ventricles, where it was first secreted, to the subarachnoid spaces, where it was finally drained away (Davson 1958). An examination of the composition of the fluid drawn from different regions failed to indicate any serious changes in composition; in fact, the constancy of the composition was remarkable (Davson 1958) so that it was concluded that the extracellular fluid of brain was, indeed, controlled by active processes, separate from those controlling the composition of the cerebrospinal fluid.

Additional support for this concept was provided by examination of the concentrations of a variety of constituents of the cerebrospinal fluid drawn as near simultaneously as possible from the various regions of the dog's cerebrospinal system, in particular the cortical subarachnoid fluid, which was chosen as one that was more likely to indicate the composition of the

Table 1. *Mean concentration of K^+ (mequiv/kg H_2O) in plasma and cerebrospinal fluids of dogs and cats. Numbers in parentheses indicate numbers of animals from which a given fluid was taken (Bito & Davson 1966)*

Plasma$_1$	Plasma$_2$	Plasma$_3$	Cist Mag	Cort Subarach	Ventr	Lumbar
4.56 ± 0.12	4.57 ± 0.14	3.97 ± 0.12	2.98 ± 0.06	2.65 ± 0.10	2.93 ± 0.08	3.22 ± 0.08
(16)	(16)	(12)	(15)	(8)	(15)	(8)

Cort Subarach/Cist Mag	0.86 ± 0.02	$P < 0.001$
Ventr/Cist Mag	0.98 ± 0.01	$P > 0.1$
Lumbar/Cist Mag	1.06 ± 0.01	$P < 0.001$

Plasma$_1$ is from blood withdrawn before anaesthesia; Plasma$_2$ from blood withdrawn immediately after anaesthesia, and Plasma$_3$ from blood withdrawn after all cerebrospinal fluid had been taken. P is the probability that the observed ratio would occur by chance.

extracellular fluid of the brain parenchyma than the lumbar fluid, since the latter, especially in the immobilized animal, is probably very stagnant and may well reflect changes due to the partial breakdown of the blood-cord barrier. In general, the results indicated a remarkable uniformity in composition, so far as Na^+, Ca^{++}, Cl^-, HCO_3^- and glucose were concerned, but the changes in concentration of K^+ that took place after the fluid had left the ventricle were quantitatively significant and of considerable interest. The results are shown in Table 1. The cortical subarachnoid fluid has a lower concentration of K^+ than the ventricular fluid, so that on its way through the cranial subarachnoid space the fluid has become less like a dialysate of plasma in that its concentration, already well below that of a plasma dialysate, has become even lower. Clearly, in this case, the extracellular fluid of brain not only has a considerably lower concentration of K^+ than that in plasma or its dialysate, but also less than that of cerebrospinal fluid. It cannot possibly be argued that the cerebrospinal fluid is imposing its composition on that of the extracellular fluid of brain; if one fluid imposes its composition on that of the other, then it must be the brain extracellular fluid imposing its composition on that of the cerebrospinal fluid. In fact, studies on the composition of the freshly secreted fluid, collected under oil from the exposed choroid plexus, indicate that the cerebrospinal fluid, as freshly secreted, has its characteristic composition (Rougemont *et al*. 1960, Ames *et al*. 1964, Sadler & Welch 1967) which may be modified by exchanges with the extracellular fluid of brain. Thus both fluids must be regarded as specific secretions, the one by the choroidal epithelial cells and the other either by the cerebral blood capillary endothelial cells or by their associated astroglia.

EXTRACELLULAR SPACE

Once the relation between brain extracellular and cerebrospinal fluids is recognized as one of mutual exchange, then a variety of phenomena become intelligible. Thus the very limited values of the sucrose-, sulphate-, and inulin-spaces of brain, by comparison with the expected value of the extra-cellular space of brain, led to the claim that there was no appreciable extracellular space in this tissue, a view that was apparently supported by the electronmicroscopy of the tissue (Horstmann & Meves 1959; see, how-ever, Van Harreveld, Crowell & Malhotra 1965). In fact, the low volumes of distribution of these extracellular markers can be attributed rather to the sink-action of the cerebrospinal fluid which, because it flows continuously over the brain-tissue, will remove slowly permeating molecules from the tissue and return them to the blood. Thus, when the cerebrospinal system was perfused with an artificial cerebrospinal fluid containing, say, ^{14}C-labelled inulin or sucrose, the measured volume of distribution was high, indicative of an extracellular space of 10–15 per cent (Davson, Kleeman & Levin 1961, Rall, Oppelt & Patlak 1962, Reed & Woodbury 1963), contrasting with a volume of distribution of only 2–4 per cent when the marker was presented intravenously (Davson & Spaziani 1959, Reed & Woodbury 1963). Because of the blood-cerebrospinal fluid barrier, the concentration of the extracellular markers in the cerebrospinal fluid is very much less than that in plasma and, in fact, it is much less than in the extracellular fluid of brain, so that the low volume of distribution of, say, ^{14}C-sucrose in brain really represents a steady-state determined by diffusion from blood into the extracellular fluid across the blood-brain barrier, together with escape into the cerebrospinal fluid, which acts as a sink

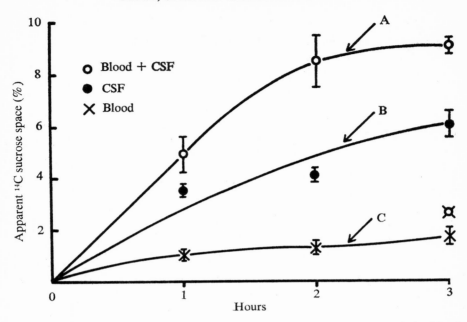

Fig. 4. Volumes of distribution of ¹⁴C-sucrose as it is presented by way of the blood (C), cerebrospinal fluid (B) or by both routes (A). (Oldendorf & Davson. *Arch. Neurol.*)

because of the low concentration in the freshly secreted fluid. Thus, as pointed out originally by Bito, Bradbury & Davson (1966), the correct way to determine the true volume of distribution of a slowly penetrating solute in the brain is to perfuse simultaneously through the ventricles and the blood; presentation of the solute through the blood alone would give an erroneously low value for the volume of distribution, due to the sink-action of the cerebrospinal fluid, whilst presentation through the cerebrospinal fluid would give a nearer approximation, by virtue of the rapidity with which exchanges occur between the two compartments, but it would still be too low because of the sink-action of the blood in the cerebral capillaries, which would drain the marker back into the blood. When these authors measured the volume of distribution of the slowly penetrating I⁻ -ion, they found that these were 5, 14 and 18 per cent, according to whether the iodide was presented by way of the blood, cerebrospinal fluid, or both simultaneously. Application of the same principle to the measurement of the sucrose-space of brain by Woodward, Reed & Woodbury (1967) and

2   A. B. Symp. III

Oldendorf & Davson (1967) and the sulphate-space by Cutler, Lorenzo & Barlow (1968) has confirmed the validity of this principle (Fig. 4).

MATHEMATICAL MODEL

When a substance is maintained at a constant concentration in the blood plasma, the course of penetration into the brain or cerebrospinal fluid will involve passage through the respective blood-brain and blood-cerebrospinal fluid barriers under the established gradients of concentration or electrochemical potential, or by specialized transport processes; net exchanges between cerebrospinal fluid and brain extracellular fluid will complicate the otherwise simple kinetic relations between the two compartments (i.e., blood-brain and blood-c.s.f.) so that the accurate formulation of the time-course of penetration from blood to brain, or blood to cerebrospinal fluid, is not easy theoretically. By making several simplifying assumptions, Davson & Pollay (1963) developed an equation describing the penetration of ^{24}Na from blood into the cerebrospinal fluid when an artificial fluid was perfused through the system. The experimental points agreed reasonably well with the theoretical curve. That equation assumes the independence of processes at the blood-brain barrier; actually the continuity of the extracellular and cerebrospinal fluids insures that processes bordering that medium are coupled, and more satisfactory models from a theoretical point of view have been developed by Patlak (1967) and by Welch (1969). Fig. 5 shows how an extended form of the latter may be used in the analysis of the penetration of ^{24}Na into cerebrospinal fluid (Curve I) and brain water (Curve II) of the rabbit. In each case the plotted points are experimental measurements, whilst the lines are solutions of the differential equation for a model of the system which includes a distributed source in the tissue, extra- and intracellular locations and diffusional relationship with a bathing fluid which is continuously renewed.

A variety of studies on the relation between cerebrospinal fluid and brain, which are the theme of later papers in this Symposium, have amply confirmed the suggestion of Wallace & Brodie that the extracellular fluid of brain, and the cerebrospinal fluid, are similar in composition; at the risk of being invidious we may mention the conclusion of Fencl, Miller & Pappenheimer (1966) that the factor determining the control of respiration-rate was the pH of the cerebrospinal fluid rather than that of the blood

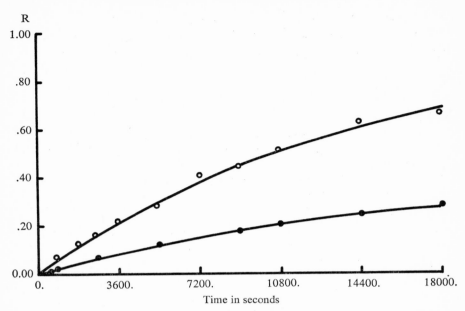

Fig. 5. Penetration of ^{22}Na into the water of cerebrospinal fluid (upper curve) and brain (lower curve) when a constant level was maintained in the plasma. The plotted points are experimental and the curves are theoretical on the basis of Welch's (1969) model. Ordinate: Ratio of activities in c.s.f. or brain-water and plasma water. Abscissa: Time in sec after establishing plasma level.

plasma, and the measurements of the responses of the resting potentials of glial cells of *Necturus* to altered K-concentration of the blood (Cohen, Gerschenfeld & Kuffler 1968) which showed that the response was determined by the concentration in the cerebrospinal fluid, rather than that in the blood.

LYMPH FUNCTION

Finally, we may point to an important function of the cerebrospinal fluid as a substitute for a lymphatic system; however "tight" the blood-brain barrier may be normally, we must envisage the escape of small quantities of blood proteins into the brain tissue, and these can only escape back to the blood through a system that flows under hydrostatic pressure from the subarachnoid spaces into the vascular system. The free connexion between subarach-

2*

noid spaces and dural sinuses, revealed by a variety of studies both functional and histological on the arachnoid villi, permits this flow; in consequence, high concentrations of proteins are prevented from building up in the tissue.

REFERENCES

Ames, A., Sakanoue, M. & Endo, S. (1964) Na, K, Ca, Mg and Cl concentrations in choroid plexus fluid and cisternal fluid compared with plasma ultrafiltrate. *J. Neurophysiol. 27*, 672–681.

Bakay, L. (1960) Studies in sodium exchange. *Neurology 10*, 564–571.

Bito, L. Z. & Davson, H. (1966) Local variations in cerebrospinal fluid composition and its relationship to the composition of the extracellular fluid of the cortex. *Exp. Neurol. 14*, 264–280.

Bradbury, M. W. B. & Davson, H. (1964) The transport of urea, creatinine and certain monosaccharides between blood and fluid perfusing the cerebral ventricular system of rabbits. *J. Physiol. 170*, 195–211.

Bito, L. Z., Bradbury, M. W. B. & Davson, H. (1966) Factors affecting the distribution of iodide and bromide in the central nervous system. *J. Physiol. 185*, 323–354.

Brightman, M. W. (1965a) The distribution within the brain of ferritin injected into cerebrospinal fluid compartments. I. *J. Cell Biol. 26*, 99–123.

Brightman, M. W. (1965b) The distribution within the brain of ferritin injected into cerebrospinal fluid compartments. *Amer. J. Anat. 117*, 193–220.

Cohen, M. W., Gerschenfeld, H. M. & Kuffler, S. W. (1968) Ionic environment of neurones and glial cells in the brain of an amphibian. *J. Physiol. 197*, 363–380.

Cutler, R. W. P., Lorenzo, A. V. & Barlow, C. F. (1968) Sulfate and iodide concentration in brain. *Arch. Neurol. 18*, 316–323.

Davson, H. (1955a) A comparative study of the acqueous humour and cerebrospinal fluid in the rabbit. *J. Physiol. 129*, 111–133.

Davson, H. (1955b) The rates of disappearance of substances injected into the subarachnoid space of rabbits. *J. Physiol. 128*, 52–53 P.

Davson, H. (1956) *Physiology of the Ocular and Cerebrospinal Fluids.* Churchill, London.

Davson, H. (1958) Some aspects of the relationship between the cerebrospinal fluid and the central nervous system. In *The Cerebrospinal Fluid.* (Ciba Foundation Symp.), pp. 189–203. Churchill, London.

Davson, H. & Pollay, M. (1963) The turnover of ^{24}Na in the cerebrospinal fluid and its bearing on the blood-brain barrier. *J. Physiol. 167*, 247–255.

Davson, H. & Pollay, M. (1963) Influence of various drugs on the transport of ^{131}I and PAH across the cerebrospinal fluid-blood barrier. *J. Physiol. 167*, 239–246.

Davson, H., Kleeman, C. R. & Levin, E. (1961) Blood-brain barrier and extracellular space. *J. Physiol. 159*, 67–68 P.

Davson, H. & Spaziani, E. (1959) The blood-brain barrier. *J. Physiol. 149*, 135–143.

Fencl, V., Miller, T. B. & Pappenheimer, J. R. (1966) Studies on the respiratory response to disturbances of acid-base balance, with deductions concerning the ionic composition of cerebral interstitial fluid. *Amer. J. Physiol. 210*, 459–472.

Goldmann, E. E. (1909) Die aussere und innere Sekretion des gesunden und kranken Organismus im Lichte der "vitalen Farbung". *Beitr. klin. Chirurg. 64*, 192–265.

Goldmann, E. E. (1913) Vitalfarbung am Zentralnervensystem. *Abh. preuss. Akad. Wiss., Phys. Math. Kl.*, No. 1. pp 1–60.

Horstmann, E. & Meves, H. (1959) Die Feinstruktur des molekularen Rindengraues und ihre physiologische Bedeutung. *Z. Zellforsch. 49*, 569–604.

Oldendorf, W. H. & Davson, H. (1967) Brain extracellular space and the sink action of cerebrospinal fluid. *Arch. Neurol. 17*, 196–205.

Olsen, N. S. & Rudolph, G. G. (1955) Transfer of sodium and bromide ions between blood, cerebrospinal fluid and brain tissue. *Amer. J. Physiol. 183*, 427–432.

Patlak, C. S. (1967) Analysis of the distribution of materials within the blood-brain-cerebrospinal fluid system. *Bull. math. Biophys. 29*, 513–531.

Pollay, M. & Curl, F. (1967) Secretion of cerebrospinal fluid by the ventricular ependyma of the rabbit. *Amer. J. Physiol. 213*, 1031–1038.

Rall, D. P., Oppelt, W. W. & Patlak, C. S. (1962) Extracellular space of brain as determined by diffusion of inulin from the ventricular system. *Life Sci. 2*, 43–48.

Reed, D. J. & Woodbury, D. M. (1963) Kinetics of movement of iodine, sucrose, inulin and radio-iodinated serum albumin in the central nervous system and cerebrospinal fluid of the rat. *J. Physiol. 169*, 816–850.

Rougemont, J. De., Ames, A., Nesbitt, F. B. & Hofmann, H. F. (1960) Fluid formed by choroid plexus. *J. Neurophysiol. 23*, 485–495.

Rudolph, G. G. & Olsen, N. S. (1956) Transfer of potassium between blood, cerebrospinal fluid and brain tissue. *Amer. J. Physiol. 186*, 157–160.

Sadler, K. & Welch, K. (1967) Concentration of glucose in new choroidal cerebrospinal fluid of the rabbit. *Nature 215*, 884–885.

Stern, L. & Gautier, R. (1921) Rapports entre le liquide céphalo-rachidien et la circulation sanguine. *Arch. int. Physiol. 17*, 138–192.

Stern, L. & Gautier, R. (1922) Les rapports entre le liquide céphalo-rachidien et les éléments nerveux de l'axe cérébrospinal. *Arch. int. Physiol. 17*, 391–448.

Stern, L. & Gautier, R. (1923) Rapports entre le liquide céphalo-rachidien des espaces ventriculaires et celui des espaces sous-arachnoidiens. *Arch. int. Physiol. 20*, 403–436.

Van Harreveld, A., Crowell, J. & Malhotra, S. K. (1965) A study of extracellular space in central nervous tissue by freeze-substitution. *J. Cell Biol. 25*, 117–137.

v. Monakow, P. (1920) Uber die Uramie. *Arch. neurol. Psychiat. 6*, 183–200.

Wallace, G. B. & Brodie, B. B. (1939) The distribution of iodide, thiocyanate, bromide and chloride in the central nervous system and spinal fluid. *J. Pharm. Pharmacol. 65*, 220–226.

Wallace, G. B. & Brodie, B. B. (1940) On the source of the cerebrospinal fluid. The distribution of bromide and iodide throughout the central nervous system. *J. Pharm. Pharmacol. 70*, 418–427.

Welch, K. (1969) A model for the distribution of materials in the fluids of the central nervous system. *Brain Res. 16*, 453–468.

Woodward, D. I., Reed. D. J. & Woodbury, D. M. (1967) Extracellular space of rat cerebral cortex. *Amer. J. Physiol. 212*, 367–370.

DISCUSSION

SEVERINGHAUS
I don't understand all the assumptions underlying the sodium curves of Dr. Welch. I presume there must be assumptions about exchange from the inside to the outside of cells, etc.

WELCH
The system was set up as a simplified model. Instead of having the complex geometry of the brain it was considered to be a single slab or sheet. It was assumed that there was a distributed source in the sheet corresponding to blood-brain exchange, and within the sheet there were cells, so that the materials could enter the cells. The sheet was considered to be bathed by a continuously renewed fluid. The bathing fluid was set up as a boundary at one side of the sheet. The other border of the sheet was assumed not to display gradients. The differential equations were set up and programmed for automatic computation by substituting various rate constants at the various borders. Actually in the particular slide that was shown the permeability of the blood-brain interface to sodium turned out to be several orders of magnitude lower than in muscle, about 8×10^{-8} cm/sec.

SEVERINGHAUS
Were the curves generated after the data had been obtained?

WELCH
That's right. They were made to see what permeability one would need to account for the experimental data.

SIESJÖ
Dr. Davson, could I anticipate the discussions to follow on the CSF-plasma potentials by asking you about the openness of the valves? If there are some valves open all the time, one would expect that they would act as a shunt.

DAVSON
I can refer to Dr. Welch who has done most of the experimental work on these valves. We have just studied the actual impedement that these valves, or these openings of the arachnoid villi, offer to large molecules. We have

perfused the ventricular system, that is to say the ventricles plus the subarachnoidal space, with solutions containing different molecules. There is absolutely no influence of the molecular weight on the rate at which the material can escape. It is as though the holes are very much larger than the biggest dextrans which we were able to use, and these had molecular weights of the order of 500,000. That tells us that these holes are there, but are they closed or open? It they are closed, would they really act as a high resistance for diffusion? I would find it rather difficult to believe that a simple flap mechanism could actually also operate as a real barrier to diffusion for small molecules and ions. Dr. Severinghaus: If you have a system which might open up when you create a hydrostatic pressure, then when it collapses, do you think it could act as a high resistance membrane? I think it is most unlikely.

SEVERINGHAUS
Yes, I should think it is possible.

DAVSON
In that case we should be able to measure a change in potential when we established a hydrostatic pressure favouring opening up of the valves.

SIESJÖ
Could you please explain the factors which determine the rate of absorption of CSF.

DAVSON
From our studies we agree entirely with the anatomical evidence, which indicates that the holes are so large that the colloid osmotic pressure exerted by the plasma proteins cannot operate. We could perhaps expect that the colloid osmotic pressure was operating in helping the fluid out because of the high concentration of proteins in the plasma. However, we have perfused the ventriculo-subarachnoid space with two solutions, the one containing a high molecular weight dextran and therefore with a very low colloid osmotic pressure, and the other with a low molecular weight dextran and with a colloid osmotic pressure about equal to that in plasma, but there was no difference in the rates of absorption. Both solutions were absorbed more slowly than one without added dextran, but this was because of the increase

in viscosity caused by the dextran. I would say that the colloid osmotic pressure theory is quite out of the question, and it indeed creates difficulties; you have to get rid of your proteins, and you have no real lymphatic system to do it with, so you must make use of some open channels through which they can go. If your channels are so small that the proteins themselves can exert a colloid osmotic pressure, then the proteins can't be absorbed and get back into the blood.

SEVERINGHAUS

Another way of estimating how big the absorption sites might be, is to determine what pressure is required for air bubbles to be reabsorbed. One can calculate the surface tension, and therefore the radius of the bubble, if air is injected into the CSF. Some years ago an experiment was done in our anesthesia department to determine what happens when N_2O diffuses into the CSF as a result of giving N_2O during pneumo-encephalogram. One sees the pressure rise in the CSF as the N_2O migrates into the cavity containing air, until a pressure between 80–100 mmHg is reached. At that point presumably arachnoid villi permit gas bubbles to pass.

QUESTION FROM SEVERAL PARTICIPANTS
Do you really mean 80–100 mmHg?

SEVERINGHAUS

Yes, 80–100 mmHg pressure at which point the gas pressure suddenly drops. I calculated that the radius of the orifice should be about 8–10 μ, assuming a surface tension of 50 dynes/cm.

ORKAND

Dr. Davson – you showed a graph from which you obtained the sucrose space of the brain. How much of the difference between the curves obtained with only CSF perfusion and those obtained with CSF and blood perfusion can one attribute to the blood volume?

DAVSON

We allow for the blood volume in the tissue during analysis. This is actually very small, only ½ per cent of the sucrose space. If you exsanguinate the animal by cutting his carotids and also cut his vertebrals, it bleeds so well that you have very little blood left behind.

ORKAND

Is there any correction in these measurements for possible uptake of sucrose in the cells?

DAVSON

No. The extracellular space might be smaller on that account.

ORKAND

Has anybody performed auto-radiography on mammalian brain to see if the 'extracellular' markers go into the cells? Nicholls & Wolfe (1967) found inulin and dextran were taken up by neurons and glial cells in the leech central nervous system.

DAVSON

I don't know really. It is always something that we have been suspicious about. Inulin is less likely to go into cells, and the extracellular space measured with inulin comes out in the same order. However, it is larger in the dog than we found in the rabbit. Sulphate may give a different space. It seems to be true of all tissues that the apparent extracellular space varies with the marker used to measure it; thus in muscle the sorbitol-space is larger than the sucrose- and inulin-spaces.

ORKAND

If one thinks of pinocytosis rather than diffusion across membranes the exact size of the molecule may not be important.

DAVSON

Yes, but I have never had much sympathy with the concept of pinocytosis, except as a means of transport for very large molecules or particles.

J. W. WOODBURY

I would like to pursue this business of the valves. It seems to me, that if there are holes that big, there would be no CSF to blood potential at all; macroscopic holes where the CSF escapes into the venous sinuses would

Nicholls, J. G. & Wolfe, D. E. (1967) Distribution of ^{14}C-labeled sucrose, inulin, and dextran in extracellular spaces and in cells of the leech central nervous system. *J. Neurophysiol. 30*, 1574–1592.

completely shunt out the potential. Actually there would be some potential but, off hand, I would expect it to be small.

DAVSON

I am not sufficiently expert on electricity. But don't we also have to suppose that there is a potential across the blood-brain barrier, and that this is created by a very large battery. Otherwise the CSF potential, as Dr. Severinghaus mentioned to me many years ago, would be shunted across the brain.

SEVERINGHAUS

One answer to this is that the potential may in fact be an ionic diffusion potential, which would exist with no barrier at all, just as you have a junction potential between liquids of different composition. For example the difference in composition between CSF and blood results in $+3$ to $+4$ mV in CSF when they form an *in vitro* liquid junction, without a membrane. The magnitude of a liquid junction potential depends on the mobilities of the various ions. Such potentials can be substantial.

J. W. WOODBURY

Are you suggesting a junction potential between isotonic solutions as large as ten millivolts?

SEVERINGHAUS

Perhaps 100 mV. It depends on the difference in composition.

J. W. WOODBURY

Are you talking about free diffusion across a boundary?

SEVERINGHAUS

Yes, if you established a liquid junction between saline and blood you find 6 mV between them with no membrane at all. If you change the ionic composition you can manipulate this potential.

J. W. WOODBURY

Six millivolts, yes, but it's hard to see how it can vary much with pH, be much larger, and be maintained in the steady state in the body.

SEVERINGHAUS

You are quite correct. pH variations within the biologic range have no effect on in vitro diffusion potentials, which are created by movements of the major ions. If the in vivo effect of pH on the EMF between CSF and blood is to be a diffusion potential, it must be assumed that the concentrations of some of the major ions had been altered at one of the boundaries. Of course there are either two or four boundaries separating blood from CSF, depending on whether diffusion is assumed to be across only endothelial walls, or also glial walls, and a small variation in the membrane potential at any one of the surfaces might be responsible. These sequential membranes along the pathway constitute a series of batteries, each of which consists of diffusion potentials in which the ions are kept out of electrochemical equilibrium by the action of the membrane.

J. W. WOODBURY

I find that hard to believe, i. e., I believe that is a spurious argument.

SEVERINGHAUS

We recently observed a baffling potential gradient within the blood stream. After removing the calvarium from a dog, catheters were placed in the sagittal sinus and external jugular vein, and the potential between the two was recorded. CO_2-induced acidosis caused the sagittal sinus EMF to rise 5 to 10 mV positive to the external jugular vein. The brain surface and the wound edges also followed the sagittal sinus potential, while the remainder of the body was at the potential of the jugular vein (unpublished observations).

J. W. WOODBURY

What you are really saying is that perhaps there is no CSF to blood potential at all.

USSING

It might be worth mentioning that within the kidney tubules there are very substantial potential differences even though the kidney tubules are open in boths ends. In the case of the CSF to blood potential it is only a matter of the length of the leak. If the leak is long enough you can have a substantial potential.

RALL

In the elasmobranch there are open channels from the ventricles through the optic nerves directly to the extracellular fluids space of the body, and the elasmobranch maintains a -15 mV potential all the time in spite of these channels (Rall 1967).

Rall, D. P. (1967) Comparative pharmacology of cerebrospinal fluid. *Fed. Proc. 26*, 1020–1023.

Volume of Cerebral Extracellular Fluids

David P. Rall & Joseph D. Fenstermacher

The basic principles involved in determining the extracellular fluid space of the brain by ventricular perfusion and diffusion are similar to those involved in measuring diffusion of a substance into a block of agar. Substances useful as extracellular fluid volume indicators cannot easily permeate cell membranes. Thus they cannot pass the solid cellular membrane of the blood-brain barrier, but can pass the permeable barrier presented by the ependyma or pia-glia.

In practice, if a steady concentration of a compound, normally limited to the extracellular fluid compartment, is maintained in the ventricular or subarachnoid space, the relative concentration as a function of both distance from the brain-fluid boundary and time can be measured. This allows for the estimation of the apparent relative volume of tissue occupied by the substance as well as the rate of movement of the substance into brain. If for any one compound the ependyma (or pia-glia) is permeable, there is no bulk flow in either direction across the ependyma (or pia-glia), and the cerebral capillaries are impermeable, the estimates of apparent extracellular volume should be valid. Evidence exists that these conditions can substantially be met.

The shape of the curve for diffusion of a substance into a block of tissue is such that the first half of the curve, with respect to concentration in the tissue, is roughly linear. Extrapolation of these points (concentration vs distance from the boundary) to the ependymal or pia-glial boundary will yield the extracellular space (ECS) for that tissue. If the curve fits the theoretical curve for diffusion, then the estimate of ECS may be valid for that segment of the experimental curve which fits the theoretical curve.

Office of the Associate Scientific Director for Experimental Therapeutics, National Cancer Institute, National Institutes of Health, Bethesda, Md. 20014, U.S.A.

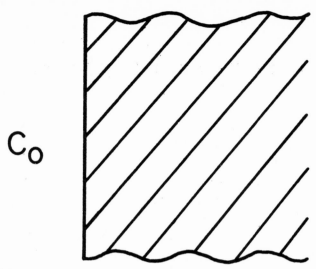

Fig. 1. Model for the diffusion process.

The model for this process is shown in Fig. 1.

The appropriate equation is shown in Fig. 2.

Analysis of the curves is aided by the use of complementary error function (erfc) graph paper which converts erfc to a linear scale (Schantz & Lauffer 1962).

A method of subarachnoid and ventricular space perfusion and tissue sampling was used to determine cortical distribution spaces for inulin and sucrose, in cerebral cortex, caudate nucleus and para-ventricular white matter. All animals were anesthetized with pentobarbital and placed in a stereotaxic head-holder. Two cranial holes were drilled with a dental drill and a size 11 dental burr. For cortical space determinations, inflow needles (Pitkin spinal needles, 20 or 22 gauge) were stereotaxically positioned over the holes and advanced through the dura and superior sagittal sinus into the supracallosal subarachnoid space. For caudate nucleus and para-ventricular white matter space determinations, a needle was similarly placed in each lateral ventricle. An outflow needle was manually placed in the cisterna magna. Patency of the system was tested by perfusing colored saline solutions from inflow to outflow needle before starting the perfusion with the labeled compounds.

The perfusion solution was a buffered isotonic salt solution containing

General Formula

$$\frac{C}{Co} = erfc\left(\frac{x}{2}\sqrt{Dt}\right)$$

Co is the concentration of the test substance in ventricular fluid.
C is concentration of test substance at distance x from the ependyma at time t.
D is the diffusion constant of the test substance.
erfc is the complementary error function.

Fig. 2. General formula for diffusion into a slab of tissue.

the labeled compound (inulin or mannitol) and a C^{14} – labeled compound (sucrose or inulin) in trace amounts. To indicate the cortical areas that were well perfused, Trypan blue was added to the perfusate. The inflow was driven by a Harvard constant infusion pump at 0.12 to 0.25 ml/mm.

At various times after beginning the perfusion, the animal was killed and the brain rapidly removed. The brain was frozen in liquid nitrogen for 15–30 seconds and coronal sections made with a Stadie-Riggs blade. For measurement of cortical spaces, areas which were stained dark blue (well-perfused) and appeared to present a flat sulci-free surface were selected for sampling. From these areas, strips of tissue running perpendicular to the cortical surface were cut and subsequently recut into a series of 0.5 mm or 1.0 mm thick blocks with a single stroke of a multi-bladed knife. Three to five blocks were cut per series. The tissue blocks were transferred from the knife to tared counting bottles and weighed. The entire duration for sampling, i.e., from the death of the animals until all samples were placed in counting vials, was ten minutes or less. Similar slicing techniques were used to obtain samples for caudate nucleus and para-ventricular white matter. Samples of inflow and outflow perfusate and arterial blood were obtained periodically throughout the experiment. All tissue and fluid samples were prepared for liquid scintillation spectrometry and counted by standard procedures.

Further details of these procedures may be found in Fenstermacher *et al.* (1970) and Levin *et al.* (in press).

One problem with these studies is that it seems likely that there is a 0.015 mm layer of adherent perfusion fluid on the first piece of brain tissue containing the ependyma or the pia-glia. Since this 0.015 mm layer has a

Table 1. *¹⁴C-sucrose and ³H-inulin spaces in dog caudate nucleus after ventriculocisternal perfusion for various times*

Time-hr.	Sucrose space	Inulin space
1	18.2	–
	(N=2)	
2	18.2	–
	(N=8)	
3	18.2	18.2
	(N=4)	(N=2)
4	17.7	16.4
	(N=14)	(N=5)
5	18.3	–
	(N=2)	
6	16.2	16.9
	(N=3)	(N=3)
Average	17.8	16.9

100 per cent concentration of the marker molecule (relative to the perfusion fluid) and the approximately 0.5 mm slice of tissue has only 10–15 per cent, a systematic error is introduced. This error adds about 1.5 per cent to the true space.

Spaces reported in this paper have been corrected for this 1.5 per cent error and are our best estimates at this time.

If the ependyma appreciably restricted the transport of an extracellular molecule between cerebrospinal fluid and brain, the size of the distribution space for that molecule should increase as the time of perfusion increases. This was experimentally tested using sucrose and inulin. The sucrose and inulin spaces measured after 1 to 6 hours of perfusion are shown in Table 1. There is no indication of an increase in the distribution spaces with time. From these data an ependymal permeability constant of *at least* 5×10^{-5} cm/sec was calculated. In qualitative terms this means that molecules with molecular weights of 5,000 or less can freely cross the ependyma.

Evidence that there is inadequate bulk flow across the ependyma to affect these results has been presented before (Rall 1967).

These observations support the concept that this method should give reliable estimates of ECS in selective portions of the brain. A summary of our data on the ECS in various portions of the brains of various species is presented in Table 2. These values varied from 14.5 to 18.4 per cent. White

Table 2. *Apparent extracellular space in mammalian brain space in per cent*

Species	Cortex		Caudate nucleus		Periventricular white matter	
	sucrose	inulin	sucrose	inulin	sucrose	inulin
Rabbit	18.4	16.1	–	–	–	–
Cat	18.3	16.9	–	–	–	–
Dog	18.0	17.3	17.8	17.7	15.5	14.5
M. mulatta	17.9	16.9	16.0	–	14.9	–

matter seemed to have a smaller space than either cortex or caudate nucleus. Cortex space did not vary with species or brain size.

REFERENCES

Fenstermacher, J. D., Li, C-L., & Levin, V. A. (1970) Extracellular space of the cerebral cortex of normothermic and hypothermic cats. *Exp. Neurol. 27,* 101–114.

Levin, V. A., Fenstermacher, J. D., & Patlak, C. S. Sucrose and inulin space measurements of the cerebral cortex in four mammalian species. *Amer. J. Physiol.* In press.

Rall, D. P. (1967) Transport through the ependymal linings. *Proc. Brain Barrier Systems Conference,* September 26–30. Amsterdam, The Netherlands.

Schantz, E. J. & Lauffer, M. A. (1962) Diffusion measurements in agar gel. *Biochemistry 1,* 658–663.

DISCUSSION

BRADBURY

This figure shows some results which are complementary and in agreement with the work of Dr. Rall. This was a preparation of the isolated frog brain which weighs about 100 mg. It will incubate very nicely *in vitro* without any disturbance in electrolyte content. This figure shows the C^{14}-inulin and the S^{35}-sulphate space as a function of time. Both these markers equilibrate very rapidly, in about half an hour, and their concentrations remain relatively constant – perhaps with a slight increase with time over the period of incubation. This largely answers the suggestion of Dr. Orkand that there is substantial intracellular penetration. The slight increase between ½ and 3 hours of incubation might be due to some degree of intracellular penetration. I might add that sucrose gives similar values, just a little bit higher. We also, in a rather crude fashion, attempted the same technique on rabbit brain as Dr. Rall used from the pial surface and came up with values very comparable to his. Robert Wright has measured diffusion of sucrose and sulphate out of the isolated optic lobes of the frog. He came up with apparent diffusion coefficients of about half of the theoretical value, all in very good agreement with Dr. Rall's results.

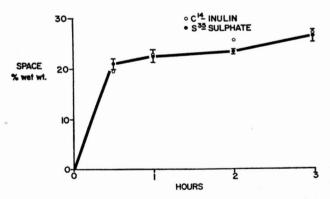

Fig. 1. ^{14}C-inulin and ^{35}-S-sulphate spaces of frog brain incubated *in vitro*.

SIESJÖ

If we take the brain out after freezing it *in situ* with liquid nitrogen, then we obtain both blood, bulk CSF fluid, and intercellular fluid. What are the relative sizes of these spaces? Is there any information about changes in the volume of the extracellular space during hyper- or hypocapnia?

RALL

I don't know how these spaces are partitioned in the whole frozen brain.

CAMERON

In Dr. Davson's laboratory we studied the effect of severe hypercapnia on the volume of distribution of ^{14}C-labelled sucrose in rabbit brain; first when the sucrose was maintained at constant plasma concentration and second, when it was introduced by means of ventriculo-cisternal perfusion. When sucrose was presented by ventriculo-cisternal perfusion there was no significant change in its volume of distribution during hypercapnia. When sucrose was introduced intravenously the volume of distribution in brain was significantly increased when compared with normocapnic controls. This change was attributed to a possible increase in the permeability of the blood-brain barrier (Cameron *et al.* 1970).

LASSEN

In experiments where sucrose or inulin is infused into the lateral ventricle and sampled downstream, even after a long time a dilution is found. Is this simply caused by secretion by the ependyma and by the choroid plexus in the lateral and 4th ventricles?

RALL

There will be a constant but very slight diffusion of the tracer substance into the brain. Now to put it into perspective, we have to use what would normally be considered enormous concentrations, 1 or 2 μCurie/ml ^{14}C-inulin or ^{14}C-sucrose in perfusion fluid to get enough counts in the pieces of tissue that we analyze. In terms of the loss of this material into the brain tissue by diffusion, it is about 1 or 2 per cent, and that is all. That is, when you start out with 100 per cent in the inflow you will end up with 98 per cent or 99 per cent in the outflow.

Cameron, I. R., Davson, H. & Segal, M. B. (1970) The effect of hypercapnia on the blood-brain barrier permeability to sucrose in the rabbit. *Yale J. Biol. Med.* 42, 241–247.

MINES

You have shown that perhaps $10\,\mu l/min$ of fluid could be formed from the brain surface. The total formation of cerebrospinal fluid in the dog brain choroid plexus is only about 50 μl of fluid/min. Would you agree that a significant proportion of the fluid is formed in this way?

RALL

I think it is quite possible that around 20 per cent of CSF may be formed within the brain substance.

D. WOODBURY

My only comments on the extracellular space are related to the changes with age. If the uptake of inulin is measured in neonatal and prenatal animals, the inulin uptake is very high, and the CSF/plasma ratios approach 1.0. During development the inulin uptake decreases as the blood-brain barrier develops. In the period before 16 days of age the ratio between the brain and CSF measures the extracellular space, because there is rapid equilibration between the two fluids. This space decreases with age until approximately 16 days and then increases after this age. This suggests that a barrier develops across the ependyma for inulin after this period of time. It is likely that there is also development of a partial barrier across the ependyma between CSF and brain. However, the evidence suggests that the extracellular space decreases from around 50 per cent in the prenatal animal to about 14 per cent in the adult rat (Ferguson & Woodbury 1969).

WELCH

At what time does the inulin space begin to increase in relation to the growth of the brain? The larger the brain, the higher the ratio might be expected to be.

D. WOODBURY

Actually, the inulin space does not increase with age, but decreases. The rapid growth of the brain occurs between 5 days and 21 days after birth.

Ferguson, R. K. & Woodbury, D. M. (1969) Penetration of ^{14}C-inulin and ^{14}C-sucrose into brain, cerebrospinal fluid, and skeletal muscle of developing rats. *Exp. Brain Res. 7*, 181–194.

However, the interstitial space decrease with age occurs only after 10 days of age, a time that corresponds to the very rapid growth stage of the brain and growth of glial cells and neuronal cell processes. The intracellular water content increases with age whereas the total water content decreases slightly with age. Again these changes correspond to the time of rapid glial and neuronal cell processes proliferation.

Siesjö

Dr. Rall: We have learned that due to the sink action of the CSF, substances like sucrose or inulin will not equilibrate between plasma and brain extracellular fluid when they are introduced into the blood. Consequently we cannot calculate the ECF volume from the plasma and whole tissue concentrations of these substances, even if the plasma concentrations are kept constant for long periods. However, v. Harreveld et al. (1966) arrived at ECF volumes of 15 to 30 per cent in the cat and rabbit brain by employing sulphate given i. v. and by using the CSF sulphate concentration as representative of the ECF concentration. If you do the same for sucrose or inulin, what kind of space do you arrive at?

Rall

I do not know. We have not done that.

van Harreveld, A., Ahmed, N. & Tanner, D. J. (1966) Sulphate concentrations in cerebrospinal fluid and serum of rabbits and cats. *Amer. J. Physiol. 210*, 777–780.

Factors Affecting CSF Production

W. W. Oppelt

CSF

The factors affecting CSF production have been of interest, both in that they may be manipulated to alleviate a pathological condition and in that they may give clues as to the basic mechanism by which the CSF is formed. It has been quite clear for years that the CSF is not a product of simple diffusion from plasma. The contents of the CSF is quite different from that of plasma in several important regards. The most striking characteristic, of course, is the very low protein concentration found in the CSF, the CSF/ plasma ratio of protein being about 0.004. Other important differences include a slight excess of Na^+ and Cl^- and a definite deficit of K^+, the CSF/plasma concentration ratio of that ion being 0.68 (Davson 1967). It is interesting that this K^+ deficit is found in vertebrates from the primitive elasmobranchs (Maren 1967) to mammals, including man. There is a deficit of Ca^{++}, however, free Ca^{++} is probably in balance between plasma and CSF. In some species there is a Mg^{++} excess (Oppelt *et al.* 1963), in others not. Glucose and urea tend to be lower in CSF, compared to plasma, and CSF pH is about 0.1–0.2 units lower than plasma pH. These concentration differences, as well as studies with inhibitors, suggest that CSF is a product of active secretion. More evidence for this will be presented below.

There has been interest for a long time in measuring the rate with which CSF is produced in the brain ventricles. Early methods for this simply involved placing a cannula into the cisterna magna and measuring the amount of CSF that dripped out per unit time. Disadvantages of this technique include the sensitivity of this method to pressure changes in the CSF, as well as the fact that the measurements must be done at a zero pressure,

Department of Pharmacology and Therapeutics and Department of Medicine, University of Florida College of Medicine, Gainesville, Florida 32601, U.S.A.

relative to the cisterna magna. Later methods of CSF production formation include the measurements of the turnover of various substances, removed by bulk flow, in the CSF. An excellent single measurement of the rate of turnover of CSF can be obtained in this way; however, the method is not useful for the continuous measurement of CSF production, such as might be desired if the effect of a drug on formation is to be measured, using a control period of formation in the same animal. The introduction of ventriculo-cisternal perfusion with an inulin-C^{14} containing buffer as a technique to measure CSF formation by Pappenheimer's group (Pappenheimer & Heisey 1963) solved many of the above-mentioned objections. A CSF-like buffer, containing traces of inulin-C^{14}, is perfused at a steady rate into one of the lateral ventricles and is allowed to exit through a cannula placed into the cisterna magna. As the buffer passes through the ventricles, newly formed CSF is added and dilutes the inulin. Therefore, by measuring dilution of inulin as it passes through the ventricles, and by knowing the rate of inflow, CSF formation can then be calculated. One can take periodic collections of outflow and thereby measure CSF formation continually, both before and after administration of a drug. Thus each animal can be used as its own control. Also, intraventricular pressure can be adjusted to the normal by raising or lowering the level of the outflow cannula. Except where mentioned, the experiments below, which describe the control of CSF formation, were all performed using ventriculo-cisternal perfusion as the technique for measuring rate of CSF production.

NORMAL RATES OF CSF PRODUCTION

CSF formation rates have been measured in a variety of animals, including goat, dog, cat, man and elasmobranch fishes. In the mammals, turnover rates of CSF, indicating CSF formation rates, are about 0.3–0.5 per cent/minute (Heisey et al. 1962; Oppelt et al. 1964, Vates et al. 1964). These rates in sharks, representing the primitive elasmobranch fishes, are considerably lower, being about 0.1 per cent/minute in dogfish living in the cold waters of the northern Maine Coast, and about 2–4 times that rate in sharks living in warmer waters. In mammals, CSF formation rates roughly correlate with choroid plexus weight, being about 0.04–0.05 ml/min/100 mg choroid plexus weight (Oppelt et al. 1964b).

CARBONIC ANHYDRASE INHIBITION

As carbonic anhydrase is present in the choroid plexus of animals studied, (Maren 1967b) it seemed likely that inhibition of this enzyme would have an effect on the rate of formation of CSF. Early studies, using more primitive techniques, mostly showed that inhibition of the enzyme with the sulfonamide carbonic anhydrase inhibitors, did occur. Some confusion, however, was present, as the administration of the inhibitor causes a temporary increase in pCO_2 of blood, which in turn increases brain blood volume, and would cause increased rate of outflow of CSF out of a cisternal cannula if this method were used to measure CSF formation. Later studies, however, using more advanced techniques, uniformly showed a decrease in CSF formation rates after administration of a variety of carbonic anhydrase inhibitors in a variety of animals (Oppelt et al. 1964). Interestingly, the maximum reduction in CSF flow produced by carbonic anhydrase inhibition is about 40 per cent, indicating that carbonic anhydrase is not alone in regulating CSF formation, and also indicating that the reaction catalyzed by the enzyme also has a significant uncatalyzed rate (Maren 1967b). An interesting study was done with the carbonic anhydrase inhibitor Benzolamide. This agent, because of its low lipid solubility and its affinity for the renal weak acid transport mechanism, can selectively inhibit carbonic anhydrase in the kidney without significantly affecting the red blood cell enzyme (Travis et al. 1964). Very low i.v. doses of this drug caused significant inhibition of CSF formation in the cat when plasma concentration of the inhibitor was too low to theoretically cause complete enzyme inhibition (Broder & Oppelt 1969). It is notable that the choroid plexus was found to concentrate the drug above that necessary to

Table 1. *CSF production in dogs after varying doses of i. v. acetazolamide*

No. of dogs	Dose mg/kg	Per cent decrease in production ± SE
5	200	43 ± 5
3	67	27 ± 4
4	22	25 ± 4
2	11	20 ± 1
3	5	15 ±13
2	1	3 ± 1

From Oppelt et al. 1964

bind to the enzyme after i.v. injection. To our knowledge, this is the first example of a drug concentrating in choroid plexus when the drug is presented from the blood side.

The mechanism by which carbonic anhydrase regulates CSF formation rates involves the accumulation of HCO_3^- on the epithelial side of the choroid plexus cell, which comes from the hydration of CO_2, catalyzed by the enzyme (Maren 1967b). Recent data suggest that carbonic anhydrase inhibitors also affect C^- secretion (Maren & Broder 1970); however, it is not clear whether this involves carbonic anhydrase or not.

INHIBITION OF SODIUM-POTASSIUM ACTIVATED ADENOSINE TRIPHOSPHATASE

Na-K ATP'ase, found in many tissues, has been shown to be important in active cation transport (Vates et al. 1964). The finding that CSF contains a small excess of Na^+ and a definite deficit of K^+, compared to plasma, suggests that this enzyme also is important in regulating CSF formation rate. The enzyme is specifically inhibited by the digitalis related cardiac glycosides, and their effect on CSF production rates has therefore been studied extensively. Studies of Na-K ATP'ase inhibition by cardio-active glycosides, such as ouabain, in vitro, indicate that enzyme inhibition is complete when drug concentration in the medium reaches $10^{-5}M$, with a dose response curve at lower concentrations. I.V. administration of ouabain to dogs and cats (Oppelt et al. 1964, Vates et al. 1964) did not result in any significant effect on CSF production rates. Calculation of theoretical ouabain concentration reached in choroid plexus after i.v. injections of maximally tolerated doses of the drug suggest that inadequate concentration of drug is reached in choroid plexus and that this may be the explanation for the lack of effect after i.v. injection.

Intraventricular perfusion of buffer containing ouabain, on the other hand, caused a significant reduction in CSF formation rates when high concentrations were used (Vates et al. 1964). This suggests that the enzyme does play a role in driving CSF formation, probably through its effect on active secretion of Na^+ in exchange for K^+. Some interesting studies in the chicken kidney with various doses of ouabain showed that there was, indeed, inhibition of Na-K ATP'ase with the resulting physiologic alterations when high doses of ouabain were used. However, low doses of the drug, which were

Table 2. *CSF production in cats after intraventricular perfusion
of varying concentrations of ouabain*

Concentration Neg Log M	Per cent change in production
5	—65
6	—45
7	—25
8	— 5
9	+13
10	+45
11	+24
12	— 3
14	+ 0.5

From Vates *et al.* 1964 and Oppelt & Palmer 1966

thought to result in tissue concentrations of about 10^{-8} to 10^{-19}M, showed stimulation of enzyme activity *in vitro* as well as the physiologic changes expected from such stimulation (Palmer & Nechay 1964). Similar studies, using varying ouabain concentrations in the ventricular perfusate of cats, showed a similar biphasic response to ouabain. At high concentrations of 10^{-4} to 10^{-6}M ouabain in the perfusate, a drastic reduction in CSF production rates with a concurrent reduction in choroid plexus Na-K ATP'ase activity was seen. When ouabain at 10^{-10}M was used, there was an increase of CSF formation rate of 45 per cent, with a roughly parallel increase in choroid plexus enzyme activity (Oppelt & Palmer 1966). This biphasic response of Na-K ATP'ase to cardio-active glycoside is quite interesting and of uncertain physiological importance. It could possibly be related to the mechanism of action of cardio-active glycosides, as therapeutic concentrations of these drugs in patients is estimated to be about 10^{-8} to 10^{-10}M (Oppelt & Palmer 1966).

The studies with cardio-active glycosides actually indicate that Na-K ATP'ase is an important factor in the regulation of CSF production, probably working through regulating the active secretion of Na^+ in exchange for K^+.

EFFECTS OF ACID–BASE ALTERATIONS

Changes in acid-base balance of body fluids might be expected to influence CSF formation rates, either by affecting enzyme systems in the choroid plexus or by altering brain blood flow, which in turn might change CSF production rates. A series of experiments in dogs were done, altering blood acid-base balance (Oppelt et al. 1963b). Metabolic acidosis was induced by i.v. infusion of HCl. This resulted in a decrease in plasma pH averaging about 0.2 units and an average decrease of 12 mM total CO_2. There was no significant change in CSF production rate. When acetazolamide was given, in addition to the metabolic acidosis, a 31 per cent decrease in CSF formation was seen. Respiratory acidosis, produced by breathing air containing increased CO_2 concentration, produced an increase of about 30 mm Hg in plasma pCO_2, but had no effect on CSF formation rates. Metabolic alkalosis alone caused a slight decrease, averaging 23 per cent in CSF production rates, with a further decrease of 45 per cent when acetazolamide was added. Respiratory alkalosis had the most significant effect on CSF production, a 46 per cent decrease. Further decrease was seen when acetazolamide was added. These results indicate that acid-base alterations do not interfere with the action of carbonic anhydrase inhibitors, and that respiratory and metabolic alkalosis themselves lower CSF formation rates. These results can be explained in two ways. It is possible that the decrease is due to the lowering of plasma pCO_2, thereby reducing the quantity of substrate available for the hydration of CO_2, which is an important reaction driving secretion of CSF. Another possibility is that the decreased brain blood flow, which probably resulted from the production of metabolic and respiratory alkalosis, caused a reduction in CSF secretion.

In recent, as yet unpublished experiments, we perfused buffers of varying pH through the ventricles of cats to determine the effect of such intraventricular acid-base changes on CSF formation rates. Rather drastic increases or decreases in ventricular perfusate pH caused significant reduction in CSF formation rates. Most likely this is due to significant changes in choroid plexus intracellular pH, causing an unfavorable environment for the enzymic reactions necessary for secretion. There may also have been local effects on choroid plexus blood flow, especially in the experiments where alkalotic perfusates were used.

MISCELLANEOUS EFFECTS

Dinitrophenol, in concentrations of 0.05mM in the ventricular perfusate, caused a 45 per cent reduction in CSF formation rates (Pollay & Davson

Table 3. *Changes in CSF production rates caused by changing the pH of the ventricular perfusate in cats*

pH of Perfusate	Per cent change from control	No. of animals
8.3	—41	4
8.0	—20	5
6.5	+25	2
6.2	—41	6

1963). This is presumably due to the effect of this substance on energy supplies (ATP) necessary for enzymic processes responsible for CSF secretion. Hypothermia also depresses CSF formation rates (Davson 1967). Corticosteroids, DOCA, norepinephrine, diphenylhydantoin, insulin hypoglycemia, neostigmine and some diuretics, had no effect on Na^{24} turnover in CSF, suggesting that they do not affect CSF formation rate (Fishman 1959). Direct studies, using ventriculocisternal perfusion, would be of interest here to measure CSF formation more directly.

PHYLOGENY OF THE CONTROL OF CSF FORMATION

It is of interest to determine whether the CSF secretion mechanism is similar in various classes in the vertebrate kingdom. The major studies in this area have been done in various species of elasmobranch fishes, a good example of a primitive vertebrate. Composition of CSF, and its relation to plasma, is surprisingly similar in shark and mammal, suggesting similar mechanisms of secretion (Maren 1967). Studies in three species of sharks with the carbonic anhydrase inhibitor, acetazolamide, and the Na-K ATP'ase inhibitor, ouabain, showed that similar reduction in CSF formation rate occurred when these drugs were given as in the mammals studied (Oppelt *et al.* 1964b, 1966). This indicates that the mechanism of CSF formation is rather ancient in the evolutionary history of animals on this planet.

SUMMARY

The CSF is a product of active secretion, taking place in the choroid plexus and probably also in the lining cells of the ventricles. Two major enzymes involved in the control of its secretion are carbonic anhydrase and Na-K

ATP'ase, as inhibition of these enzymes causes significant reduction in CSF formation rates. Metabolic and respiratory alkalosis also reduce CSF production, either by decreasing plasma pCO_2, and thus reducing the substrate necessary for the hydration of CO_2, or by affecting brain blood flow. Blood acid-base disturbances do not interfere with the action of carbonic anhydrase inhibitors. Similar mechanisms and control of CSF secretion appear to be present in vertebrates as primitive as elasmobranch fishes.

REFERENCES

Broder, L. E. & Oppelt, W. W. (1969) Effect of benzolamide on cerebrospinal fluid formation. *J. Pharmacol. exp. Ther. 169,* 271–276.

Davson, H. (1967) *Physiology of the Cerebrospinal Fluid.* Little Brown & Co., Boston.

Fishman, R. A. (1959) Factors influencing the exchange of sodium between plasma and cerebrospinal fluid. *J. clin. Invest. 38,* 1698–1708.

Heisey, S. R., Held, D. & Pappenheimer, J. R. (1962) Bulk flow and diffusion in the cerebrospinal fluid system of the goat. *Amer. J. Physiol. 203,* 775–781.

Maren, T. H. (1967) Special body fluids of the elasmobranch. In *Sharks, Skates and Rays,* ed. Gilbert, Mathewson & Rall. The Johns Hopkins Press, Baltimore, Md.

Maren, T. H. & Broder, L. E. C. (1970) The role of carbonic anhydrase in anion secretion into cerebrospinal fluid. *J. Pharmacol. exp. Ther. 172,* 197–202.

Oppelt, W. W., Adamson, R. H., Zubrod, C. G. & Rall, D. P. (1966) Further observations on the physiology of elasmobranch ventricular fluid. *Comp. Biochem. Physiol. 17,* 857–866.

Oppelt, W. W., MacIntyre, I. & Rall, D. P. (1963) Magnesium exchange between blood and cerebrospinal fluid. *Amer. J. Physiol. 204,* 959–962.

Oppelt, W. W., Maren, T. H., Owens, E. S. & Rall, D. P. (1963b) Effects of acid-base alterations on cerebrospinal fluid production. *Proc. Soc. exp. Biol. (N. Y.) 11,* 86–89.

Oppelt, W. W. & Palmer, R. F. (1966) Stimulation of cerebrospinal fluid production by low doses of intraventricular ouabain. *J. Pharmacol. exp. Ther. 154,* 581–585.

Oppelt, W. W., Patlak, C. S. & Rall, D. P. (1964) Effect of certain drugs on cerebrospinal fluid production in the dog. *Amer. J. Physiol. 206,* 247–250.

Oppelt, W. W., Patlak, C. S., Zubrod, C. G. & Rall, D. P. (1964b) Ventricular fluid production rates and turnover in elasmobranchii. *Comp. Biochem. Physiol 12,* 171–177.

Palmer, R. F. & Nechay, B. R. (1964) Biphasic renal effects of ouabain in the chicken: Correlation with a microsomal Na-K stimulated ATP'ase. *J. Pharmacol. exp. Ther. 146,* 92–98.

Pappenheimer, J. R. & Heisey, S. R. (1963) *Drugs and Membranes,* ed. Hogben, C. A. (First Int. Pharmacol. Meeting, Vol. 4), pp. 95–105. Pergamon Press, Oxford.

Pollay, M. & Davson, H. (1963) The passage of certain substances out of the cerebrospinal fluid. *Brain 86,* 137–150.

Travis, D. M., Wiley, C., Nechay, B. R. & Maren, T. H. (1964) Selective renal carbonic
    anhydrase inhibition without respiratory effect: Pharmacology of 2-benzenesulfona-
    mido-1,3,4-thiadiazole-5-sulfonamide (CL 11366). *J. Pharmacol. exp. Ther. 143*, 388–
    394.
Vates, T. S., Bonting, S. L. & Oppelt, W. W. (1964) Na-K activated adenosine tri-
    phosphatase and formation of cerebrospinal fluid in the cat. *Amer. J. Physiol. 206*,
    1165–1172.

DISCUSSION

AMES

Have you tried, or have others tried a carbonic anhydrase inhibitor and oubain together to see if the effects are additive?

OPPELT

We have tried this about 2 or 3 times, and they did not appear to be additive.

SEGAL

We used ouabain and Diamox together. Diamox was given intravenously (100 mg/kg) and ventriculo-cisternally (20 mg/100 ml perfusion fluid) and ouabain 10^{-5} Mol in the perfusion fluid in rabbits. There was no further decrease in CSF secretion rate compared to that obtained with either inhibitor alone. I found in all 60 per cent inhibition of secretion without an additive effect.

AMES

To secrete fluid through a membrane that is relatively impermeable to all ions, without creating much of a potential change, it would be necessary to transport both a cation and an anion. This may be what happens at the choroid plexus. One might postulate that acetazolamide acts on chloride transport and ouabain on sodium transport and that is why they both reduce the volume of CSF formed, but without an additive effect. Do you think that hyperventilation acted by reducing blood flow? In the system that we used, in which we exposed the choroid plexus of cats, there was a dramatic constriction of the vessels when we hyperventilated the animals. It was easy to believe that this was sufficient to reduce blood flow to a level that limited secretion.

MAREN

One certainly can speculate that there might be vascular changes. However, in every system that we have ever studied, respiratory alkalosis always mimics the effect of acetazolamide. All you need to do is to hyperventilate, for example, and you will have an alkaline urine with exactly the same composition as if you had given acetazolamide. Similarly, if you cause hyperventilation in a dog you will get the same effects on pancreatic secretion as following acetazolamide. I therefore view these results as being part of that chemical change and in some way due to substrate (CO_2) depletion, or less delivery of CO_2 per unit time to the tissue, in hyperventilation. In the brain, this effect would certainly be augmented by vasoconstriction.

ORKAND

It seems essential to me to know whether or not choroidal blood flow is maintained constant during these procedures. Is there evidence one way or the other in your preparations? (See Macri *et al.* 1966).

AMES

We observed the vessels in the choroid plexus when applying acetazolamide topically. I don't think there was any evidence of a change in the blood flow.

D. WOODBURY

Dr. Reed in our laboratory did some studies on the combination of acetazolamide and ouabain, and he noted an additive effect. He tried it both ways, i.e. either giving ouabain first or acetazolamide first. In each case the CSF secretion was reduced to about 50 per cent of normal and then decreased to 25 per cent of normal when the other agent was added.

PLUM

Ouabain is capable of causing rather marked morphological changes in the ependymal wall, when introduced into the ventricles. Did you have any histology in the animals when using these concentrations? Can one be confident that the effect of ouabain is on a sodium-potassium ATP-ase, or might it not be due to a more widespread action?

OPPELT

I do not have histology. It certainly is true that these high concentrations may have other effects. I have done the same thing in the eye, which may

Macri, F. J., Politoff, A., Rubin, R. & Rall, D. P. (1966) Preferential vasoconstrictor properties of acetazolamide on the arteries of the choroid plexus. *J. Neuropharmacol.* 5, 109–115.

not be completely comparable, but there we observed, for example, changes in pupil size. These high concentrations of ouabain are not innocuous to the animal, and there is approximately a 25 per cent mortality due to respiratory arrest when using 10^{-4} Mol/l ouabain in the perfusion fluid.

SKINHØJ

Do you know about any drug, or any principle, which is able to accelerate the production? It might be useful in some clinical situations with low pressure syndromes.

OPPELT

No, and I may mention that we got neither stimulation nor reduction by giving the drug intravenously.

SEGAL

We did not find any acceleration of CSF production with drugs such as vasopressin and amphotericin B (Davson & Segal 1970).

CAMERON

Ouabain administered into the ventricles causes considerable hyperventilation (Cameron 1967). Did you follow the Pco_2 of these animals? The fall of Pco_2 in respiratory alkalosis could also contribute to the fall in secretion rate.

OPPELT

We did not notice any significant hyperventilation, but we did not measure Pco_2.

BRADBURY

Dr. Parsons from Oxford demonstrated for small intestine that there is active transport of both bicarbonate and chloride and apparently this is strongly inhibited by Diamox, but there is no carbonic anhydrase in the tissue. Would you like to comment on the possibility that the effect of Diamox on the choroid plexus is unrelated to its action on carbonic anhydrase?

Davson, H. & Segal, M. B. (1970) The effect of some inhibitors and accelerators of sodium transport on the turnover of ^{22}Na in the cerebrospinal fluid and the brain. *J. Physiol. (Lond.) 209*, 131–154.
Cameron, I. R. (1967) The respiratory response to injection of ouabain into the cerebral ventricles. *Resp. Physiol. 3*, 55–63.

MAREN

That is not correct. There is carbonic anhydrase in the small intestine. That has been shown many times (Maren 1967). There do appear now to be some effects of acetazolamide unrelated to carbonic anhydrase, demonstrated *in vitro* with very high concentrations (on cornea, turtle bladder and perhaps frog skin). But in a tissue such as choroid plexus, where there is enzyme and where the CO_2 function is involved, and where low doses of the drug are effective, I think we should follow William of Occam and say that acetazolamide is working on carbonic anhydrase.

BRADBURY

I listened to Dr. Parsons speaking some weeks ago and he specifically showed a slide at that time according to which a high activity carbonic anhydrase was present in high concentrations in the stomach, both high and low activity carbonic anhydrase in the large bowel, but no detectable amounts of either in the small intestine.

MAREN

But we have made experiments with the jejunum and the ileum repeatedly, and others have also shown carbonic anhydrase in those tissues. I am going to show tomorrow a slide that I think may convince you that there is a relationship between the type of activity that we have discussed now, and the carbonic anhydrase content.*

PLUM

Can one separate the effects of benzolamide on choroid plexus carbonic anhydrase from indirect effects of respiratory acidosis on the cerebral vascular bed? Does benzolamide penetrate the glial cell?

Maren, T. H. (1967) Carbonic anhydrase: Chemistry, physiology, and inhibition. *Physiol. Rev. 47*, 595–781.

Carter, M. J. & Parsons, D. S. (1968) Carbonic anhydrase activity of mucosa of small intestine and colon. *Nature. 219*, 176–177.

* *Bradbury:* Dr. Parsons has since confirmed that there is a relatively small content of carbonic anhydrase in both jejunum and ileum (Carter & Parsons 1968). He believes that it is insufficient to be related to the active transport of chloride or bicarbonate by these tissues or its inhibition by Diamox.

MAREN

Benzolamide does not produce the effect on cerebral blood flow that acetazolamide does, because it does not get into the red cell and therefore it does
not produce a respiratory acidosis and an increase in cerebral blood flow
(Maren 1967). So far as we know, however, this drug affects CSF flow in
the same way as acetazolamide. As Oppelt just showed, it appears to be
secreted into the choroid plexus from the blood side, just as for the kidney.
This appears to be the first demonstration of such an effect, for any drug.
But we do not know about its uptake into glia.

OPPELT

This is of course dose dependent. Using much higher doses one can get a
respiratory acidosis, i. e. a red cell effect.

COHEN

You mentioned the changes in substrate or in cerebral blood flow as possibly
contributing to a decrease in CSF formation with alkalosis. I wonder whether
this might be a direct pH effect on carbonic anhydrase or on other enzymes
involved in CSF production. In particular, do you know the pH dependency
of carbonic anhydrase?

MAREN

In this range it is neglibible (perhaps 2–3 fold) in view of the large enzyme
excess. I think the point about respiratory alkalosis is one of the clearest
things that Dr. Oppelt has shown, and it is a general phenomenon, as I said
before. It always mimics carbonic anhydrase inhibition, and it is at least
separable from blood flow, since it occurs in organs where this is not an
issue. By this I mean it is not primarily a vascular phenomenon. It appears
due to less CO_2 delivered to tissues in hypocapnia; in regions where hypocapnia lowers blood flow this would increase the effect.

Maren, T. H. (1967) Carbonic anhydrase: Chemistry, physiology, and inhibition. *Physiol. Rev. 47*, 595–781.

The Blood-Brain Barrier
Facts and Questions

Christian Crone

It is quite appropriate to discuss the blood-brain barrier in a symposium on "Ion Homeostatis of the Brain". An understanding of the mechanisms involved in the homeostatic functions requires detailed information about the permeability of the membranes which separate brain from plasma. Essentially two membrane systems govern the exchange: the choroid plexus and the blood-brain barrier. The surface area of the blood-brain barrier is at least 5000 times that of the chorioid plexus, and the permeability of the blood-brain barrier is therefore of great importance for the composition of the brain interstitial fluid.

The mere fact that a question with the particular formulation – homeostasis of an *organ* – can be raised signifies that exchange between plasma and brain extracellular fluid is different from exchange in other organs. Nobody would ask a similar question in connection with, say, the liver or muscle. There is, of course, a homeostatic regulation for these organs, but the lungs and the kidneys take care of this. However, if for some reason the plasma composition is altered, the extracellular fluid in these organs follows this change passively. This is not the case in the brain.

It is natural to stress that the concept of homeostasis refers to stability of the *extracellular* fluid. This, at least, was what Claude Bernard considered when he formulated the concept of the stability of the internal environment. But there is an equally interesting problem connected with the homeostatic mechanisms involved in the stabilization of the *interior of cells*. There are many similarities between regulation of the cell interior and regulation of the brain interstitial fluid. This led Krogh (1946) to use the analogy between the blood-brain barrier and cell membranes in general. He rather conceived

Institute of Medical Physiology, Dept. A, University of Copenhagen, Denmark
28, Juliane Maries Vej, DK 2100 Copenhagen Ø, Denmark

the brain extracellular fluid as being separated from blood by a membrane with cellular characteristics. In a cell the composition of the interior is the result of the net effect of "pumps" and "leaks" in the plasma membrane. Similarly, the composition of the brain interstitial fluid is determined by pumps and passive leaks in the blood-brain barrier and in the choroid plexus, respectively.

Both structures, cell membranes and the blood-brain barrier, are highly permeable to lipophilic gases and to other non-polar substances. Cells are not protected against substances with many lipophilic groups and neither is the brain. Although it is correct to stress the low permeability of the blood-brain barrier to most substances, it should not be forgotten that the brain is defenseless against a certain group of substances, as are cells.

ANATOMICAL ASPECTS

The most spectacular progress in the field of the blood-brain barrier has come from the work of Brightman, Karnovsky and Reese (Reese & Karnovsky 1967, Bodenheimer & Brightman 1968, Brightman & Reese 1969). It has been convincingly shown that the capillaries in brain differ from those in other organs. The endothelial cells are surrounded by a continuous belt of tight junctions which are tight for molecules down to a molecular weight of 2000 (Brightman, Reese & Feder 1970).

The endothelial cells are covered by foot-processes from astrocytes. The covering is not complete. The spaces between the glial processes are so large as to permit the passage of protein-markers with a molecular weight of 40,000.

From purely anatomical considerations, the most reasonable structure to be thought responsible for the low permeability between blood and brain is the capillary wall itself. Whether the possible regulatory functions in the homeostasis are performed by the brain endothelium is unknown. Experiments have not been designed which clearly distinguish between the two possibilities, endothelium or glial end-feet. One view point, however, is not tenable, namely that the brain capillaries have permeability characteristics similar to muscle capillaries. There can be no doubt that the permeability of the capillaries is smaller, but how much is the question.

A physiologist's concept of the structural basis for homeostatic regulation of brain interstitial fluid is seen in Fig. 1 (from Cohen, Gerschen-

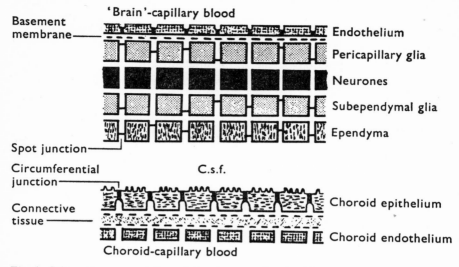

Fig. 1. Schematic representation of the structures involved in the exchange of materials between the blood, cerebrospinal fluid and cells within the vertebrate brain. The intercellular spaces between endothelial cells of "brain" capillaries are occluded by circumferential junctions *(zonulae occludentes)* which prevent the escape of proteins, such as peroxidase, from the blood. Circumferential junctions between choroid epithelial cells also act as a physical barrier for the escape of materials from the blood into the cerebrospinal fluid. (Reproduced from Cohen, Gerschenfeld & Kuffler, 1968, by courtsey of *J. Physiol.*).

feld & Kuffler 1968). A similar scheme was suggested independently by Brightman & Reese (1969).

PHYSIOLOGY

There are two different ways of assessing the permeability of the blood-brain barrier: either the uptake in brain with time is determined under conditions where the concentration of marker substance in the blood is kept constant, or the loss from blood as it flows through the brain is determined.

The difficulty with the first approach, the tissue-analysis method, is that many other factors besides the permeability of the blood-brain barrier influence the time-course of rise of concentration of marker substance in brain tissue. If there is an uptake of the substance in the cells in the brain it is clear that the rate of cellular uptake complicates the picture. Another dis-

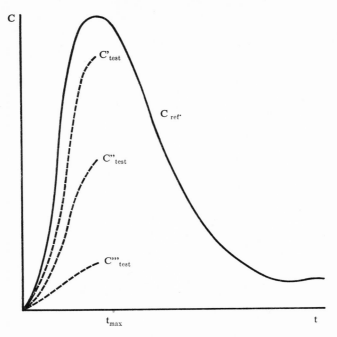

Fig. 2. Schematic drawing of time-concentration curves in the effluent blood from an organ obtained after single injection into the afferent vessel. C_{ref}: reference substance which does not leave the capillaries. C_{test}: various permeable test substances.

advantage is that fast transfer processes cannot be studied, because brain tissue cannot be taken out very rapidly for analysis.

The other approach has been described several times (Crone 1961, 1965a, Agnew & Crone 1967, Crone & Thompson 1970). It consists in an intra-carotideal injection of a mixture of albumin-bound dye and various test substances. The injection is immediately followed by sampling of venous outflow from the superior sagittal sinus. From an analysis of the dilution curves (Fig. 2) one obtains information about the rate of transfer across the blood-brain barrier. The advantage of this methodology is its high time-resolving power. Its disadvantage is that some test substances, for example small ions like K^+ or Na^+, separate within the vessels from the protein-bound dye reference, so-called Taylor diffusion (Taylor 1953, Lassen & Crone 1970).

The information which has come from studies with the indicator diffusion

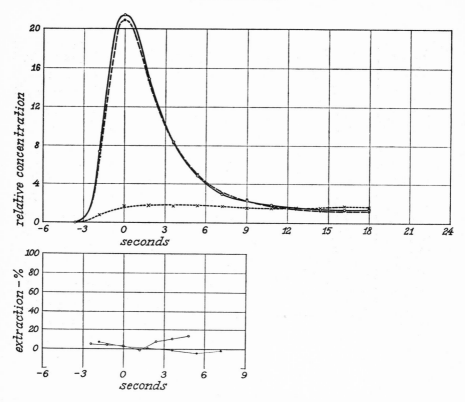

Fig. 3. The permeability of brain capillaries to propanol and glycerol. The upper part of the figure shows the time-concentration curves for Evans Blue Dye (o——o), glycerol (● – ●) and for propanol (x – – – x). The lower part of the figure shows the extractions of glycerol.

technique is that the permeability of the blood-brain barrier to even small polar substances is very limited. The presence of lipophilic and hydrophilic groups in a molecule is decisive for whether a given substance passes rapidly or slowly into the brain. This point is well illustrated in Fig. 3, which shows that the introduction of 2 OH-groups in the molecule of propanol (thereby changing it to the highly polar D-glycerol) dramatically reduces the transcapillary escape rate, reducing the transcapillary loss from 95 to 3 per cent. Other experiments with the same technique have shown that D-glucose passes the blood-brain barrier by facilitated diffusion (Crone 1965b). Furthermore, the blood-brain barrier distinguishes between the two optical isomers D- and

Fig. 5. Autoradiographic studies of the distribution of tritiated mannitol and glucose in rat brain 10–20 seconds after an intravenous injection of the substances. Stain: Methylene Blue.

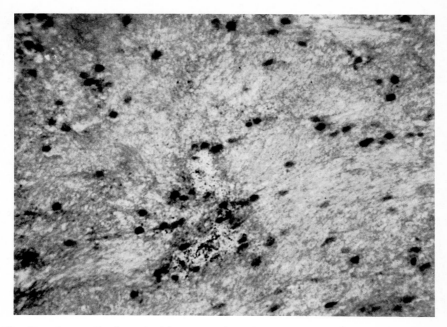

Fig. 5a. The localization of tritiated mannitol. Grains are only found intravascularly. Magnification: 100 ×. Section from cerebellar cortex.

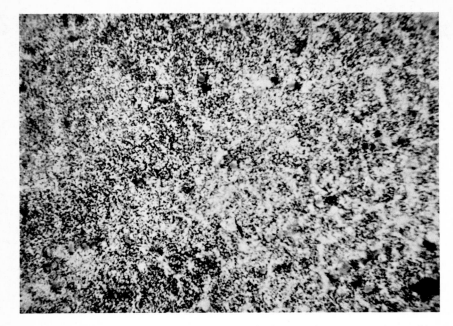

Fig. 5b. The localization of tritiated glucose. Grains are found everywhere with no signs of any preferred localization. Magnification: 100 ×. Section from cerebellar cortex.

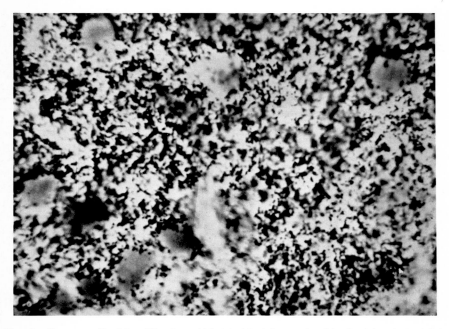

Fig. 5c. Same as 5b. Magnification: 400 ×. Nuclei are devoid of tritiated material.

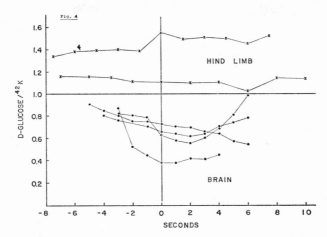

Fig. 4. Ratios between ¹⁴C-D-glucose and ⁴²K in the effluent blood from brain (lower part of figure) and hind limb (upper part of figure) after a single injection into the afferent vessel. A ratio above 1 signifies that ⁴²K has left the circulation faster than D-glucose. A ratio below 1 signifies that D-glucose has escaped faster. (From unpublished experiments by Crone & Thompson).

L-glucose (Crone & Thompson 1970). In brief, the blood-brain barrier shows several of the characteristics of a cell membrane. This behaviour is not reconcilable with the presence of a leaky membrane.

Another way of demonstrating the difference between the blood-brain interphase and the capillaries in other organs is to compare the relative concentrations of various test molecules or ions in the outflow from an organ immediately after an intra-arterial injection (the relative concentration is the concentration in the effluent relative to that in the injection solution). The thinking in connection with this method is best understood from inspection of Fig. 4.

The figure shows comparisons between brain and hind limb. The ratio in the effluent between ¹⁴C-D-Glucose and ⁴²K is below 1 in the brain and above 1 in the hind limb (mainly muscle). In a passive porous membrane more K⁺ than glucose would escape (because of a faster diffusion). This is the picture in the hind limb. In the brain the pattern is opposite. This finding cannot possibly be explained by a blood-brain interphase which behaves as a passive porous membrane. Yudilevich (1970) has revived the old hypothesis that the capillaries in brain are rather permeable, but that the glial envelope is impermeable and responsible for the blood-brain barrier characteristics.

His idea is that the capillaries being leaky let substances pass through according to the diffusion coefficients. At the glial level two things can happen: (1) some substances are "reflected" back to the blood, because of impermeability of the glial envelope; (2) others are let through (for example D-glucose). Such an analysis is, however, not reconcilable with the findings in Fig. 4. If Yudilevich's interpretation were correct, more potassium would be lost from the blood in the first few samples than glucose (reflecting the passive transcapillary loss) and the first samples would have a D-glucose/K^+-ratio above 1. This was never found.

Other results from studies of blood-brain barrier permeability are shown in Table 1, where ratios of outflow concentrations of various combinations of substances were investigated. Brain and hind limb were compared. The fact that the K/mannitol ratio is 1 in brain, despite the fact that K^+ diffuses faster than mannitol, is explained by the presence of a very impermeable membrane which prevents both species from leaving the blood, giving a ratio of 1 in the effluent. In the hind limb, however, the K/mannitol ratio is clearly below 1, as expected in a passive permeable membrane.

It is seen that the K/Na ratio is indistinguishable from 1. Again the simplest explanation for this finding is that the blood-brain barrier is virtually impermeable for both these ions. If this were not the case, more K^+ than Na^+ would have left owing to the faster diffusion of K^+.

The glucose/mannitol data corroborate earlier findings. In the brain the transfer of D-glucose away from the blood is faster than that of D-mannitol. In the hind limb the ratio was close to 1, as expected in a capillary membrane with a more pronounced passive leak.

These experiments do not give us information about the exact rate with which these ions and non-electrolytes pass the blood-brain barrier, but they indicate, that the blood-brain barrier is extremely tight to even small ions. Unfortunately for the problems connected with the origin of the D.C.-potential difference between blood and brain interstitial fluid, a detailed knowledge of the exact permeabilities of the various charged species is necessary, but not available. So far, it has not been possible to determine these parameters. In view of the importance of the relative permeabilities of charged species, the main conclusion is to stress the need for other and better experimental approaches.

In connection with these experiments, it is pertinent to mention the experiments by Fenstermacher & Johnson (1966) where the permeability of the

Table 1. Mean ratios of relative outflow concentrations after injection in supplying artery. Inflow ratio: 1.

*Dog Brain**		
^{42}K/*Mannitol	1.023 ± 0.014 (SE)	6 experiments
*Glucose/*Mannitol	0.678 ± 0.058	4 experiments
^{42}K/^{22}Na	0.988 ± 0.006	6 experiments
*Dog Hind Limb***		
^{42}K/*Mannitol	0.842 ± 0.008 (SE)	10 samples
	0.716 ± 0.017	23 samples
*Glucose/*Mannitol	0.945 ± 0.003	9 samples
	1.001 ± 0.004	11 samples

* ^{14}C or ^{3}H
** Means for 4–6 experiments, each yielding 6–11 serial sample values
*** Means of single experiments, SE for the number of samples indicated

blood-brain barrier was estimated by an osmotic approach. They found that the blood-brain barrier had pores with an equivalent pore diameter of 15 Å. This figure fits very well the general picture of the blood-brain barrier as a cellular membrane. Wright & Prather (1970) have studied the reflection coefficient of the chorioid plexus epithelium to a series of non-electrolytes and have obtained results which are qualitatively similar to those obtained on the blood-brain barrier.

DO GLIA CELLS NOURISH NEURONES?

The view has been held that passage through glia cells of glucose is a necessity in order for the substance to reach the neurones (Dempsey 1958). One function of the glia cells should be to nourish the neurones. No convincing proof of this theory has so far been delivered. In collaboration with W. F. Agnew* We tried to make a direct attack on the problem. The idea was that if the theory were correct it should be possible after a single administration of tritiated glucose to find the glia cells containing tritiated glucose at a time when the neurones had not received the glucose from the glia cells. The experiments were based on autoradiographic demonstration of the localization of tritiated glucose in rat brain.

The technique consisted in a single rapid intravenous injection of tritiated

* Huntington Memorial Hospital, Pasadena, California.

glucose. 30 seconds after the injection the brain was cut out and immediately frozen in isopentane cooled with an acetone dry ice (CO_2) mixture.
Sections of brain tissue were made with a microtome in a cryostat at -20 °C.
The specimens were 5–8 μ thick. They were then stored in a glass container
submerged in the freezing mixture and transferred to a freeze-drying appara-
turs and dried. Care was thus taken to keep the specimens at at least -20 °C
until the water was removed. The dry tissue sections were then transferred
to a microscope slide, a film of photographic emulsion (Ilford K5) was
mounted and the specimens were stored in a refrigerator (at 4° C) for
1–2 months. Controls were always made with sections from brains of
uninjected rats in order to ensure that artifacts were not present (in view
of the long exposure time). Similar experiments with tritiated mannitol were
also performed because it is generally agreed that this substance only pene-
trates into the brain interstitial fluid very slowly. The mannitol experiments
thus served as control for the diffusion of the tritiated compounds during
the preparation.

Figs. 5a, b, c show the results. It is seen that mannitol is localized
exclusively intravascularly. On the other hand glucose is spread over the
entire tissue. It was not possible to find any preferred localization of glucose
and we concluded that we had not been able to demonstrate the presence of
glucose in glia cells before it could be demonstrated in the neurones.

This "negative" result speaks against the "feeder-theory", which in my
eyes should be disregarded until somebody has demonstrated newly injected
glucose in glia cells before it reaches the neurones. Only dynamic studies
can prove this theory. A special formulation of the "feeder-theory" is the
above mentioned view point that passage through capillary-near glia cells
is an obligatory step in the transfer of hydrophilic substances from blood
to brain (see also Pappenheimer 1970).

WHY A BLOOD-BRAIN BARRIER?

The most commonly accepted answer to this question is that a tight blood-
brain barrier makes it possible to keep a composition of the brain interstitial
fluid which is different from that of plasma. The investigations of Bradbury
& Davson (1965), Cserr (1965), and Cohen, Gerschenfeld & Kuffler (1968)
have amply proved that the regulation of the interstitial fluid is very effective
over a wide range of changes in plasma concentrations of potassium. If the

low potassium concentration is important for the function of the neurones and glia cells, we see a clear necessity for a blood-brain barrier. It may be a difficulty for this viewpoint that the membrane potential of neurones is rather insensitive to changes in external potassium concentration in the low potassium range (between 2–10 mM). On the other hand, the glia cell membrane potentials, even in this range, are remarkably sensitive to changes in potassium concentration (Kuffler, Nicholls & Orkand 1966).

It is interesting, however, to consider other possibilities for the function of the blood-brain barrier. The brain continually produces and secretes transmitter substances. As every neurone is close to a capillary, there is a possibility for loosing the secreted transmitter, if there were no blood-brain barrier. Conversely, after it has been discovered that the amino acid L-glutamate serves as excitatory substance to certain cortical neurones (Krnjevic 1970), the necessity of a structure which prevents glutamate in plasma to reach the neurones is obvious.

Another possibility to consider is whether the blood-brain barrier has a function connected with the presence of the cerebrospinal fluid. Vertebrates, all of which have a blood-brain barrier (Davson 1967), have cerebrospinal fluid, while the invertebrates, among which many do not have a true blood-brain barrier, do not have a cerebrospinal fluid. It seems likely that in order to keep a volume of cerebrospinal fluid the permeability of the capillaries should be small. The system would be badly designed if the cerebrospinal fluid could escape back to blood through leaky capillaries. This aspect of the function of the blood-brain barrier has not been thoroughly considered so far.

REFERENCES

Agnew, W. F. & Crone, C. (1967) Permeability of brain capillaries to hexoses and pentoses in the rabbit. *Acta physiol. scand. 70,* 168–175.

Bodenheimer, T. S. & Brightman, M. W. (1968) A blood-brain barrier to peroxidase in capillaries surrounded by perivascular spaces. *Amer. J. Anat. 122,* 249–267.

Bradbury, M. W. B. & Davson, H. (1965) The transport of potassium between blood, cerebrospinal fluid and brain. *J. Physiol. (Lond.) 181,* 151–174.

Brightman, M. W. & Reese, T. S. (1969) Junctions between intimately apposed cell membranes in the vertebrate brain. *J. Cell Biol. 40,* 648–677.

Brightman, M. W., Reese, T. S. & Feder, N. (1970) Assessment with the electron-microscope of the permeability to peroxidase of cerebral endothelium and epithelium in mice and sharks. In *Capillary Permeability,* ed. Crone, C. & Lassen, N., pp. 468–476. Munksgaard, Copenhagen.

Cohen, M. W., Gerschenfeld, H. M. & Kuffler, S. W. (1968) Ionic environment of neurones and glial cells in the brain of an amphibian. *J. Physiol. (Lond.) 197,* 363–380.

Crone, C. (1961) The diffusion of some organic non-electrolytes from blood to brain tissue. Thesis (in Danish). Munksgaard, Copenhagen.

Crone, C. (1965a) The permeability of brain capillaries to non-electrolytes. *Acta physiol. scand. 64,* 407–417.

Crone, C. (1965b) Facilitated transfer of glucose from blood into brain tissue. *J. Physiol. (Lond.) 181,* 103–113.

Crone, C. & Thompson, A. M. (1970) Permeability of brain capillaries. In *Capillary Permeability,* ed. Crone, C. & Lassen, N., pp. 446–455. Munksgaard, Copenhagen.

Davson, H. (1967) *The Physiology of the Cerebrospinal Fluid.* J. & A. Churchill Ltd., London.

Dempsey, E. W. 1958) Discussion in *Biology of Neuroglia,* ed. Windle, W. F., p. 41. Charles C. Thomas, Springfield.

Fenstermacher, J. D. & Johnson, J. A. (1966) Filtration and reflection coefficients of the rabbit blood-brain barrier. *Amer. J. Physiol. 211,* 341–346.

Kuffler, S. W., Nicholls, J. G. & Orkand, R. K. (1966) Physiological properties of glial cells in the central nervous system of amphibia. *J. Neurophysiol. 29,* 768–787.

Krogh, A. (1946) The active and passive exchanges of inorganic ions through the surfaces of living cells and through living membranes generally. Croonian Lecture. *Proc. roy. Soc. B 133,* 140–200.

Krnjević, K. (1970) Glutamate and γ-aminobutyric acid in brain. *Nature.* In press.

Lassen, N. & Crone, C. (1970) The extraction fraction of a capillary bed to hydrophilic molecules. With a discussion of the role of diffusion between laminar streams (Taylor's effect). In *Capillary Permeability,* pp. 48–59. Munksgaard, Copenhagen.

Pappenheimer, J. R. (1970) Transport of HCO_3^- between brain and blood. In *Capillary Permeability,* ed. Crone, C. & Lassen, N., pp. 454–458. Munksgaard, Copenhagen.

Reese, T. S. & Karnovsky, M. J. (1967) Fine structural localization of a blood-brain barrier to exogenous peroxidase. *J. Cell Biol. 34,* 207–217.

Taylor, G. I. (1953) The dispersion of solute matter in solvent flowing slowly through a tube. *Proc. roy. Soc. A 219,* 186–213.

Wright, E. M. & Prather, J. W. (1970) The permeability of the frog chorioid plexus to nonelectrolytes. *J. Membr. Biol. 2,* 127–149.

Yudilevich, D. L. (1970) Serial barriers to blood-tissue transport studied by the single injector indicator diffusion technique. In *Capillary Permeability,* ed. Crone, C. & Lassen, N., pp. 115–129. Munksgaard, Copenhagen.

DISCUSSION

BRADBURY

I would like to point out that your results on the apparent impermeability of the blood-brain barrier to sodium and potassium would be completely compatible with results obtained by intravenous infusion and sampling of the brain. On the other hand, sampling of the brain after intravenous infusion does enable a distinction to be made between the low permeabilities to sodium and potassium.

WELCH

I think, that by comparing appearances in the brain, the potassium ion is about 10 times as permeable as the sodium ion.

CRONE

The experiments which we have performed with sodium and potassium do not allow definite conclusions as to differences between the rates of transport of the two ions from blood into brain.

SIESJÖ

The remarkable thing about the CSF composition is the stability of the potassium, hydrogen, calcium, and magnesium ion concentrations. Is there any information about the concentrations of these ions in the other creatures you were talking about. Is there a less perfect regulation?

CRONE

I would refer you to the papers by Rall (1962, 1967). I don't think there is a less perfect regulation, but the requirements to the regulatory system may be smaller in view of the extraordinary stability of the environment, sea water.

Rall, D. P. (1962) The structure and function of the cerebrospinal fluid. In *The Cellular Functions of Membrane Transport,* ed. Hoffmann, J., pp. 269–282. Prentice Hall, Inc., New Jersey.
Rall, D. P. (1967) Comparative pharmacology of cerebrospinal fluid. *Fed. Proc. 26,* 1020–1023.

SIESJÖ

You have asked the question why a blood-brain barrier is needed. Isn't it needed because the potassium and the hydrogen ion concentrations, as well as the calcium and magnesium ion concentrations, are functionally important?

CRONE

The point is that the concentration in the blood of these ions does not vary much. It is not at all obvious why the central nervous system has such great requirements to ionic stability that a special regulatory system (the blood-brain barrier) is necessary. Neurones are virtually insensitive to changes in potassium concentration around the normal values. The glial cells, however, monitor changes in potassium concentration even in the low concentration ranges. This may or may not be important.

SØRENSEN

What is the relative permeability of the blood-brain barrier to anions and cations of similar size? In the case of the lactate ion we are faced with the problem that we have to invoke a permeability which is several orders of magnitude larger than the permeability to for instance glycerol (which is about the same size) in order to explain the elimination of lactate at the rate at which it occurs. This fact suggest that the blood-brain barrier either is particularly "permeable" to lactate or that it in general is more permeable to anions than to cations.

CRONE

We have made a few experiments with radioactive chloride, but they are a little difficult to interpret, due to the carriage of chloride with the red cells. However, the main impression is that there is no significant difference between the behavior of the positive and the negative ions, during the passage through the brain.

SEVERINGHAUS

Dr. Nemoto in our laboratory is completing some work on the transport of lactate between blood and brain. It is really not quite finished, but it seems clear that the blood-brain barrier is several times more permeable to L-lactate than D-lactate. The uptake of L-lactate by brain can be blocked by saturation of the blood with a large amount of cold lactate, suggesting that there is a transport facilitation.

SIESJÖ
Don't we have to take into account the fact that lactate is an acid which will also exist in the unionized form?

SØRENSEN
If lactate was eliminated from the brain as lactic acid, we would have to invoke an even larger permeability, because the concentration of lactic acid in brain extracellular fluids is less than 1/1000 of the concentration of lactate.

WADDELL
The solubilities of the lactate ion and the unionized lactic acid are very similar. Both are very polar so one would guess that the permeability of membranes to the two types of molecules would be similar.

SØRENSEN
Dr. Severinghaus, I would like to have a little more information about how the results on facilitated lactate diffusion were obtained. As far as I know it is very difficult to obtain this information because we are talking about a metabolite.

SEVERINGHAUS
Dr. Nemoto injected ^{14}C-labelled L- or D-lactate intravenously into anesthetized rats within 1 minute after hepatectomy and killed the rats by decapitation at different times varying from 15 seconds to 20 minutes after injection. He then assayed the whole brain for ^{14}C activity. ^{32}P-labelled red cells given simultaneously permitted correction for the amount of blood left in the brain. After 1 minute, the brain contained about 0.4 per cent of the injected L-lactate and about 0.15 per cent of the injected D-lactate activity. Virtually none of the ^{14}C activity in the brain at 1 minute was acid labile or precipitable as glucose, pyruvate or malate as determined by the Barker-Summerson copper-lime treatment. This would indicate that the ^{14}C activity in the brain was due to labelled lactate.

AMES

I was particularly interested in Dr. Crone's last comments about the role of the blood-brain barrier in maintaining CSF volume. I quite agree that it is hard to see how CSF could be present in any appreciable quantities in the absence of a barrier; for the osmotic force exerted by the serum proteins would draw the CSF back into the blood vessels if the walls of these vessels were freely permeable to the smaller solutes. This is a novel consideration to me and most entertaining. Brightman & Reese (1969) have reported an interesting finding from their horseradish peroxidase studies. They showed that, in just those areas where the blood-brain barrier is absent (i. e. area postrema and median eminence), the ependyma *does* have continuous tight junctions. One can imagine these as being sort of "plasma sniffing" areas, where the neurons are exposed to plasma contents, the latter being kept from leaching away by the ependymal barrier.

CRONE

There is also the aspect that some of the cells in the brain are neurosecretory cells producing polypeptides, which, of course, have to enter the blood. In those areas the capillaries seem to be different and there is an absence of the blood-brain barrier judging from penetration of dye from blood into tissue.

Brightman, M. W. & Reese, T. S. (1969) Junctions between intimately apposed cell membranes in the vertebrate brain. *J. Cell. Biol. 40,* 648–677.

Transepithelial Potentials and Ion Transport

Hans H. Ussing

The title of this talk really poses two questions: (1) How do transepithelial potentials influence ion transports, and (2) how do ion transports influence transepithelial potentials? Even in the case of inanimate homogeneous membranes these two questions present formidable difficulties, and a complete solution in the case of multilayer structures like epithelia is hardly feasible. However, by making suitable simplifying assumptions, useful results may be obtained.

One approach is the flux ratio analysis (Ussing 1949a). The "membrane", which in this treatment just means an unstirred sheet, separating two well stirred solutions, is treated as a "black box", and we only want to know how the whole structure influences the flux ratio for the different ionic species present. The flux ratio equation (sometimes called the independence equation) states that for an ionic species passing through a membrane without interacting with other moving particles and without being subject to active transport, the flux ratio is independent of conditions in the membrane phase and is determined solely by the electrochemical potential difference across the membrane for the ion in question.

It has been generally assumed that the fluxes should be measured under steady-state conditions. Actually, this limitation is not necessary (Ussing 1970b). If the flux ratio for an independently diffusing ion is calculated from the amounts of two ideal tracers which pass through the membrane in opposite directions, the value of the flux ratio is the same from the moment of appearance of the isotopes on the opposite sides of the membrane until the time of steady-state flux. Thus, if a system is changing due to treatment with a drug, a hormone, or other chemical agent, or because of general deterioration, the flux ratio may still give correct information with respect

Institute of Biological Chemistry, University of Copenhagen, 2 Øster Farimagsgade, DK-1353 Copenhagen K, Denmark.

to the presence or absence of interactions (e. g. active transport), provided that the fluxes are measured for a period which is short compared with the rate of change of the potential and resistance "profiles" inside the membrane. If conditions within the membrane can be considered constant during the experiment, a change in the flux ratio with time must mean that the ion in question must be able to follow more than one pathway through the membrane: The faster pathway may dominate the flux ratio initially whereas the slower ones will dominate later. In this way, one may for instance be able to disclose the simultaneous existence of a passive and an active transport path.

An example of behaviour in agreement with the flux ratio equation is presented by chloride passing through the isolated frog skin. If sodium chloride is present on both sides of the skin, chloride normally moves from the outside to the inside solution (Huf 1935) but the flux analysis shows (Koefoed Johnsen et al. 1952) that the movement is passive and that the reason for the passage is the electric potential difference of up to 170 mV (inside positive) which is maintained by the skin as long as sodium (or lithium) ions are present in the outside medium. The movement of sodium, on the other hand, is almost exclusively active (Ussing 1949b). Indeed, it is this active transport of sodium which is the source of the electric potential difference across the skin. This is clearly shown in particular by the short-circuiting technique (Ussing & Zerahn 1951): When the potential across a skin with identical sodium-containing solutions on both sides is maintained at zero by an applied external E. M. F., the current generated by the skin is exactly equal to the difference between the influx and the efflux of sodium. This difference is equal to the net transport of sodium. The flux ratio for sodium under these conditions is usually between 100 and 20, whereas for a passive ion, the flux ratio ought to be one. Thus sodium passes almost exclusively due to active transport. Chloride and other anions seem to behave passively. The potassium fluxes are very small indeed and do not contribute measureably to the over-all picture. The net potassium transport during short circuiting may be slightly positive or negative. Recent experiments (see Table 1) where the influx and efflux of potassium were measured on paired skin halves in the presence of Inderal (which inhibits the glandular activity) indicate that the influx is larger than the efflux. The table also illustrates that the flux ratio is constant during a period when the absolute values of the fluxes are still far from the steady state values. This

Table 1.

After add. of isotope	cm $\times$ sec^{-1} $\times$ 10^8		"P$_{in}$"/"P$_{out}$"
	"P$_{in}$"	"P$_{out}$"	
15'	8	4	2.0
30'	15.2	4.4	3.5
45'	24.8	7.2	3.4
60'	27.6	8.8	3.1
120'	39.0	11.0	3.6

Determination of non-steady state flux ratios for potassium ions on short-circuited frog skins (R. temporaria). Influx and efflux were determined simultaneously on paired skin halves with 42-K. The non-steady state fluxes are expressed as apparent permeability coefficients, "P$_{in}$" and "P$_{out}$".

slight inward transport of K is seen when the K-concentration in the bathing solutions is 2mM, but it vanishes when the K-concentration is increased to, say, 20 mM. Thus, we can still say that the active sodium transport is solely responsible for the electric asymmetry of the frog skin. The flow of passive ions like chloride under the influence of the potential (in non-shorted skins) represents a shunt for the "sodium battery". An equivalent circuit of the frog skin would then consist of a sodium battery in series with a sodium resistance and shunted by a conductance represented by passive ions.

One can predict from the equivalent circuit just mentioned that the skin potential is usually an involved function of passive and active transports, but that one should be able to measure the "true" electromotive force of the sodium-battery if the shunt could be reduced to zero. Technically this situation can be approached either by treating the skin with a trace (10^{-5} molar) CuSO$_4$, which reduces the chloride permeability appreciably, or by replacing chloride by the more slowly penetrating sulfate ion.

Both procedures, especially with R temporaria, often give very high and stable potentials.

With such skins it was possible for us to show (Koefoed Johnsen & Ussing 1958) that the outside of the skin behaved towards changes in ionic composition as if it were a sodium electrode whereas the inside of the skin behaved like a potassium electrode. Thus the potential seemed to be the sum of a sodium diffusion potential and a potassium diffusion potential. Still we had every reason to believe that active sodium transport was the source of the potential. These two apparantly conflicting views could be reconciled if we made the following three assumptions: (1) The inward facing cell membrane has properties similar to those of nerve and muscle fibres, viz., it is highly permeable to K and Cl, but slightly permeable to Na (and sulfate). (2) The outward facing membrane is highly permeable to Na and also permeable to Cl, but little permeable to K and sulfate. (3) The inward facing membrane only is provided with an active transport mechanism which maintains the cellular sodium low and the potassium high.

The above-mentioned two membrane hypothesis with suitable modifications has been applied successfully to account for the relationship between potential and transports in many epithelia. Thus in toad bladder, frog skin and many other epithelia, strophanthin inhibits the ion transport when applied from the serosal side only (where the ion pump is supposed to be located), whereas amiloride inhibits only when applied on the apical side of the epithelium. In the frog skin sodium transport is stimulated by high concentrations of bicarbonate on the inside, whereas this ion is without much effect on the outside. On the other hand, CO_2 inhibits the transport more when applied from the outside than from the inside (Funder *et al.* 1967). One gets the impression that the site which is acted upon by bicarbonate and CO_2 is located so that it is placed between two barriers with different permeability characteristics. Similarly, changes in osmotic pressure have quite different effects on the frog skin (and the toad bladder) depending on whether the change takes place on the inside or the outside (Ussing 1965). Thus an increase in osmotic pressure on the inside usually increases the resistance (and inhibits sodium transport) whereas an increase on the outside leads to a violent drop in electric resistance.

Whereas these and many other cases of asymmetrical behaviour of epithelia may agree with a simple two membrane structure, there are observations which can be accounted for only on the basis of a more detailed picture of the anatomical arrangement of the cells in the epithelium.

Measurements of intracellular potentials in the frog skin epithelium with microelectrodes led Ussing & Windhager (1964) to propose that the epithelium cells were interconnected to a three-dimensional network by low resistance bridges, forming a functional cyncytium. The intercellular spaces were supposed to form a continuous system of slits and pores in relatively free connection with the inside bathing solution, whereas they were more or less completely closed toward the outside bathing solution.

A similar structure was proposed independently by Farquhar & Palade

(1964). These authors also demonstrated the presence of ATP-ase along all the surfaces facing the interspaces, whereas the enzyme was absent on the surface facing the outside bathing solution. Furthermore, they drew attention to the fact that low resistance connections between neighbouring cells can be demonstrated in, for example, salivary glands of insects (Loewenstein 1964). (For the present Symposium it may be of interest to recall that glia cells also seem to be connected by low-resistance bridges, cf. Kuffler 1966).

For the revised two-membrane model of the frog skin then, the sodium-selective membrane is still the outward-facing surface of the first living cell layer in the epithelium (just underneath the unicellular corneum). The potassium-selective membrane with the sodium pump, however, would be the total surface of epithelium cells facing the intercellular spaces.

Experiments performed in our laboratory (Smith, in press) have indeed revealed that the skin has two capacities in series, of which the outer one is of the order of one microfarad per cm^2 whereas the inner one is about 50 times larger. This result is compatible with the assumption that the outer condensor is the outer surface of the first living cell layer, whereas the inner one is the total inner surface of the epithelium facing the interspaces. A single cell layer could hardly possess a capacity of the observed magnitude.

If we accept the picture of the epithelium outlined above, certain important consequences are apparent. In the first place, the long winding intercellular path will give rise to a diffusion delay for ions (and other particles) passing through the skin. For ions such as potassium which are present in low concentration in Ringer's and in high concentration in the cells, the system may act like an ion exchange column so that, for instance, a ^{42}K-ion which is present in the outer part of the interspace system is much more likely to enter a cell than to pass through the interspace system into the inside bathing solution.

Furthermore, the shape of the interspace system and its relative narrowness may allow the concentration of certain substances in the interspace system to deviate appreciably from the respective concentrations in the inside bathing solution. This fact may be responsible for many of the cases where epithelia fail to comply with the predictions from the simple two-membrane model.

It has been pointed out (see, for instance, Diamond 1962) that the transport of sodium chloride into the long and narrow interspaces in the gall bladder epithelium may lead to a "standing gradient" of this electrolyte which may lead to constant osmotic flow of water (and other easily diffusible substances) from the lumen to the serosal side of the organ.

Under normal conditions the outward facing side of the frog skin is too tight for more than minute amounts of water to be transported in this fashion. If, however, the osmotic pressure of the outside bathing solution is made higher than that of the inside solution, the epithelial permeability increases dramatically, and it seems that a shunt-path is created through the epithelium (Ussing 1965, 1970a). Under these conditions one may get a coupled transport of solutes from the outside to the inside of the skin which can best be explained as anomalous solvent drag (Ussing 1969).

The question may be asked whether all cell layers in the frog skin participate to the same extent in the transport of sodium and thus in the development of the skin potential. For the time being he question cannot be answered with certainty. Recent experiments have shown, however, (Voûte & Ussing 1968, 1970) that if the sodium transport is increased by sending an ingoing current (for example twice the short-circuit current) through the skin, there is a strong swelling of the first living cell layer (counting from the outside) whereas the other cell layers remain unchanged. If a similar current is passed in the outward direction, the same cell layer shrinks whereas there is virtually no change in the rest of the epithelium. These observations may suggest that most of the handling of sodium is performed by the reacting cell layer. However, it still remains to be proven that the changes are due to changes in the sodium content.

The above considerations have been mainly concerned with the explanation of epithelial potentials in terms of a two-membrane model of the epithelial cell provided with specific ionic selectivities and an active transport of sodium. Many electrophysiological observations can be explained in terms of such a model.

One should not forget, however, that bioelectrical potentials may arise from other active transport processes. Thus it was found several years ago (Hogben 1951) that the potential of the gastric mucosa is due to active chloride transport, and both active chloride transport and active transport of bicarbonate have been observed. In insects (but probably not in vertebrates) a sodium-independent potassium transport seems to play an important role for the maintenance of potentials (see, for instance, Harvey & Nedergaard 1964).

However, a survey of the literature will reveal (see, for instance, Keynes

1970) that most of the electric "output" of epithelia is due to the sodium pump.

REFERENCES

Diamond, J. M. (1962) The mechanism of solute transport by the gall bladder. *J. Physiol. 161*, 474–502.

Farquhar, M. G. & Palade, G. E. (1964) Functional organization of amphibian skin. *Proc. nat. Acad. Sci. (Wash.) 51*, 569–577.

Funder, J., Ussing, H. H. & Wieth, J. O. (1967) The effects of CO_2 and hydrogen ions on active Na transport in the isolated frog skin. *Acta physiol. scand. 71*, 65–76.

Harvey, W. R. & Nedergaard, S. (1964) Sodium-independent active transport of potassium in the isolated midgut of Cecropia silkworm. *Proc. nat. Acad. Sci. (Wash.) 51*, 757–765.

Hogben, C. A. M. (1951) The chloride transport system of the gastric mucosa. *Proc. nat. Acad. Sci. (Wash.) 37*, 393–395.

Huf, E. (1935) Versuche über den Zusammenhang zwischen Stoffwechsel, Potentialbildung und Funktion der Froschhaut. *Pflügers Arch. ges. Physiol. 235*, 655–673.

Keynes, R. D. (1970) From frog skin to sheep's rumen: A survey of transport of salts and water across multicellular structures. In press.

Kofoed-Johnsen, V., Levi, H. & Ussing, H. H. (1952) The mode of passage of chloride ions through the isolated frog skin. *Acta physiol. scand. 25*, 150–163.

Kofoed-Johnsen, V. & Ussing, H. H. (1958) The nature of the frog skin potential. *Acta physiol. scand. 42*, 298–308.

Kuffler, S. W. & Nicholls, J. G. (1966) The physiology of neuroglial cells. *Ergebn. Physiol. 57*, 1–90.

Loewenstein, W. R. & Kanno, Y. (1964) Studies on an epithelial (gland) cell junction. I. Modifications of surface membrane permeabiltiy. *J. Cell Biol. 22*, 565–586.

Smith, P. (1970) Passage of alternating current across frog skin. *Acta physiol. scand.* In press.

Ussing, H. H. (1949 a) The distinction by means of tracers between active transport and diffusion. *Acta physiol. scand. 19*, 43–56.

Ussing, H. H. (1949 b) The active ion transport through the isolated frog skin in the light of tracer studies. *Acta physiol. scand. 17*, 1–37.

Ussing, H. H. & Zerahn, K. (1951) Active transport of sodium as the source of electric current in the short-circuited frog skin. *Acta physiol. scand. 23*, 110–127.

Ussing, H. H. & Windhager, E. E. (1964) Nature of shunt path and active transport path through frog skin epithelium. *Acta physiol. scand. 61*, 484–504.

Ussing, H. H. (1965) Relationship between osmotic reactions and active sodium transport in the frog skin epithelium. *Acta physiol. scand. 63*, 141–155.

Ussing, H. H. (1969) The interpretation of tracer fluxes in terms of membrane structure. *Quart. Rev. Biophys. 1*, 365–376.

Ussing, H. H. (1970 a) Tracer studies and membrane structure. In *Capillary Permeability*, ed. Crone, C. & Lassen, N. Munksgaard, Copenhagen.

Ussing, H. H. (1970 b) The use of the flux ratio equation under non-steady state conditions. In *Festschrift for Kenneth Cole*. In press.

Voûte, C. L. & Ussing, H. H. (1968) Some morphological aspects of active sodium transport. The epithelium of the frog skin. *J. Cell Biol. 36*, 625–638.

Voûte, C. L. & Ussing, H. H. (1970) The morphological aspects of shunt-path in the epithelium of frog skin. *Exp. Cell Res.* In press.

DISCUSSION

MAREN

Is the effect of amiloride unique for the frog skin system?

USSING

As far as I know amiloride acts in the same way on kidney, on toad bladder, and on frog skin, that is, it inhibits transport immediately. The moment amiloride is added to the outside bathing solution, the short circuit current drops to zero or to a very low value, and within seconds of its removal the current is back to the full value again. It does not take any time for diffusion, and it doesn't seem to change the metabolism. It just stops the entry of sodium.

MAREN

Is there any other drug which has this effect?

USSING

Progesterone seems to act in a similar way. It may have a very slight effect on the inside of the frog skin but when added to the outside solution there is an immediate inhibition, which can readily be washed away again.

SIESJÖ

Could the decrease in sodium transport, observed when the CO_2 tension was increased, be explained by competition between hydrogen ions and sodium ions for a common carrier?

USSING

There have been quite a lot of very careful studies on hydrogen ion transport in the frog skin. Compared to the sodium transport, the hydrogen transport is virtually nonexistent (Friedman et al. 1967, Funder et al. 1967). It might

Friedman, R. T., LaPrade, N. S., Aiyawar R. & Huf, E. G. (1967) The chemical basis for the [H^+] gradient across the isolated frog skin. Amer. J. Physiol. 212, 962–972.

Funder, J., Ussing, H. H. & Wieth, J. O. (1967) The effect of CO_2 and hydrogen ions on active Na transport in the isolated frog skin. Acta Physiol. Scand. 71, 65–76.

Fuhrman, F. A. (1952) Inhibition of active sodium transport in the isolated frog skin. Amer J. Physiol. 171, 266–278.

be that sodium ions and hydrogen ions are competing for some carrier sites, but that the hydrogen ions are not being transported. In some systems the hydrogen ion will compete both for the sites and for the transport, whereas in the frog skin apparently, it can inhibit the site, but it cannot be transported. If it was transported we should have been able to draw a current from the skin when changing the pH of the bathing solution. In this context, I think it is rather interesting to point out that Fuhrman (1952) found that sulphonamides cause 50 per cent reduction in sodium transport.

SØRENSEN

In the experiments you were quoting, the pH changes were extreme. The P_{CO_2} was around 500 mmHg. Is there any indication of a diphasic response when lowering pH? I am referring to the fact that we later are going to hear about an opposite effect of pH on potentials. Is it possible that you are dealing with so extreme conditions, that you knock out the whole system, including the metabolism?

USSING

At a P_{CO_2} of 500 mmHg the metabolism is not knocked out, but certainly such conditions are extreme. We are normally running the frog skin with a P_{CO_2} of practically zero and are probably working near the optimum of the activity. When we increase the P_{CO_2} we are changing the cellular pH. First there is a slight stimulation on Na transport (at 4 mm CO_2) and then an inhibition, but also when we go to very extreme basic pH values we get an inhibition. However, we haven't been so interested in that end of the curve, but I know that we need a pH of 9 to 10 before we get inhibition. This seems to be rather unphysiological.

DC Potentials between CSF and Blood

H. H. Loeschcke

In 1924 Lehmann & Meesmann (1924) published a paper "On the existence of a Donnan-equilibrium between blood and ocular fluid and cerebrospinal fluid respectively". They observed potentials of $+6$ to $+15$ mV between CSF and the external jugular vein in anesthetized cats and rabbits. This study has been overlooked by later investigators including myself but Lehmann & Meesmann's (1924) results have been amply confirmed. Such experiments are listed in Table 1. Measurements were made on cats, rabbits, rats, dogs, goats and humans.

NORMAL VALUES

With the exception of results presented by Tschirgi & Taylor (1954, 1958), all the investigations listed here show the CSF to be slightly positive ($+3$ ... $+14$ mV) with respect to the reference electrodes. Tschirgi & Taylor found slightly negative potentials and state that the potential may vary between negative and positive values, depending upon the depth of anesthesia and the state of the acid-base equilibrium of the blood. In contrast to other investigators, in most of their experiments they measured the potential of the *surface of the brain cortex* against jugular blood. The meninges were opened. It seems quite probable that the brain was not covered with cerebrospinal fluid and this may have altered the situation. To what extent these experiments may or may not be compared with those in which the electrode was in CSF will be discussed later. Potentials of the brain surface against blood or indifferent electrodes located, for example, on the nasal bone have been observed by a number of authors, and the history of these investigations is as old as that of the electroencephalogram (Brazier 1963); for recent references see O'Leary & Goldring 1964, Caspers & Speckmann

Institut für Physiologie der Ruhr-Universität Bochum, D-4630 Bochum, Germany.

Table 1. DC potentials of CSF in warm blooded animals. Normal values.

Authors	Year	Animal	mV	"Hot" electrode	Ref. electrode
Lehmann & Meesmann	1924	cat, rabbit an.	+ 6 ... + 15	4th ventr.	ven. jug. ext.
Loeschcke	1956	rabbit, anesth.	+ 12.4 ± 1.8*	cisterna	occipital bone
Tschirgi & Taylor	1958	rat, rabbit an. cat, dog an.	− 1 ... − 5	brain surface	ven. jug. ext.
Mottschall & Loeschcke	1963	cat an.	+ 5.3 ± 5.4*	cisterna	occip. joint
Severinghaus, Mitchell, Richardson & Singer	1963	man awake dog an.	+ 3 ± 0.5** + 4 ± 1**	lumbar CSF cisterna	? ?
Held, Fencl & Pappenheimer	1964	goat awake dog an.	+ 6.8 + 6.1	cisterna lat. ventr. cisterna	ven. jug. ext. ven. jug. ext. ven. jug. ext.
Welch & Sadler	1965	rabbit an.	+ 14	lat. ventr.	chor. plex. interstitium
Loeschcke	unpublished	cat an.	+ 3.2 ± 1.9*	cisterna magna cisterna pontis	atlanto occ. joint sinus of dura ven. jug. ext.
Schöne & Loeschcke	1969	cat an.	+ 6.1 ± 4.1*	cisterna magna	chor. plex. interstitium
		cat, rabbit an.	+ 3.3 ± 4.3*	mock CSF	isolated chor. plex. interstitium

* standard deviation.
** standard error?

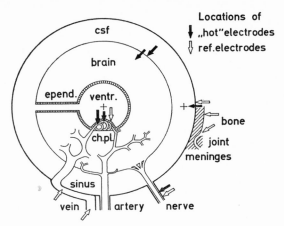

Fig. 1. The anatomical situation with indication of location of electrodes in several studies.

1969. Usually, however, instead of absolute values only potential changes have been reported. Hirsch *et al.* (1968b), in the isolated perfused dogs head, gave absolute values of DC-potentials if pCO_2 or pO_2 were varied but in their preparation it is difficult to state what is normal. Furthermore, potentials were taken from the outside of the parietal dura against the frontal bone. The inflow of blood into the head was connected to earth. This unusual technique makes it impossible to compare the data with those listed in Table 1 although the relative changes agree well with the relative changes reported by other investigators.

LOCATION OF THE ELECTRODES AND SPATIAL DISTRIBUTION OF POTENTIALS

In the last column of Table 1 it may be seen that the reference electrodes have been located at widely varying sites. Most of them are indicated in Fig. 1 which schematically depicts the anatomical situation. What influence has the location of the reference electrode on the height of the potential measured? Table 2 gives data from two experiments in anesthetized cats.

In these experiments the Calomel half cells against each other in KCL or NaCl solutions were without potential. In the experiment of Dec. 14 the atlanto-occipital membrane and the atlanto-occipital joint were exposed from the dorsal side and in the experiment of Dec. 18 from the ventral side. The "hot" electrode therefore was introduced into the cisterna magna

Table 2. Influence of location of reference electrodes on CSF potential.
Cats anesthetized with chloralose-urethan. Calomel electrodes, 2 m KCl Agar bridges
(unpublished experiments).

Date	Site of electrode	Site of reference electrode	Potential mV
Dec. 14, 1965	Cisterna magna	Atlanto-occipital joint	+ 5
		Sinus lat. dors.	+ 2
		Vena jug. ext.	+ 1
Dec. 18, 1965	Cisterna pontis	Atlanto-occipital joint	+ 3.8
		Sinus lat. ventr.	+ 2.5
		Vena jug. ext.	+ 3.4

on Dec. 14 and into the cisterna pontis on Dec. 18. In both exposures venous sinuses imbedded between two sheets of the dura can be recognized laterally running in rostro-caudal direction. These vessels, since not indicated in books on the anatomy of the cat available to the author, have been named sinus lateralis dorsalis and ventralis, respectively, for convenience. On Dec. 18 the potentials derived by the use of three references were very similar; the one measured against the sinus lateralis ventralis was slightly lower than the other two. Somewhat larger differences occurred on Dec. 14. It may be stated, however, that changes of the potentials during inhalation of CO_2 or injection of HCl in both experiments were almost perfectly equal in all three leads. This will be shown later (Fig. 4).

The situation becomes much clearer in Fig. 2. Using here a similar schematic drawing as in Fig. 1, the resistances measured in a single experiment in an anesthetized cat between the indicated points are presented. The data indicate that resistances between all 3 reference points (occipital bone, atlanto-occipital joint and jugular vein) are small in comparison to the resistance through the meninges measured between cisterna magna and either occipital bone or jugular vein. All three reference electrodes therefore pick up the potential of the outside of the meninges against the CSF. The potential differences between the reference electrodes which may be calculated from Table 2 are not systematic and may partly depend upon the degree of lesion by surgery of the local cells or of depolarization by potassium chloride leaking out of the agar bridges.

The cerebrospinal fluid as a layer of high conductivity is surrounded by the brain on one and the meninges on the other side which are both

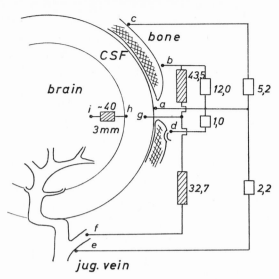

Fig. 2. The physical situation as demonstrated in a single experiment on an anesthetized cat (29.4.1970). Resistances (1000 c/sec) have been measured by an impedance bridge between several sites of electrodes. The voltage applied was between 2 and 4 V. The resistance of the electrode pair (7 kΩ) (Hg, HgCl, KCl-Agar) has been subtracted from the measurements. Numbers in the Fig. represent resistances in kΩ. Location of the electrodes on the outside of the atlanto-occipital membrane (a), the bone of the skull 10 mm and 26 mm rostral of the electrode on the atlanto-occipital membrane (b, c), in the atlanto-occipital joint (d), on the outside of the external jugular vein (e), inside of the same vein (f), cisterna magna (g), dorsal surface of medulla oblongata (h), 3 mm inside the medulla oblongata (i).

structures of low conductivity as compared with CSF or the tissue outside of the skull. This leads to the postulate that in all CSF there is a rather homogeneous level of potential, either against the interior of the brain or the blood or against the extracranial tissues including the jugular vein. The extracranial tissue would be electrically connected to the brain or the blood vessels of the brain by such bridges as the blood vessels themselves, the sheaths of cranial nerves, and possibly connections in the olfactory area. Similarly, because of the high conductivity of the extracranial tissues, the potential level there should be homogeneous and possibly similar to the level of brain blood vessels. Small deviations may be imagined where local sources of potential exist mainly in structures injured by surgery or as a consequence of local depolarization of cells under the reference electrodes by KCl leaking out of the electrode system.

Systematic studies on the role of the position of the CSF electrode are not available. Kao & Loeschcke (1965) in anesthetized cats, observed slightly differing potentials (2–3 mV) against one reference in the jugular vein between electrodes in the lateral ventricle, the third ventricle and the cisterna magna. These differences were maintained if blood pH was changed by injections of HCl or $NaHCO_3$. All other authors introduced only one electrode into the cerebrospinal fluid space. The high conductivity of CSF as compared with brain matter would suggest a rather homogeneous potential of CSF against reference. Since, however, the paths of CSF connecting the ventricles with each other are narrow, thereby increasing resistances, some potential difference seems to be quite possible depending upon the site or sites of the source of the potential. Even in punctures of the choroid plexus by Welch & Sadler (1965) small differences of potential have been obtained at different points of the plexus.

The situation may be different if potentials are picked up from the surface of the brain. In this case and especially so when the surface is dry, it may be assumed that the electrode picks up potentials between neuronal elements as well as potentials of that local CSF which may have leaked out of the brain under the electrode. From this aspect differences between brain surface and CSF potentials which will be described later may be understood.

A slowly moving electrode was used in rabbits by Loeschcke (1956). The electrode penetrated the atlanto-occipital membrane, the cisterna magna, the posterior part of the fourth ventricle and the medulla oblongata in one set of experiments and the meninges of the convexity of the brain the subdural (capillary) space, the cortex, and the lateral ventricle in another set of experiments. Glass capillaries with tips measuring 0.1 to 0.5 mm in diameter served as electrodes. As soon as the electrode pierced the meninges, the potential rose rectangularly from zero to about +12 mV, sometimes in 2 steps in the region of the medulla oblongata and a little less in the convexity. As it entered the medulla or the cortex, the potential dropped more or less smoothly to values around zero, and if the electrode tip left the medulla on the opposite side the potential again became positive; as it passed the lateral ventricle a positive peak was observed. It is questionable, however, if this procedure allows definite conclusions about the spatial distribution of potential inside the brain matter, because injury potentials may contribute more or less, according to the momentary location of the electrode tip. Woody *et al.* and Besson *et al.* (1970) used electrodes placed inside the brain to record the effects of disturbances of the acid-base balance of the blood. They state that the potential changes, if picked up from different depths inside the brain or from the surface, were almost identical in direction and amplitude, although the absolute values which are not presented might differ.

The first ones using microelectrodes in CSF potential studies were Welch & Sadler (1965). They exposed the choroid plexus of a lateral ventricle of rabbits and punctured it with a capillary electrode. The CSF was found to be $+64$ mV against the interior of the ependymal cells and $+14$ mV against the interstitium of the plexus. No difference of potential between the interstitial tissue and the lumen of a venule was observed.

Schöne & Loeschcke (1969) punctured the choroid plexus of anesthetized cats of the fourth ventricle and observed potentials of CSF against interstitium of about $+6$ mV. Isolated plexuses of cats or rabbits were punctured with microelectrodes, and average transependymal potentials of CSF against interstitium of $+3.3$ mV were determined.

It is interesting that Nicely (1955), in the frog, observed positive potentials (10 mV) of the interior of a nerve sheath against the outside. Nerve sheaths are prolongations of the meninges and their interior fluid is connected to CSF. The small positive potentials (1 .... 3 mV) observed by Patlak (1964) between brain ventricles and the extradural tissue of the dogfish (squalus acanthias) do not deviate much from the results in mammals. The data of Hogben *et al.* (1960) in the same animal, however, show the opposite polarity.

Most of the more recent investigators agree that it is necessary to use electrodes of the same type as hot and reference electrodes. For example, Hg–HgCl or Ag–AgCl electrodes should be used, and the contact with tissue fluid should be made with KCl bridges of high concentration of KCl. 0.5, 2, 3 molar or saturated KCl have been used in different studies. The KCl bridge usually was solidified by agar gel. These rules have not been observed in all investigations.

FACTORS INFLUENCING CSF POTENTIALS

Lehmann & Meesmann (1924) observed that the potentials between the CSF or the ocular fluid and the blood decreased if the CSF contained

6*

proteins or if the brain was artificially perfused with protein-free solutions. At this time the influence of CO_2 or hydrogen ions on DC potentials was not known, and since these factors have not been kept constant the protein concentration has not been the only important variable in their experiments. The authors' conclusion, that the observed potentials might be Donnan potentials, cannot be accepted in the light of more recent information on the ion concentrations of CSF, which do not follow a Donnan distribution, as will be discussed later.

The effect of CO_2 inhalation on cortical potentials in rats, rabbits, cats, and dogs was first mentioned by Tschirgi & Taylor (1954) and described in extenso in 1958 and was independently observed in transmeningeal potentials of the rabbit by Loeschcke (1956b). Tschirgi & Taylor in addition described potential shifts in the same direction in metabolic acidosis. Held, Fencl & Pappenheimer (1964) established a quantitative linear relation of the CSF potential to arterial pH in respiratory and metabolic acidosis and in anesthetized dogs found an average slope of 32 mV/pH in respiratory acidosis and of 43 mV/pH in metabolic acidosis and similar results in awake goats. Mottschall & Loeschcke (1963) observed positive shifts in metabolic acidosis in cats; inhalation of more than 5 per cent CO_2, however, caused the transmeningeal potential to drop. This species difference has recently been confirmed by Woody et al. (1970) measuring potential changes of the cortical surface or of the interior of the brain against the jugular vein. In these studies in *cats* and *rhesus monkeys* respiratory acidosis caused negative and metabolic acidosis positive shifts of the potential. The observation of Held et al. (1964) that the slope of the potential against arterial pH was less in respiratory than in metabolic acidosis may mean that in the dog as well in respiratory acidosis a counteracting effect in negative direction is superposed upon the positive effect of arterial pH observed in metabolic acidosis.

The time course of CSF potential changes in respiratory and metabolic acidosis have been described by Loeschcke (1956b), Mottschall & Loeschcke (1963) and Held et al. (1964), time courses of cortical potentials by Tschirgi & Taylor (1958) and a number of authors including the most recent papers of Woody et al. (1970) and Besson et al. (1970) where references may be found. The time course of the decay of the transmeningeal potential of rabbits after killing the animal was described by Loeschcke (1956a). The same author (1956b) described a moderate drop of the transmeningeal potential of the rabbit during inhalation of 7 per cent of O_2. This diminution was not more than could be expected from the accompanying decrease of pCO_2 caused by the hypoxic hyperventilation. This result is important insofar as this is the only situation in which the response of the CSF potential differs in *quality* from the response of the cortical potential. In severe hypoxia there is a very marked negative shift of the cortical potential, and the same is the case in complete ischemia after an initial positive shift (Hirsch *et al.* 1968a, b, Caspers & Speckmann 1969). In contrast to this, as already mentioned, the transmeningeal potential after death of the animal (judged by stop of circulation and respiratory arrest) decays exponentially to zero. The comparison, however, of the two types of experiment is difficult, because in the measurements of transcortical potential the absolute values of the potentials are not known and the "terminal depolarisation" may therefore be a decay to zero.

Held *et al.* (1964) studied the influence of ion concentrations in ventriculocisternal perfusion fluid. With variation of the potassium concentration the slope was -1 mV per meq/l. The potential remained unaffected by concentration changes of HCO_3^-, H^+, Na^+ and Cl^-. Variation of K^+ in the blood plasma between 4 and 11 meq/l was without influence. 10^{-6} m ouabain in the ventricular fluid reduced CSF formation and potential.

With most ions Welch & Sadler (1965) found similar effects on the transependymal potential of the choroid plexus in the lateral ventricle of the rabbit. Only the effect of Na^+ differed insofar as diminution of the sodium concentration in CSF was followed by an increase in the potential. In the experiments of Schöne & Loeschcke (1969) in isolated choroid plexus of cats and rabbits, stepwise replacement of sodium by potassium caused depolarisation. Isotonic replacement of Na^+ by choline$^+$ again was followed by a depolarisation of the potential. Potassium was constant in this latter experiment. The depolarisation for a given diminution of sodium was equal in both experiments, which means that the depolarisation obtained by replacing sodium by potassium was an effect of the diminution of the sodium concentration rather than of an increase of the concentration of potassium. Ouabain diminished the potential as in the experiments of Held *et al.* (1964) and Welch & Sadler (1965). It should be kept in mind, however, that the situation in the isolated plexus is quite different from that of a plexus *in situ*, inasmuch as the blood and interstitial phase are not continuously replaced and probably equilibrate soon with the bathing fluid by leaks or passive fluxes. The situation, therefore, may be more comparable to that of a frog's skin immersed on both sides in the same solution.

In introducing this discussion it may be stated that there is not necessarily one source of the DC potential. Several different sources may contribute and the magnitude of their contributions may vary from site to site. The type of potential from different sources may not be identical.

A. Nature of CSF potentials

In Lehmann & Meesmann's (1924) pioneer paper the DC potentials of CSF and ocular fluid against the jugular vein have been considered as Donnan potentials. At their time it was believed that pH of both fluids was strongly on the alkaline side and that the chloride concentration in the fluids is much above that of the blood. Obviously pH measurements were erroneous because of the loss of CO_2. These data qualitatively would have supported a Donnan distribution though Donnan's r would have deviated more from 1 than might have been expected. More recent data on ion concentrations, for example those of De Rougemont et al. (1960), Ames et al. (1964), or of Fencl et al. (1966) clearly indicate that there is no Donnan distribution between the blood and the CSF or ocular fluid. The fluid formed by the choroid plexus (Ames et al. 1964), however, is very similar to an ultrafiltrate, only Mg^{++} and Ca^{++} showing major deviations and sodium being only slightly more concentrated in plexus fluid than in plasma ultrafiltrate. Using Ames' (1964) data and calculating r from choroid plexus fluid concentration over plasma concentration for Na^+ yields r = 0.97, for chloride r = 1.04. Both would be normal figures for r, and if the abnormalities of the concentration ratios of the bivalent ions Ca^{++} and Mg^{++} are neglected, this may be considered as a distribution close to Donnan's equilibrium. The different concentration of ions in CSF, as sampled from the cisterna, may then be explained by secondary exchange processes with the blood, or addition of metabolites, or of fluid of different composition not produced by the choroid plexus or a combination of all three factors. In such a hypothesis indeed a Donnan potential would be expected across the ependyma of the choroid plexus but not generally between CSF and blood. This potential, however, would be about +1 mV. It would not explain the measured potentials.

If the data of Ames *et al.* (1964) in the cat are used to calculate maximal concentration potentials (Nernst) of plexus fluid against blood plasma, these would be for Na⁺, Cl⁻ and K⁺ + 0.8, + 1.2 and + 7.7 mV, and those of cisternal fluid against plasma would be in the same order of ions + 0.8, + 2.2 and + 13 mV. If the potential between the CSF and the blood would be a concentration potential, this would be determined by all ions according to their individual permeabilities and would approximately follow Gold-mann's equation which may be written as follows for CSF and blood plasma

$$E = \frac{RT}{F} \ln \frac{[Na^+]_{pl} \cdot P_{Na} + [K^+]_{pl} \cdot P_K + [H^+]_{pl} \cdot P_H + [Cl^-]_{CSF} \cdot P_{Cl} + [HCO_3^-]_{CSF} \cdot P_{HCO_3}}{[Na^+]_{CSF} \cdot P_{Na} + [K^+]_{CSF} \cdot P_K + [H^+]_{CSF} \cdot P_H + [Cl^-]_{pl} \cdot P_{Cl} + [HCO_3^-]_{pl} \cdot P_{HCO_3}}$$

if bivalent ions are neglected. In the fluids on both sides of the membrane sodium and chloride concentrations are high in comparison to the other ions, especially potassium. The potential is determined by these ions. If potassium should contribute appreciably to the potential, it would be necessary to assume a very much higher permeability for this ion than for sodium and for chloride. If the potassium concentration in CSF, however, is increased markedly in the experiment, a depolarisation of the CSF potential (in dogs) occurs as described by Held, Fencl & Pappenheimer (1964). No effect, however, could be observed after changing blood plasma potassium concentration. This, in the view of the Goldmann equation, may be interpreted as meaning that the ependymal cell membrane on the side exposed to CSF is permeable enough to allow some contribution of the potassium potential to the total potential, while on the interstitial side of the same cell, permeability to potassium relative to the permeabilities of the other ions is less. (See, however, discussion).

Summarising, it may be stated that Donnan potentials do not contribute appreciably to the CSF potentials and that it is not probable that concentration potentials contribute much more, though some influence of the latter cannot be excluded.

A positive answer finally must be given to the question if active ion transport is able to cause potentials of the observed magnitude. This concept is based on the observation that ouabain, which is considered as an inhibitor of active transport mechanisms, introduced into CSF diminishes the potentials of the choroid plexus *in vitro* and *in situ* appreciably and that the same is the case with the potentials measured in the cisterna against the jugular vein. The data on ion concentrations in CSF of cats of Ames *et al.*

(1964), for example, would not be against the assumption that sodium ion is transported into the CSF, water and the other ions following passively. The low concentrations of K^+ and Ca^{++} in plexus fluid are not contradictory; the relatively high concentration of magnesium, however, may need an additional explanation in the future.

A completely different concept with regard to the nature of *cortical* potentials has been proposed by several investigators (see Caspers & Speckmann 1969). These authors believe and give good arguments that this potential reflects the state of polarisation of superficial neurons and that the changes of it are a compound effect of changes of polarisation, for example of postsynaptic membrane potentials. There is no doubt that under the influence of afferent impulse traffic in a population of neurons, a dynamic state of potential difference between the postsynaptic membrane of the soma and the dendrites and the efferent axon develops, and that even on the dendritic branches such potential gradients may exist. Such potentials would in a statistical way be picked up by an electrode on the cortical surface against any indifferent electrode mainly if the neurons are oriented perpendicularly to the surface. The most convincing example of such *neuronogenic* cortical DC potentials is seen in rhythmic seizures in which the bursts of cortical activity are accompanied by a negative DC potential shift if the electrode is on the focus. The fact that the negativity on such a focus is surrounded by a positive area indicates that this is a more local phenomenon. Synchronous changes of pH and pCO_2 in the jugular vein have been observed by Caspers & Speckmann (1969), but they state that "comparative evaluations of the concomitant DC displacements do not reveal any significant differences as to voltage and time course of the shifts whether pH changes turn out to be alkaline, acidic or biphasic".

In steady states of CO_2 inhalation or of metabolic acidosis, however, all authors agree that cortical potentials and transmeningeal potentials react in the same direction and approximately with the same amplitude. The question arises whether these potential shifts are neuronogenic or created by active pump mechanisms or both. If the active transport on the blood-tissue interface is able to cause potential gradients perpendicularly to the cortical surface, of course it is to be expected that these potentials are superimposed on potentials of neurogenic origin along the neurons. Postsynaptic potentials measured by intracellular electrodes may well reflect them. It has been observed by Caspers & Speckmann (1969) that part of the nerve cells of the central nervous system show polarisation and part depolarisation of postsynaptic potentials if CO_2 is inhaled. At this moment it is impossible to decide whether these effects are primary effects on the postsynaptic membrane itself or effects of different origin superimposed on the cellular potentials. In that case the position of the neuron in the electric field may be the determining factor in deciding if a hyper- or depolarisation will be observed.

One of the effects which is probably neuronogenic is the terminal negative shift of the cortical potential in severe hypoxia which is considered as a hypoxic depolarisation of neuronal membranes. This type of negative shift has not been observed in transmeningeal potential measurements. In the experiments of Loeschcke (1956b) in the rabbit, a slight depolarisation in hypoxia was observed and this could be accounted for by the diminution of pCO_2. After death of the rabbit the transmeningeal potential dropped to zero and not to a strongly negative level as seems to be case with the cortical potential. Furthermore, the time constant is much longer than that in the terminal depolarisation of the cortex. If this result should be confirmed by a direct observation in the same animal it would permit the conclusion that the transmeningeal potential measured on the atlanto-occipital membrane does not reflect the neuronogenic components of the potentials which may be observed on the cortex. If this were true, since the cortical potential reacts to respiratory and metabolic acidosis in the same way as the transmeningeal potential, the effects of both types of acidosis would be non-neuronogenic. This conclusion is not yet definite. More experimental data are needed. It seems, however, to be the best working hypothesis at the moment.

Woody et al. (1970) and Besson et al. (1970) measured the cerebral blood flow (CBF) at the same time as cortical potentials. In cats and rhesus monkeys they found a good correlation between increase of CBF and negative shifts of the cortical potential. The correlation holds in CO_2 inhalation, sleep, arousal, and alteration of blood flow by drugs.

In their view "the correlation seems to be sufficiently great to warrant the hypothesis of some relationship between the two". This relationship suggests to them that the potential shifts in CO_2 inhalation may indicate their nature as blood-brain barrier potentials. Furthermore, as the authors state, the "administration of drugs such as nembutal and strychnine in sufficient amounts to disrupt neuronal activity" does not alter the character of the potential shift with CO_2. They reach the same conclusion, as derived

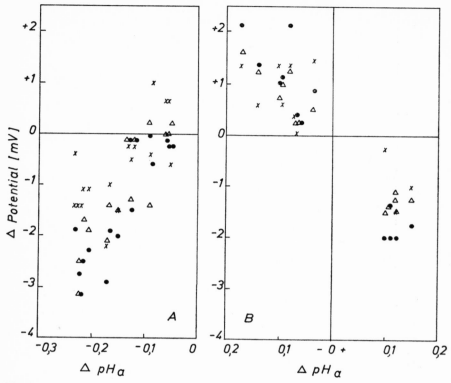

Fig. 3. Changes of transmeningeal potential caused by changes of arterial pH in respiratory acidosis (A) and in metabolic acidosis or alkalosis (B) in an anaesthetized cat (14.12.1965). The slopes have opposite signs in the two types of experiments. Hot electrode in cisterna magna, three reference electrodes: × in atlanto-occipital joint, Δ in sinus lateralis and ● in external jugular vein (see Table 2).

from the experiments in severe hypoxia, that "transcortical potential differences, such as might be expected from potentials of neuronal origin, do not comprise a significant factor in these potential shifts".

It should be mentioned that the correlation between CBF and potential shifts is not so general as it may seem. In the cat in metabolic acidosis the shift is in opposite direction to that in respiratory acidosis. In both cases, however, in the steady state an increase of cerebral blood flow is expected. In the dog and the rabbit, for example, the shifts in both types of acidosis are in the same direction but opposite to that in respiratory acidosis in the cat. Woody *et al.* (1970) take refuge from this difficulty under the hypo-

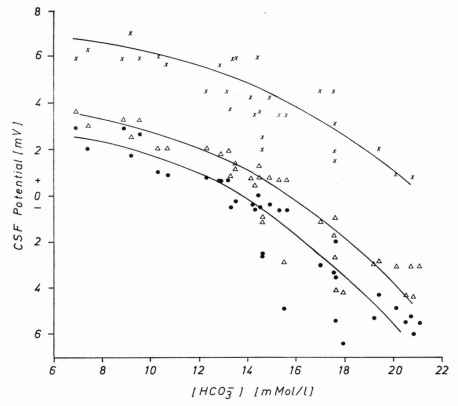

Fig. 4. All data of transmeningeal potential of a long-lasting experiment (same as Fig. 3) plotted against plasma bicarbonate concentration including controls, respiratory acidosis by CO_2 inhalation, metabolic acidosis by i.v. HCl injection and metabolic alkalosis by i.v. $NaHCO_3$ injection. Three reference electrodes (see Table 2). This plotting suggests a *unique* dependance of potential upon plasma bicarbonate concentration. The relative changes using three reference electrodes (as in Fig. 3) are almost identical.

thesis that there are two different effects causing the positive shift in metabolic acidosis and the negative one in respiratory acidosis.

As for the opposite reaction of the cat to severe respiratory acidosis and to metabolic acidosis, experiments of Loeschcke (unpublished) may give a clue. Arterial pH and endtidal pCO_2 were recorded in cats anesthetized with chloralose-urethan simultaneously with the potential between the cisterna magna or the cisterna pontis against 3 different reference electrodes (on occipital bone, on the atlanto-occipital joint and the jugular vein). In Fig. 3 the potential changes are plotted against plasma pH separately for CO_2 inhalation (left) and metabolic acidosis (HCl i. v.) or alkalosis ($NaHCO_3$ i. v.). In Fig. 4 the data from the same cat in an experiment lasting many hours were plotted against plasma bicarbonate concentration, which was calculated from pH and endtidal pCO_2. It turns out that the potentials in both types of acidosis or alkalosis now follow a unique function. This may be interpreted as meaning that the potential depends upon the plasma bicarbonate concentration rather than the plasma hydrogen ion concentration. As is well known, $[HCO_3^-]$ varies conversely with $[Cl^-]$. Therefore the potential may as well depend upon the chloride concentration instead of HCO_3^- so that the experiment does not allow a decision between both. It does, however, suggest that more attention should be paid to the anions than has been the case so far.

The physiological role of the DC potentials

There are two lines of thought about the role played by the DC potentials of CSF.

(1) There is no doubt that the potentials between CSF and blood, for example across the choroid plexus or the brain capillary walls, influence the distribution of ions between the two phases. The magnitude of the potential must be known to the physiologist who wants to find out whether a certain kind of ion is in electrochemical equilibrium or not. The potentials in fact are not very high, rarely more than $+15$ mV. Their influence on the distribution of ions therefore is not too great. Several authors, for example Pappenheimer (1967) or Severinghaus et al. (1963), discussed this aspect of the potential. Since it is partly an active transport potential it is an expression of the processes taking part in CSF production and may therefore be called a "blood brain barrier potential". This aspect has been discussed by Tschirgi & Taylor (1954, 1958), Loeschcke (1956), Held et al. (1964), Welch & Sadler (1965).

(2) The potential may influence neurons. Creutzfeldt et al. (1962) discussed this aspect as did Caspers & Speckmann (1969) recently. How much it may influence activity of neurons electrotonically depends on the gradient along these neurons which it may constitute. The spatial distribution in a microscopic sense of the gradients inside the brain matter should be known better for this purpose. In Creutzfeldt's calculation such an influence would

be small if effective at all. Still some influence must exist, and the DC potential may help a cell to discharge when otherwise the afferent impulse traffic would just be subthreshold. Loeschcke (1956a) discussed the question whether DC potentials in the region of the medulla may act in such a way on respiratory neurons. It was not possible, however, to stimulate respiration by local application of direct current on the surface of the medulla, even at such spots where electrical stimulation of respiratory movements by rectangular pulses was possible.

B. Sources of CSF potentials

The discussion of the anatomical and physical situation led to the view that CSF is charged (usually positive) against indifferent electrodes outside the skull and that there is not much difference where the reference electrode is located. It is questionable whether CSF is charged against the matter of the brain. The experiments of Loeschcke (1956a) may suggest that there is a pretty steep gradient from the surface to the interior of the brain, for example about 10 mV/0.1 mm (rabbit). These experiments, however, are not conclusive because it is not easy to decide whether or not injury potentials of brain structure play a role in the measurement.

It seems to be certain that one of the sources of the CSF potential is the choroid plexus. Since no potential difference exists between the blood and the interstitium the ependyma must be considered as the source of the potential. This has been established by Welch & Sadler (1965) and by Schöne & Loeschcke (1969) by puncturing the plexus. Even in the isolated plexus a (diminished) potential has been observed by the latter authors. The choroid plexus potential at least partly is dependent upon an active transport process since it is strongly reduced by ouabain.

It is conceivable that the choroid plexus would be the only battery which charges the CSF against the blood. It may be discussed if in the meninges a similar battery is located. The very steep gradient of potential across the meninges does not necessarily support this hypothesis because the conductivity of this membrane is very low in comparison to CSF or to the tissue in the neck. Only the observation that the resistance between the jugular vein and the CSF is about as high as that of the meninges makes it difficult to believe that it is possible to use the jugular vein as prolongation into brain of an electrode picking up the potential of brain blood against CSF.

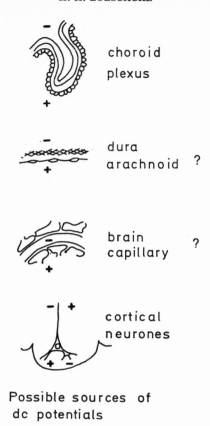

Possible sources of
dc potentials

Fig. 5. The possible sources of CSF – DC potentials. Only the choroid plexus and the neurons on the surface of the brain can so far be considered as contributing batteries with some certainty. The meninges and the walls of the brain capillaries possibly contribute.

This difficulty would not exist if in the meninges a battery of the same type delivering the same potential as in the choroid plexus could be assumed. The histology, however, is not in favour of this. The dura contains no continuous layer of cells like the ependyma. The arachnoid does, although the cells are flat and do not suggest activity.

The capillaries of the brain covered with the glial membrane may behave similarly to the choroid plexus and produce similar potentials. If so, on a section of the brain the potential would be distributed in a local pattern of gradients. A macro-electrode introduced may not pick up anything else than an average charge which may be close to zero and only on the most superficial layer of the brain a gradient may become observable with such a technique. Such a concept would fit well into the experimental data of Loeschcke (1956a).

All potentials so far mentioned in this chapter may be called blood-brain barrier potentials.

Mainly on such parts of the brain where neurons are oriented perpendicularly to the surface, the situation is prone to be involving the picking up of potentials of neuronal origin, mainly if such potentials are synchronized in the population of cells. These potentials may form a source of potential parallel to the already mentioned DC potentials of the blood-brain barrier. They are most convincingly seen in seizures or in terminal hypoxic depolarisation. In distinction to the blood-brain barrier potentials, these are more local phenomena, though probably contributing everywhere on the cerebral and cerebellar cortex.

REFERENCES

Ames, A. III, Sakanoue, M. & Endo, S. (1964) Na, K, Ca, Mg and Cl concentrations in choroid plexus fluid compared with plasma ultrafiltrate. *J. Neurophysiol. 27,* 672–681.

Besson, J. M., Woody, C. D., Aleonard, P., Thompson, H. K., Albe-Fessard, D. & Marshall, W. H. (1970) Correlations of brain d-c shifts with changes in cerebral blood flow. *Amer. J. Physiol. 218,* 284–291.

Brazier, M. A. B. (1963) Historical introduction. The discoverers of the steady potentials of the brain: Caton and Beck. In *Brain Function,* ULCA Forum in Medical Sciences, pp. 1–13. University of California Press.

Caspers, H. & Speckmann, E. J. (1969) DC potential shifts in paroxysmal states. In *Basic Mechanisms of the Epilepsies,* ed. Jasper, Ward & Pope, pp. 375–395. Little, Brown and Company, Boston.

Creutzfeldt, O. D., Fromm, G. H. & Kapp, H. (1962) Influence of transcortical d-c currents on cortical neuronal activity. *Exp. Neurol. 5,* 436–452.

Fencl, V., Miller, T. B. & Pappenheimer, J. R. (1966) Studies on the respiratory response to disturbances of acid-base balance, with deductions concerning the ionic composition of cerebral interstitial fluid. *Amer. J. Physiol. 210,* 459–472.

Held, D., Fencl, V. & Pappenheimer, J. R. (1964) Electrical potential of cerebrospinal fluid. *J. Neurophysiol. 27,* 942–959.

Hirsch, H., Scholl, H., Paschke, G. & Schmidt-Schönbein, H. (1968a) Die Veränderung der corticalen Gleichspannung bei kompletter und inkompletter Ischämie des Gehirns. *Pflügers Arch. ges. Physiol. 301,* 334–343.

Hirsch, H., Scholl, H., Dickmann, H. A., Eisoldt, J., Gaehtgens, P., Mann, H. & Krankenhagen, B. (1968b) Die corticale Gleichspannung des Hundegehirns bei Veränderung des arteriellen pO_2 und pCO_2. *Pflügers Arch. ges. Physiol. 301*, 344–350.

Hogben, C. A. M., Wistrand, P. & Maren, T. H. (1960) Role of active transport of chloride in formation of dog-fish cerebrospinal fluid. *Amer. J. Physiol. 199*, 124–126.

Kao, F. F. & Loeschcke, H. H. (1965) Bestandspotentiale im Gebiet der Liquorräume. *Naturwissenschaften 52*, 562–563.

Lehmann, G. & Meesmann, A. (1924) Über das Bestehen eines Donnangleichgewichtes zwischen Blut und Kammerwasser bzw. Liquor cerebrospinalis. *Plfügers Arch. ges. Physiol. 205*, 210–232.

O'Leary, J. L. & Goldring, S. (1964) DC Potentials of the brain. *Physiol. Rev. 44*, 99–125.

Loeschcke, H. H. (1956a) Über Bestandspotentiale im Gebiet der Medulla oblongata *Pflügers Arch. ges. Physiol. 262*, 517–531.

Loeschcke, H. H. (1956b) Über den Einfluss von CO_2 auf die Bestandspotentiale der Hirnhäute. *Plfügers Arch. ges. Physiol. 262*, 532–536.

Mottschall, H. J. & Loeschcke, H. H. (1963) Das transmeningeale Potential der Katze bei Änderung des CO_2-Druckes und der H^+ Ionenkonzentration. *Pflügers Arch. ges. Physiol. 277*, 662–670.

Nicely, M. (1955) Measurement of the potential difference across the connective tissue sheath of frog sciatic nerve. *Experientia 11*, 199–200.

Pappenheimer, J. R. (1967) The ionic composition of cerebral extracellular fluid and its relation to control of breathing. *Harvey Lect. 61*, 71–94.

Patlak, C. S. (1964) Potential difference of ventricular fluid *in vivo* and *in vitro* in the dogfish. *Fed. Proc. 23*, 211.

De Rougemont, J., Ames III, A., Nesbett, F. B. & Hofmann, H. F. (1960) Fluid formed by choroid plexus. A technique for its collection and a comparison of its electrolyte composition with serum and cisternal fluids. *J. Neurophysiol. 23*, 485–495.

Schöne, H. & Loeschcke, H. H. (1969) Bestandspotentiale am Plexus chorioideus des 4. Ventrikels von Katze und Kaninchen in vitro. *Pflügers Arch. ges. Physiol. 306*, 195–209.

Severinghaus, J. W., Mitchell, R. A., Richardson, B. W. & Singer, M. M. (1963) Respiratory control at high altitude suggesting active transport regulation of CSF pH. *J. appl. Physiol. 18*, 1155–1166.

Tschirgi, R. D. & Taylor, J. C. (1954) A steady bioelectric potential between the blood and the cerebrospinal fluid (CSF). *Fed. Proc. 13*, 154.

Tschirgi, R. D. & Taylor, J. C. (1958) Slowly changing bioelectric potentials associated with the blood brain barrier. *Amer. J. Physiol. 195*, 7–22.

Welch, K. & Sadler, K. (1965) Electrical potentials of choroid plexus of the rabbit. *J. Neurosurg. 22*, 344–351.

Woody, C. D., Marshall, W. H., Besson, J. M., Thompson, H. K., Aleonard, P. & Albe-Fessard, D. (1970) Brain potential shift with respiratory acidosis in the cat and monkey *Amer. J. Physiol. 218*, 275–283.

Influences of Respiratory Acidosis and of Cerebral Blood Flow Variations on the DC potential

J. M. Besson*, C. D. Woody** & W. H. Marshall**

The studies that have been carried out on the DC potential (or steady potential) have been centered on its variations and its absolute value. Everyone agrees that a difference of potential exists between the cortex and another part of the body used as a reference, the surface of the cortex always being positive. The meaning of this difference of potential is very complicated owing to the interference of various factors of neuronal and extraneuronal origin (for further details, see O'Leary & Goldring 1964).

The variations of the DC potential have been studied during natural modifications of physiological conditions (Wakefulness and sleep) or during artificial modifications such as central stimulation, spreading depression, respiratory or metabolic acidosis, anoxia and drug injection. The DC potential is particularly sensitive to the variations of blood pH. Respiratory acidosis or metabolic acidosis in different species (rat, rabbit, dog, goat) provoke a positive DC shift (Goldensohn *et al.* 1951, Held *et al.* 1964, Kjällquist & Siesjö 1968, Loeschecke 1956, Tschirgi & Taylor 1958).

There is a relationship between the brain DC potential and blood pH which parallels the postulated physical chemical formulation for electrochemical potentials generated by H ion gradients across the blood brain barrier. The relationship between the DC potential and the blood pH has been examined in a previous paper (Loeschcke 1970); we will only study the neg-

Laboratoire de Physiologie des Centres Nerveux, Faculté des Sciences, Université de Paris, 4, Avenue Gordon-Bennett, F-75 – Paris (16°), France.
  * Laboratorie de Physiologie des Centres Nerveux, Faculté des Sciences, Université de Paris, 4 Avenue Gordon-Bennett, Paris (16°), France.
 ** Laboratory of Neurophysiology, National Institute of Mental Health, Bethesda, Maryland 20014, U.S.A.

ative variations observed during respiratory acidosis in cats and monkeys. These negative deflections had already been described by Mottschall & Loeschcke (1963) on the cat and by Meyer *et al.* (1962) on the monkey.

This report can be divided in two parts: to start with, we will study the negative deflections observed during respiratory acidosis and their correlation with the increase of the cerebral blood flow (CBF). Secondly, the use of different pharmacological modifications will enable us to confirm the relationship between CBF and DC potential. (Cf. Besson *et al.* (1970) and Woody *et al.* (1970) for experimental procedures and techniques.)

NEGATIVE DC SHIFTS DURING RESPIRATORY ACIDOSIS

Despite what is generally believed, especially in other species, a negative DC shift is generally observed during respiratory acidosis in the cat and monkey. Respiratory acidosis, therefore, does not only provoke a positive deflection. In other words, the results depend a good deal on the animal species, as the same experiments carried out on the dog and rabbit give positive deflections. In Fig. 1 are shown a series of examples of positive and negative DC shifts in various species.

These results do not depend on the recording conditions, as we used different types of electrodes and different amplifiers. This is confirmed by the fact that, if we compare our results with those given by Held *et al.* (1964) on the amplitude of the positive deflection compared with the variation of blood pH in the dog, they are both similar (roughly 32 mV/pH unit). Tschirgi & Taylor (1958) and Held *et al.* (1964) placed the reference electrode in the jugular vein; we did not notice much difference in the results, whatever the place of the electrode: in a blood vessel (jugular vein, carotid artery), on a muscle, on a subcutaneous tissue, on the frontal sinus or on the posterolateral occiput.

The DC shifts affect the whole of the CNS, as we were able to observe it at different levels: cortical, thalamic, bulbar, spinal, in the third ventricle, and in the cisterna magna. This suggests an extraneuronal origin for these variations. This is confirmed by the fact that negative DC shifts during respiratory acidosis remain after use of different pharmacological substances that modify neuronal mechanisms, such as intravenous injections of high doses of Nembutal or locally applied KCl or strychnine (Fig. 2) on the cortex.

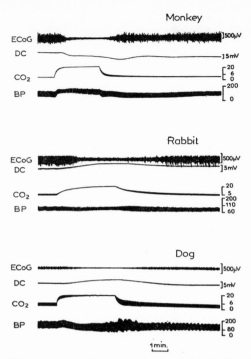

Fig. 1. DC shifts in different species during respiratory acidosis. Simultaneous recordings of percentage of CO_2 expired in the trachea (CO_2), femoral arterial blood pressure (BP), electrocorticogram (ECoG) and DC potential (DC). In this graph, as in those that follow, positive DC shift is figured by an upward deflection. Note that respiratory acidosis induces a negative DC shift in the monkey but positive deflections in rabbit and dog.

With between 6 to 20 per cent of CO_2, the amplitude and the slope of the negative deflections increased with the percentage of inhaled CO_2, but on the other hand marked differences existed between preparations.

An important experimental observation is that a lack of protection of the cortex against traumatic or physical deterioration is capable of reversing the DC shift induced by the inhalation of CO_2 in the cat and monkey. Generally speaking, respiratory acidosis starts by provoking a negative DC shift, but, after several hours of recording, several inhalings or several hypoventilation periods, a reversal of the polarity often appears and the response becomes positive monophasic (Fig. 3).

The negative DC shift is also reversed when by hypoventilation the prep-

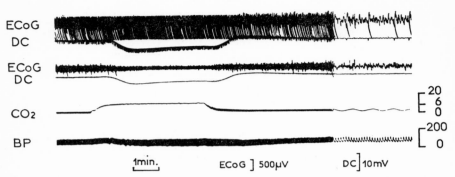

ECoG
DC

ECoG
DC

CO₂   ⎡ 20
      ⎢ 6
      ⎣ 0

BP   ⎡ 200
      ⎣ 0

1min.   ECoG] 500µV   DC]10mV

Fig. 2. Negative DC shift during respiratory acidosis after application of strychnine on one cerebral hemisphere. Simultaneous recordings of DC potential on both hemispheres show the existence of the same DC shifts despite the fact that ECoG on one hemisphere presents paroxystic activity due to strychnine.

aration is made hypoxic. This reversal of polarity is not necessarily irreversible: if the preparation receives a normal ventilation, a negative deflection reappears, but if the hypoxia is severe, it is no longer possible to get a negative DC shift.

Experimental trauma is also capable of reversing a negative DC shift during respiratory acidosis. If pressure is applied to one of the monkey's hemispheres, and the variations in the DC potentials recorded, the pressure side shows a positive deflection, whereas there is still a negative deflection in the other hemisphere.

Of course, all the intermediate stages are possible between positive and negative deflections, in which case the variations of the DC potential become multiphasic (Fig. 4). Simultaneous recordings of the cortical pH and the DC potential show the correlation between the two phenomena when there is a positive deflection.

A negative DC shift is often preceded by a low aplitude and short duration positive deflection. As shown in Fig. 5, this initial positive variation follows a reduction of the cortical pH. A reduction of cortical pH appears 10 to 15 seconds after the beginning of the variation of the end tidal CO_2. There seems to be an important relationship between O and 15 seconds after the variation of pH. The negative DC shift then appears 5 to 25 seconds after the initial positive deflection.

The data obtained in the cat and the monkey under respiratory acidosis clearly show that two factors are acting in opposite direction on

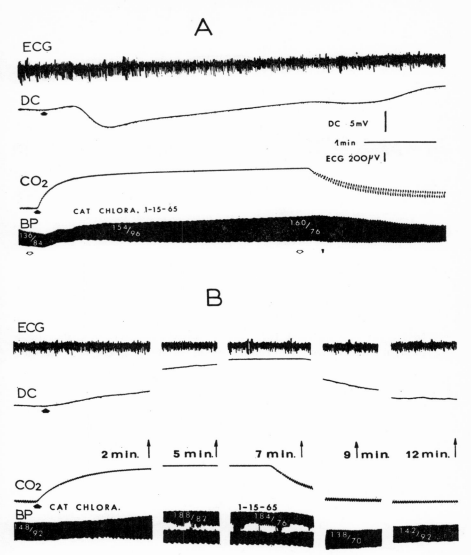

Fig. 3. Inversion of DC shift (cat) during respiratory acidosis. In A: the first inhalation of CO_2 provokes a negative DC shift. In B: four hours later on the same animal, an inversion appears of the response that becomes positive monophasic.

the variation of the DC potential. The positive deflection seems to be associated with the pH variation. We shall now investigate the different factors that may influence the appearance of the negative deflection.

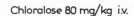
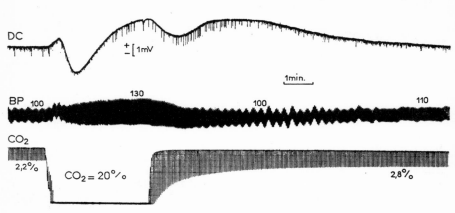

Fig. 4. Multiphasic variations of the DC potential during respiratory acidosis.

By comparing the recordings from a number of preparations, we noticed that, when significant arterial hypertension followed the inhalation of CO_2, the gradient of the onset of the negative deflection increases. We therefore thought that factors controlling blood pressure intervene. The use of sympatholytic substances strengthened this hypothesis: after the abolition of the hypertensive reaction, the amplitude and the slope of the negative DC shift were reduced in a significant way, but without the direction of the

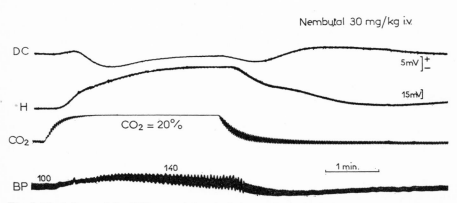

Fig. 5. Variations of the DC potential and of the cortical pH during respiratory acidosis. – H ions increase upward. Note the appearance of a small amplitude and short time initial positive DC shift associated with the beginning of the pH variation.

variation being affected. Recordings on animals that had undergone a spinal transsection at the level of CI enabled us to set aside the possibility of the influence of the hypertensive reaction in the appearence of a negative DC shift. In these cases a slight hypotension is produced by the inhaling of CO_2. However, if the DC shifts produced by respiratory acidosis are compared before and after the spinal transsection on the same animal, an important increase in the amplitude and gradient in the negative DC shift may be observed after the section.

Despite the fact that the hypertensive reaction does not seem to have great importance, circulatory factors certainly intervene, since a significant reduction of the amplitude of the negative deflection appears on a spinal animal if previously the pressure level of these preparations has been increased by epinephrine infusion. There is thus a relationship between the initial blood pressure and the amplitude of the negative deflection induced by respiratory acidosis.

The last point observed led us to the consideration of the possible relationship between the effects of CO_2 on the CBF and the negative DC shifts. CO_2 is a vasodilatator and considerably increases the CBF (Kety & Schmidt 1948). We therefore simultaneously recorded the variation of the DC potential and of the CBF. We used two methods for measuring the CBF, one using a flow probe system on the carotid, the other based on the use of a heated silicon diode Thermistor (Besson & Aleonard 1970). With both techniques we were able to prove the relationship between the increase of the CBF and the negative DC shift in respiratory acidosis.

As shown in Fig. 6 a quantitative relationship exists between the two phenomena:

If, on the same preparation, one progressively reduces the inhaling time of a gaseous mixture rich in CO_2, the negative DC shift and the increase of the CBF are reduced in the same way (Fig. 6A).

When, during the same period, an animal inhales mixtures containing various percentages of CO_2 (Fig. 6B), the negative DC shift and CBF increase with the percentage of CO_2.

These results, obtained from experiments on the cat and the monkey, indicate that in respiratory acidosis, two factors are conflicting in the determination of the DC potential. The variation of the pH is closely related to the positive deflection. It therefore becomes important to see whether, in other circumstances, the variations of CBF were likely to influence the

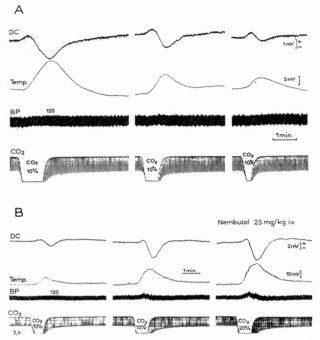

Fig. 6. Correlations between the negative DC shift and the increase of CBF during respiratory acidosis. CBF is measured with a silicon diode thermistor (Temp); an increase is figured by an upward deflection. In A: inhalation of the same mixture during various periods. In B: the increases of negative DC shift and CBF with increasing percentages of CO_2 inhaled during the same period.

potential or if their action was only due to the circulatory changes consequent to the inhaling of CO_2.

DC SHIFTS DURING CHANGES IN CBF

Central stimulation and pharmacological means were used to modify CBF to investigate the relationship between CBF and the DC potential variations.

In order to show clearly the relationship between the two phenomena, we generally used fairly high doses of pharmacological products that induced marked circulatory modifications. For this reason, autoregulation mechanisms (Lassen 1964) have little importance here.

As our studies did not concern the action of certain pharmacological substances on the CBF, we thought it better to start by showing the relationship between the variations of CBF and the DC potential and then to try and see how our results compared to those published by different authors working on the two phenomena separately in more physiological conditions, in which self-regulation mechanisms may intervene (such as in the wakefulness and sleep cycle). We shall examine successively the effects of hypertensive and hypotensive substances and the variations induced by the stimulation of the mesencephalic reticular formation.

HYPERTENSIVE DRUGS

Epinephrine

The effects of epinephrine on the CBF have been debated for a long time. It appears that a local application or an intra-arterial injection of weak doses of epinephrine produces a slight vasoconstriction of the cerebral blood vessels and a slight reduction of CBF (Dumke & Schmidt 1943, Fog 1939, Wolff 1936). On the other hand, an intravenous injection provokes an increase in the arterial blood pressure and an increase in CBF.

With the cat and the monkey an intravenous injection of epinephrine induces a significant negative DC shift (Fig. 7A). The amplitude of the variation is of several millivolts. Important variations, however, exist from one preparation to another. If one simultaneously records the DC shifts and the variations of the CBF, one notices that these two factors vary in the same way. As shown in Fig. 7B, the blood flow increase is closely related to a negative DC shift, the modifications of CBF preceding the DC shift by about 15 sconds. The amplitude of the negative DC shift and the importance of the circulatory variation increase with the dose. Infusions of epinephrine enabled us to keep the DC potential at a certain level of negativity for a long time. Epinephrine has an effect on the entire CNS, for we noticed its effects at the cortical and subcortical levels and also in functionally different structures. This last finding suggests an extraneuronal origin for the variations, but it seemed necessary to prove it, since the negative DC shift could perfectly well be due to the cortical activation induced by epinephrine (Vanasupa *et al.* 1959). Two other findings confirm the extraneuronal origin of the variations. Negativity induced by epinephrine may be observed in anaesthetized preparations (pentobarbital

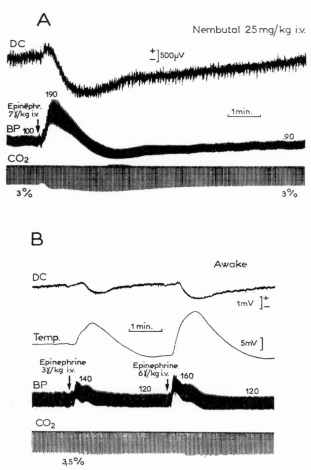

Fig. 7. Variations of the DC potential induced by intravenous injection of epinephrine. In A: Negative DC shift of long duration. In B: For different doses of epinephrine a quantitative relationship exists between negative DC shift and CBF increase.

or chloralose) or in awake animals; when anaesthetized the arousal reaction is absent (Rothballer 1956). On the other hand, after destruction of the reticular formation by coagulation, epinephrine still works. This enables us to set aside the possibility of adrenergic activation. The results, and especially those obtained by simultaneous recordings of CBF and DC potential, show the close relationship existing between the negative deflection and the increase of CBF induced by an intravenous injection of epinephrine.

Three other experimental facts strengthen this hypothesis:

(1) The increase in the CBF induced by an intravenous injection of epinephrine depends greatly on the peripheral arterial hypertension. In order to show the importance of this hypertension, we used some Yohimbine which reverses the hypertensive properties of epinephrine. If one compares the amplitude of the variations, before and after the intravenous injection of Yohimbine, one notices that for the same dose of epinephrine, the abolition of the hypertensive effects provokes (Fig. 8) a significant reduction in the negative DC shift.

(2) Inhaling of gaseous mixtures that are rich in CO_2 is associated with a considerable increase of CBF (Kety & Schmidt 1948). An injection of adrenalin no longer induces a negative DC shift in a cat inhaling CO_2. In this case epinephrine has no action on CBF as the flow is already considerably increased by the vasodilatator effect of CO_2. This explains the abolition of the negative deflection of the DC potential.

(3) Kety & Schmidt (1946) showed that a reduction of PCO_2 in man is associated with an impairment of CBF. On the same preparation, we injected the same dose of epinephrine for different percentages of alveolar CO_2 (the pump volume being changed, but not the speed). We noted that, when the percentage of alveolar CO_2 was reduced, the negative DC shift increased. This means that the amplitude of the negative DC shift increases when the initial CBF is low. On the other hand, the negative deflection is less important when the initial CBF is high.

Two other elements should be considered. To start with, we occasionally observed monophasic positive variation of the DC potential after administration of epinephrine. These preparations were in an important state of hypoxia and the cerebral blood vessels were dilatated. In this case, it seems probable that the deflection is due to a vasoconstrictor effect of epinephrine.

Secondly, we must say that our animals were paralyzed by flaxedil. Recordings on non-curarized animals proved that the negative DC shift during respiratory acidosis is constantly present, whereas the negative deflection induced by epinephrine is considerably reduced or even reversed.

OTHER HYPERTENSIVE DRUGS

Neosynephrine and Heptamyl (Cardiomid Heptominol) also enabled us to get negative DC shifts. But generally speaking, the variations were less

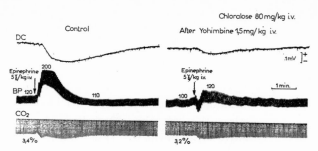

Fig. 8. Influence of Yohimbine on negative DC shift produced by epinephrine. After suppression of the hypertensive effect of epinephrine by Yohimbine, a considerable reduction of the negative DC shift appears.

noticeable with these substances, and in 20 per cent of the cases a monophasic positive DC shift appeared.

As for the effects of Norepinephrine, the results vary with the different authors, apparently owing to the type of injection and the dose (Bovet *et al.* 1957, Ingvar 1958, Ingvar & Söderberg 1958, King *et al.* 1952, Moyer *et al.* 1954, Sensenbach *et al.* 1953): an intra-arterial or an intravenous injection of small doses of Norepinephrine inducing a mild hypertension produces a slight decrease of CBF. On the other hand, intravenous injections of relatively high doses produce an increase of CBF and a negative DC shift, but in 19 per cent of cases a monophasic positive deflection appeared. All the same, the essential point is that, for the same animal and for pressure modifications of the same intensity, the amplitude of the negative DC shift is smaller than with epinephrine (Fig. 9). These facts agree with the data given by Ingvar & Söderberg (1958) who showed that, in the same circumstances, the flow increase produced by epinephrine is more marked than with Norepinephrine.

HYPOTENSIVE DRUGS

Effects obtained with different hypotensive agents, such as acetylcholine, histamine, ganglionic blocking agents, eventually depend upon blood pressure variations induced by the administration of these drugs. For our demonstration, we shall use acetylcholine. Despite the existence of a cerebral vasodilatation, an intravenous injection of acetylcholine starts by bringing the blood pressure and the CBF down (Norcross 1938, Wolff 1936). This temporary

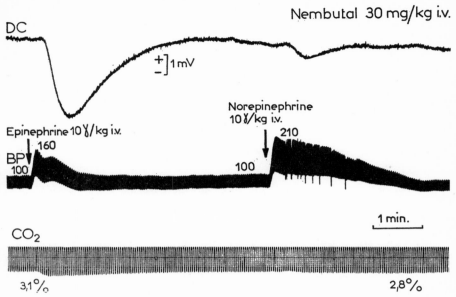

Fig. 9. Comparison of the effects of intravenous injections of epinephrine and Norepine-phrine. The injection of Norepinephrine provokes a more important increase of blood pressure than epinephrine, but note that the negative variation of the DC potential is smaller.

fall in blood pressure is followed by an important increase of CBF when the blood pressure has crept back to its initial level (Lubsen 1941, Norcross 1938, Wolff 1936).

Simultaneous recordings of DC potential and CBF show that the effects of acetylcholine depend to a large extent on the degree of hypotension. In every case, we observed a good relationship between the variations of CBF and the DC potential. As shown in Fig. 10A, when an injection of acetylcholine only induces an increase of the flow, it appears just before a negative DC shift.

On the other hand, when such an injection only induces a decrease of the CBF (Fig. 10B), it appears just before a positive deflection.

Besides these two types of monophasic deflections, i. e., reduction of flow associated with a positive DC shift or an increase in CBF with a negative DC shift, it is possible to record biphasic variations showing both types of deflections. As shown in Fig. 10C, during the fall in blood pressure produced by acetylcholine, for a short time, there is a low amplitude short duration positive DC shift (in some cases, there are no variations whatsoever) whereas the recovery of the blood pressure and the negative deflection take place at the same time. The amplitude of that deflection that increases with the variations of pressure can be of several millivolts.

The same sort of results have also been obtained with histamine and ganglionic blocking agents.

Thanks to these experiments on hypotensive substances, we have been able to confirm the relationship existing between the variations of CBF and the DC potential.

Indeed, we have already seen that an increase of CBF is generally associated with a negative DC shift. It therefore seemed logical to expect that a reduction of the flow by hypotension should be associated with a positive DC shift. But, for relatively low blood pressures not exceeding 70 mm/Hg, the positive DC shifts are of small amplitude. This agrees with the works carried out on the variation of CBF during hypotension, indicating that the brain is remarkably well protected against the fall of the blood pressure. A reduction of the cerebral vascular resistance which keeps a suitable flow despite hypotension explains this protection (Shenkin 1951). This shows that a decrease in the blood flow associated with a positive DC shift is more easily shown during marked hypotension on animals with an initially high CBF.

On the other hand, the vasodilatator effects of acetylcholine and histamine are related to a negative DC shift. This therefore confirms indirectly our results with hypertensive substances.

VARIATIONS OF CBF AND DC POTENTIAL BY RETICULAR STIMULATION

Electrical stimulation of the reticular mesencephalic formation induces fluctuations of the DC potential on the one hand (Arduini et al. 1957, O'Leary et al. 1958) and, on the other hand, an increase of the arterial blood pressure

---

Fig. 10. Variations of CBF and DC potential induced by intravenous injections of acetylcholine. In A: Acetylcholine induces an increase of CBF which slightly precedes the negative DC shift. In B: Acetylcholine provokes a decrease of CBF and a positive DC shift. Note that both variations take place in two phases. In C: Mixed deflection: positive DC shift during hypotension followed by a negative DC shift during the recovery period.

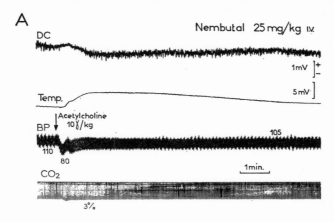

A

DC

Nembutal 25 mg/kg I.V.

1mV]+
         −

Temp.

5 mV]

BP

Acetylcholine
10 ɣ/kg

110

80

105

CO₂

1min.

3%

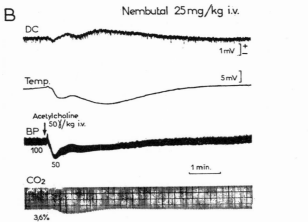

B

Nembutal 25 mg/kg i.v.

DC

1mV]+
        −

Temp.

5 mV]

BP

Acetylcholine
50 ɣ/kg i.v.

100

50

1 min.

CO₂

3,6%

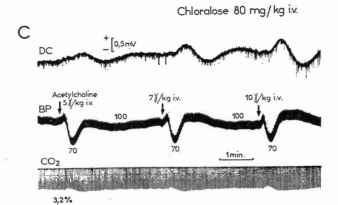

C

Chloralose 80 mg/kg i.v.

DC

+
− [0,5mV

BP

Acetylcholine
5ɣ/kg i.v.

7ɣ/kg i.v.

10 ɣ/kg i.v.

100

100

70

70

70

1min.

CO₂

3,2%

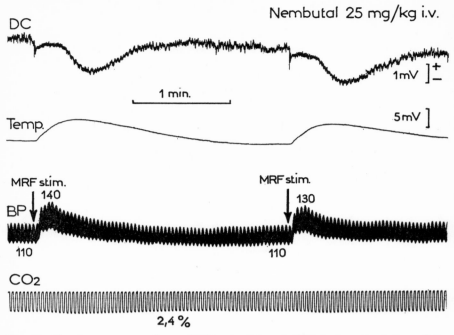

Fig. 11. Simultaneous recordings of DC potential and CBF during stimulation of the mesencephalic reticular formation. The first negative DC shift, of short duration and small amplitude, precedes the increase of CBF. The variation of the blood flow seems in close relationship with the second negative DC shift of large amplitude.

and of CBF (Ingvar 1958). We therefore made a simultaneous recording of these two factors (Fig. 11) during reticular stimulation. Arterial blood pressure and CBF are increased and are associated with a negative DC shift. The negative DC shift usually takes place in two phases. On the DC graph there is a small amplitude, short duration deflection to start with; then there is a second, longer lasting deflection with the increase of CBF. This second deflection alone seems related to the increase of CBF. This was confirmed by modification of our experimental conditions. We abolished the increase of CBF due to reticular stimulation by previously bringing the flow close to its maximum by the inhaling of CO_2 (Fig. 12). Under these conditions, the first negative deflection persists despite a slight reduction, but one can no longer observe the second deflection. This therefore seems to be related to the variations of the CBF and the initial change of DC seems due to neuronal factors resulting in the stimulation of reticular formation.

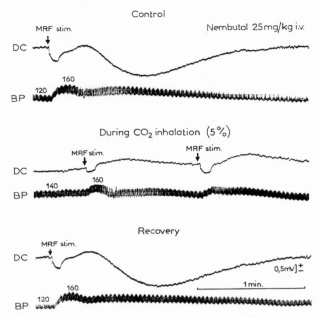

Fig. 12. Effects of respiratory acidosis on the DC shifts induced by mesencephalic reticular stimulation. Note that during the inhaling of CO_2, the second negative DC shift that was present on the control preparation is abolished.

DISCUSSION

It was generally believed that respiratory acidosis induces a positive DC shift. This positive deflection is supposed to be due to the gradient of H ions across the blood brain barrier (Held *et al.* 1964, Tschirgi & Taylor 1958). We have shown in the cat and monkey, as opposed to the rabbit, dog, goat, and rat, that inhalation of a gas mixture rich in CO_2 produces a negative DC shift. During respiratory acidosis two factors seem to influence the DC potential: first, an increase of the CBF owing to respiratory acidosis and entailing a negative DC shift; secondly, as has been shown by many authors, variation of pH producing a positive deflection.

Technical problems cannot explain the differences observed between species, as we have recorded negative DC shifts with the cat and the monkey and positive ones with the dog and rabbit, using the same electrodes. Furthermore, on the same preparation (cat or monkey) it is possible to record variations in opposite directions with the same electrode when physiological conditions are modified.

By simultaneous recordings of the DC potential and of the cortical pH, we were able to establish a close relationship between positive DC shifts and variation of the cortical pH during respiratory acidosis. As the origin of the positive DC shift has been thoroughly considered during this Symposium, we shall not go over it again but shall briefly consider the possible influence of circulatory effects.

To start with, we must insist on the fact that the negative DC shifts that we observed with the cat and the monkey, which had already been described by Mottschall & Loeschcke (1963), depend a lot on the physiological state of the preparations. Hypoxia and trauma reduce or cancel the negative variations and the positive DC shift induced by the pH variations appears. This inversion may be due to the by-passing of autoregulation processes which are extremely sensitive to experimental conditions (Langfitt et al. 1966, Lassen 1964, Rapela & Green 1964).

The occurrence of a positive deflection during hypoxia may be explained as follows: before inhaling CO_2 the CBF is already maximal owing to the lack of O_2 (Kety & Schmidt 1948). The increase of the CBF will therefore be much less than in normal conditions and a positive DC shift due to the pH will prevail. The inversion of the negative DC shifts after traumatisms may be explained by the findings of Symon (1963) who noticed that injured arteries contract instead of dilating during the inhaling of CO_2.

Studies carried out on the dog by Held et al. (1964) showed a positive DC shift of 42 mV/pH unit during metabolic acidosis, whereas the positive deflection was of only 32 mV/pH unit in respiratory acidosis. The difference between the two types of acidosis has not been explained, but our results concerning the influence of circulatory phenomena enable us to propose an explanation. During respiratory acidosis the effects of the increased CBF combat the variation due to the hydrogen ions. The deflection thus induced is therefore less important than during metabolic acidosis where, if PCO_2 remains unchanged, the variations of pH induce little change in the CBF (Harper & Bell 1963).

Simultaneous recordings of DC potential and CBF show that the negative shifts are closely related to the increase in CBF during respiratory acidosis. This relationship between CBF and DC potential was confirmed by the injection of drugs which alter CBF. Increased CBF is associated with a negative DC shift, whereas decreased CBF is associated with a positive DC shift. These results were obtained with quite high doses of pharmacological agents, and it is probable that our experimental conditions did not respect self-regulating mechanisms especially with hypertensive substances; but it seemed necessary at first to show the influence of variations of the CBF on the DC potential. On the other hand, when considering acetylcholine, one may notice that a close relationship exists between changes in CBF and the DC potential, as opposite effects on variations of the flow may be obtained according to the preparation or to the dose of substance injected but, whatever the type of modification recorded, a negative DC shift always appears with an increase of the CBF and a positive DC shift with the decrease of the flow.

Central stimulation of the reticular formation enabled us to confirm the relations between CBF and DC potential, in which case the abolition of the negative DC shift when inhaling CO_2 is particularly significant.

The relationship existing between the modification of the DC potential and the CBF with the cat and the monkey is sufficiently well established to think that certain modifications of the CBF have more influence on the DC shifts than neuronal factors. This may be particularly true when considering DC shifts appearing during different states of sleep. For instance, when passing from intense wakefulness to slow wave sleep, a positive DC shift (Tabushi et al. 1966, Wurtz 1967) is associated with a slight reduction of CBF (Hull et al. 1965, Wurtz 1967), and when passing from a slow wave sleep to paradoxical sleep, a negative DC shift (Tabushi et al. 1966, Wurtz 1967) is associated with an increase of the flow (Kanzow et al. 1962, Kety 1967).

Difference of polarity of the DC shift observed with different species during respiratory acidosis is another important problem. As respiratory acidosis induces an increase of the CBF, whatever the species, we have no reasonable explanation to propose. But the administration of drugs, as respiratory acidosis, induces DC shifts in the rabbit and the dog which are in opposition to those observed with the cat and monkey.

This report certainly does not mean that the variations of the CBF represent the direct mechanism producing modification of the DC potential. As mentioned by Sokoloff & Kety (1960), the cerebral circulation is essentially regulated by chemical means which adjust the blood flow to the tissue metabolism. Therefore, the variations of the DC potential are probably due

8*

to complex metabolic modifications or other phenomena concerning the blood brain barrier which are simultaneously accompanied by brain circulatory variations.

REFERENCES

Arduini, A., Mancia, M. & Mechelse, K. (1957) Slow potential changes elicited in the cerebral cortex by sensory and reticular stimulation. *Arch. ital. Biol. 95*, 127–138.

Besson, J. M. & Aleonard, P. (1970) Utilisation d'un monocristal de silicium pour l'étude des modifications du débit sanguin cérébral par variation de dispersion thermique. *C. R. Acad. Sci. (Paris) 270*, 163–165.

Besson, J. M., Woody, C. D., Aleonard, P., Thompson, H. K., Albe-Fessard, D. & Marshall, W. H. (1970) Correlations of brain DC shifts with changes in cerebral blood flow. *Amer. J. Physiol. 218*, 284–291.

Bovet, D., Virno, M., Gatti, G. L. & Carpi, A. (1957) Action de l'Adrénaline et de la Noradrénaline sur la circulation cérébrale. *Arch. Int. Pharmacodyn. 110*, 380–409.

Dumke, P. R. & Schmidt, C. F. (1943) Quantitative measurements of cerebral blood flow in the macaque monkey. *Amer. J. Physiol. 138*, 421–431.

Fog, M. (1939) Cerebral circulation. I. Reaction of pial arteries to epinephrine by direct application and intravenous injection. *Arch. Neurol. Psychiat. (Chic.) 41*, 109–118.

Goldensohn, E. S., Shoenfeld, R. L. & Hoefer, P. F. A. (1951) The slowly changing voltage of the brain and the electrocorticogram. *Electroenceph. clin. Neurophysiol. 3*, 231–236.

Harper, A. M. & Bell, R. A. (1963) The effect of metabolic acidosis and alkalosis on the blood flow through the cerebral cortex. *J. Neurol. Neurosurg. Psychiat. 26*, 341–344.

Held, D., Fencl, V. & Pappenheimer, J. R. (1964) Electrical potential of cerebrospinal fluid. *J. Neurophysiol. 27*, 942–959.

Hull, C. D., Buchwald, N. A.,Dubrovsky, B. & Garcia, J. (1965) Brain temperature and arousal. *Exp. Neurol. 12*, 238–246.

Ingvar, D. H. (1958) Cortical state of excitability and cortical circulation. In *Reticular Formation of the Brain*, ed. Jasper, H. H. *et al.*, pp. 381–408. Little, Brown & Co., Boston.

Ingvar, D. H. & Söderberg, U. (1958) Cortical blood flow related to EEG patterns evoked by stimulation of the brain stem. *Acta physiol. scand. 42*, 130–143.

Kanzow, E., Krause, D. & Kuhnel, H. (1962) Die Vasomotorik der Hirnrinde in den Phasen desynchronisierter EEG-Aktivität im natürlichen Schlaf der Katze. *Pflügers Arch. ges. Physiol. 274*, 593–607.

Kety, S. S. (1967) Relationship between energy metabolism of the brain and functional activity. In *Sleep and Altered States of Consciousness*. (Proc. of the Association for Research in Nervous and Mental Disease), pp. 39–47. Williams and Wilkins Company, Baltimore.

Kety, S. S. & Schmidt, C. F. (1946) The effects of active and passive hyperventilation on cerebral blood flow, cerebral oxygen consumption, cardiac output, and blood pressure of normal young men. *J. clin. Invest. 25*, 107–119.

Kety, S. S. & Schmidt, C. F. (1948) The effects of altered arterial tensions of carbon dioxide and oxygen on cerebral blood flow and cerebral oxygen consumption of normal young men. *J. clin. Invest. 27*, 484–492.

King, B. D., Sokoloff, L. & Wechsler, R. L. (1952) The effects of L-epinephrine and L-nor-epinephrine upon cerebral circulation and metabolism in man. *J. clin. Invest. 31*, 273–279.

Kjällquist, A. & Siesjö, B. K. (1968) Regulation of CSF pH-influence of the CSF/plasma potential. *Scand. J. clin. Lab. Invest.*, Supp. 102, I : C.

Langfitt, T. W., Weinstein, J. D. & Kassell, N. F. (1966) Vascular factors in head injury. In *Head Injury*, ed. Caveness, W. F. & Walker, A. E., pp. 172–194. Lippincott, Philadelphia.

Lassen, N. A. (1964) Autoregulation of cerebral blood flow. *Circulat. Res.*, Suppl. I, XIV and XV, 1–204.

Loeschcke, H. H. (1956) Ueber den Einfluss von CO_2 auf die Bestandpotentiale der Hirnhaute. *Pflügers Arch. ges. Physiol. 262*, 532–536.

Loeschcke, H. H. (1970) The DC Potential between CSF and Blood. In *Ion Homeostasis of the Brain*, ed. Siesjö, B. K. & Sørensen, S. C. Munksgaard, Copenhagen.

Lubsen, N. (1941) Experimental studies on the cerebral circulation of the unanaesthetized rabbit. III. The action of ergotamine tartrate and of some vasodilatator drugs. *Arch. néerl. Physiol. 25*, 361–365.

Meyer, J. S., Gotoh, F., Tazaki, Y., Hamaguchi, K., Ishikawa, S., Nouailhat, F. & Symon, L. (1962) Regional cerebral blood flow and metabolism *in vivo*. *Arch. Neurol. 7*, 98–119.

Mottschall, H. J. & Loeschcke, H. H. (1963) Messugen des transmeningealen Potentials der Katze bei Aenderungen des CO_2-Drucks und der H^+ Ionenkonzentration im Blut. *Pflügers Arch. ges. Physiol. 277*, 662–670.

Moyer, J. H., Morris, G. & Snyder, H. (1954) A comparison of the cerebral hemodynamic responses to Aramine and Norepinephrine in the normotensive and hypotensive subject. *Circulation 10*, 265–270.

Norcross, N. C. (1938) Intracerebral blood flow: an experimental study. *Arch. Neurol. Psychiat. (Chic.) 40*, 291–299.

O'Leary, J. L., Kerr, F. W. L. & Goldring, S. (1958) The relation between spinoreticular and ascending cephalic systems. In *Reticular Formation of the Brain*, ed. Jasper *et al.*, pp. 187–202. Little, Brown & Co.

O'Leary, J. L. & Goldring, S. (1964) DC potentials of the brain. *Physiol. Rev. 44*, 91–125.

Rapela, C. E. & Green, H. D. (1964) Autoregulation of canine cerebral blood flow. *Circulat. Res.*, Suppl. I, XIV and XV, 1–205.

Rothballer, A. B. (1956) Studies on the adrenaline-sensitive component of the reticular activating system. *Electroenceph. clin. Neurophysiol. 8*, 603–621.

Sensenbach, W., Madison, L. & Ochs, L. (1953) A comparison of the effects of L-norepinephrine, synthetic L-epinephrine and U-S-P epinephrine upon cerebral blood flow and metabolism in Man. *J. clin. Invest. 32*, 226–232.

Shenkin, H. A. (1951) Effects of various drugs upon cerebral circulation and metabolism in man. *J. appl. Physiol. 3*, 465–471.

Sokoloff, L. (1959) Action of drugs on cerebral circulation. *Pharmacol. Rev. II*, 1–85.

Sokoloff, L. & Kety, S. S. (1960) Regulation of the cerebral circulation. *Physiol. Rev.* *40*, II, 38–44.

Symon, L. (1963) Effects of vascular occlusion on middle cerebral arterial pressure in dogs and Macacus rhesus. *J. Physiol. 165*, 62 p.

Tabushi, K., Hishikawa, Y., Ueyama, M. & Kaneko, Z. (1966) Cortical DC potential changes associated with spontaneous sleep in cat. *Arch. ital. Biol. 104*, 152–162.

Tschirgi, R. D. & Taylor, J. L. (1958) Slowly changing biolectric potential associated with the blood brain barrier. *Amer. J. Physiol. 195*, 7–22.

Vanasupa, P., Goldring, S., O'Leary, J. L. & Winter, D. (1959) Steady potential changes during cortical activation. *J. Neurophysiol. 22*, 273–284.

Wolff, H. G. (1936) The cerebral circulation. *Physiol. Rev. 16*, 545–596.

Woody, C. D., Marshall, W. H., Besson, J. M., Thompson, H. K., Aleonard, P. & Albe-Fessard, D. (1970) Brain potential shift with respiratory acidosis in the cat and monkey. *Amer. J. Physiol. 218*, 275–283.

Wurtz, R. H. (1967) Physiological correlates of steady potential shifts during sleep and wakefulness. II. Brain temperature, blood pressure, and potential changes across the ependyma. *Electroenceph. clin. Neurophysiol. 22*, 43–53.

DISCUSSION

Siesjö

Dr. Loeschcke, I would like to add that Dr. Kjällquist (1970) found in rats a potential of about $+4$ mV. Furthermore, in the rat the potential varies with the plasma pH and not with the bicarbonate concentration. Because the potential varies with the pH of plasma, a comparison between the potential values obtained by various investigators would be more meaningful if they were related to the arterial pH values. I noted that the slope of the line $\triangle E/\triangle$ pH in metabolic acidosis and alkalosis in the cat was about 10 mV per pH unit which is less than ¼ of the slope which Held, Fencl & Pappenheimer (1964) reported for dogs.

Dr. Loeschcke and Dr. Besson, does the negative potential change in cats shift towards a positive value if you maintain the hypercapnia for a longer period, say one hour?

Loeschcke

The plot of E versus bicarbonate is based on all results from the same cat during perhaps seven hours, but they are not obtained while staying on a particular concentration of CO_2 for a time longer than 10 minutes.

Besson

The periods of hypercapnia were maintained only for short periods of time. However, we had constant negative deflections for 15 or 30 minutes; in other experiments we also had diphasic "negative-positive" shifts.

Cameron

Dr. Loeschcke showed a slide from the work of Held, Fencl & Pappenheimer (1964), in which they showed that changes in CSF potassium concentration affect the potential difference, but that changes in plasma potassium concentration do not. I studied the potential difference measured

Kjällquist, A. (1970) The CSF/blood potential in sustained acid-base changes in the rat. With calculations of electrochemical potential differences for H^+ and HCO_3^-. *Acta physiol. scand. 78*, 85–93.

Held, D., Fencl, V. & Pappenheimer, J. R. (1964) Electrical potential of cerebrospinal fluid. *J. Neurophysiol. 27*, 942–959.

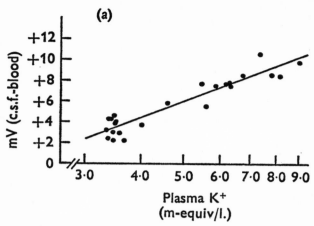

Fig. 1. The effect of increasing plasma [K$^+$] on the CSF-blood potential difference (reproduced by kind permission of the editors of J. Physiol.)

between an electrode in cisternal CSF and another in the external jugular vein during 2 hours of acute hyperkalemia in dogs. Acute hyperkalemia was induced while the arterial pH was held constant. Figure 1 shows the CSF-blood potential difference plotted against plasma potassium concentration. There is an increase in the positivity of the CSF as the plasma potassium concentration increases. The slope of this line is 16.3 mV change in the potential difference per tenfold change in the plasma potassium concentration. In another group of experiments the CSF potassium concentration was also measured; the potential difference can therefore be expressed against the log of the ratio between CSF potassium concentration and plasma potassium concentration. For a tenfold change in the ratio of CSF potassium concentration to plasma potassium concentration the change in potential would be 19.3 mV.

Furthermore, the relation between CSF-blood potential difference and arterial pH has been studied at two levels of plasma potassium cencentration. In Fig. 2 the slope of the line during normokalemia is 25 mV/pH unit. During acute hyperkalemia the relation between the potential and the arterial pH is changed so that the potential change is only 13 mV/pH unit. Therefore changes in plasma potassium concentration as well as changes in arterial pH affect the potential difference and it is possible to demonstrate an interaction between the two factors.

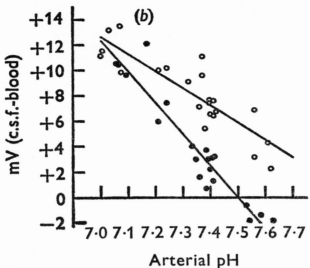

Fig. 2. The relation between the CSF-blood potential difference and arterial blood pH at a normal plasma [K$^+$], 2.8–4.0 mEq/l (closed circles) and at an increased plasma [K$^+$], 5.5–7.0 mEq./l (open circles). Reproduced by kind permission of the editors of *J. Physiol.*

SØRENSEN

The potential difference varies with changes in plasma pH. Welch & Sadler (1965) and Held, Fencl & Pappenheimer (1964) showed that the potential is not affected if pH is changed in bulk CSF. Dr. Severinghaus and I did some experiments where we examined the effect of a cerebral acidosis on the potential (Sørensen & Severinghaus 1970). Because the potential might be generated across the capillary endothelium, we induced an acidosis in brain interstitial fluid by exposing the dog to severe hypoxia for two hours. We measured the relation between plasma pH and the potential difference between CSF and blood before, at the end of the two hour period and just

Welch, K. & Sadler, K. (1965) Electrical potentials of the choroid plexus of the rabbit. *J. Neurosurg. 22,* 344–349.

Held, D., Fencl, V. & Pappenheimer, J. R. (1964) Electrical potential of cerebrospinal fluid. *J. Neurophysiol. 27,* 942–959.

Sørensen, S. C. & Severinghaus, J. W. (1970) The effect of cerebral acidosis on the CSF-blood potential difference. *Amer. J. Physiol. 219,* 68–71.

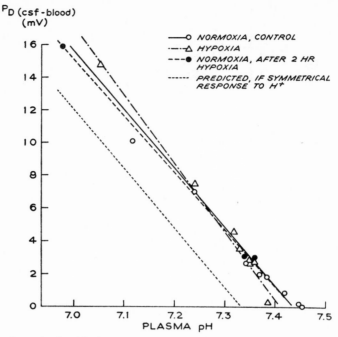

The effect of cerebral acidosis on the relationship between plasma pH and the CSF-blood potential difference. (Reproduced with permission of the editors of Amer. J. Physiol.)

after we had relieved the hypoxia. The figure shows the result from one experiment. When cerebral acidosis is created in this way the potential is still similarly related to change in plasma pH indicating that cerebral acidosis does not have any effect on the potential and therefore indicating that the cell layers separating blood and CSF are asymmetric in terms of the effect of pH on the potential.

USSING

There is something which should be mentioned regarding the difference between the short-circuit current response of frog skin and the potential response of CSF to Pco_2 changes. In the work of Funder, Wieth, and myself (1967) on frog skin we measured the effect of Pco_2 on the short circuit

Funder, J., Ussing, H. H. & Wieth, J. O. (1967) The effect of CO_2 and hydrogen ions on active Na transport in the isolated frog skin. *Acta physiol. scand. 71*, 65–76.

current as well as on the potential, and the effects were far from being identical. If we consider the equivalent circuit of an epithelium we have a sodium battery and a chloride shunt, through which passive ions go. When we change the pH we may influence both the battery and the shunt. Regarding the CSF-blood potential one may thus consider the possibility that a decrease in pH increases the shunt resistance so that one gets an increase in potential even though the sodium transport may be somewhat inhibited.

Neuron-Glia Relations and Control of Electrolytes

Richard K. Orkand

Neurons and glial cells each constitute about half the cellular volume of the nervous system. They can be distinguished from each other on the basis of a variety of anatomical and physiological criteria (Kuffler & Nicholls 1966). Anatomists readily identify glial cells by their staining properties and shape, e. g. the absence of an axon and their location around neurons and between neurons and capillaries. Most hypotheses of glial function originate from anatomical studies. These include suggestions that glial cells serve to insulate, support, feed, repair and control the environment of neurons. The one known function of glial cells is that oligodendroglia enwrap the axons of neurons to form myelin. The functions of the other large class of glial cells, the astrocytes, remain speculative. Glial cells may be identified physiologically by their high resting potentials (up to -90mV as compared to -60 to -70mV for neurons) and lack of an active membrane response following depolarization.

NEURON-GLIA RELATIONS

In the gray matter of the central nervous system, neurons are usually surrounded either by the processes of astrocytes or by other neurons. The channels between the apposed cells are narrow, only a few hundred Å wide (Horstmann & Meves 1959). However, such narrow channels do not seem to hinder greatly the movement of ions or small molecules. When the normal bathing solution surrounding a central nervous system tract, such as the optic nerve, is exchanged for one in which sucrose substitutes for sodium, the action potentials in the axons are readily abolished. They rapidly recover

Zoology Dept., University of California Los Angeles, California 900/24, USA.

when the normal [Na] is returned (Kuffler *et al.* 1966). The possibility that the solutions exchange through the glial cells rather than the intercellular channels is ruled out by the observation that the membrane potential of the glial cells is not much affected by the exchange of solutions. The glial resting potential depends on a high intracellular [K] (see below). If isotonic sucrose moved through glial cells, the potassium would be diluted and the resting potential decreased.

Direct evidence that even large molecules such as ferritin (100 Å in diameter) can move through the extracellular clefts has been obtained in electron microscopic studies of mammals (Brightman 1965). Following injection into the cerebral ventricles, the electron-dense ferritin molecules can be seen primarily in the intercellular clefts between neurons and glia. It can be concluded from these studies that the system of intercellular clefts is the primary pathway for diffusion of substances in the immediate vicinity of the neurons and glia (Nicholls & Kuffler 1964).

The question arises whether the glial cells modify the constituents of the fluid in the narrow clefts, thereby controlling the environment of the neurons. Under steady-state conditions there is no evidence for such a role on the part of the glia. In experiments using the leech central nervous system, Nicholls & Kuffler (1964) compared the resting and action potentials of neurons surrounded by glial cells and neurons in contact with the external bathing solution after the glial coverings were surgically removed. When the composition of the bathing solution was varied by changing [Na] and [K], the changes in resting and action potentials were similar in the glial covered and naked neurons. Within the limits of detection of their method, it appeared that the ionic composition of the fluid surrounding the neurons was not altered by the glial cells. In a subsequent study Nicholls & Baylor (1969) found that the negative afterpotential in the neurons following repetitive stimulation essentially disappears after removal of the glial covering. This result is consistent with the view that the negative afterpotential results from the accumulation of K released from active axons into the clefts between axon and glia (Frankenhaeuser & Hodgkin 1956). The glial membrane acts as a barrier to the diffusion of potassium away from the axons.

Anatomical studies of neurons and glia in the central nervous system do not provide evidence for specialized regions of contact between the two types of cells. Neurons do form special appositions with each other at synapses. Occasionally the membranes of glial cells come in close apposition and form "gap" junctions (Brightman & Reese 1969). These junctions are the presumed sites where ions flow readily from one glial cell to the next, forming an electrical syncytium analagous to that in heart muscle. If there is a specific transfer of information from neurons to glia, it occurs without a special anatomical relation between the two types of cells.

PHYSIOLOGY OF NEUROGLIAL CELLS

Physiological measurements of neuroglial cells have been made in an invertebrate, amphibia and mammals *in vivo* and in tissue culture (Kuffler & Nicholls 1966, Dennis & Gerschenfeld 1969, Wardell 1966). These studies allow the following conclusions: Glial cells have resting potentials of up to −90mV, i. e., larger than those recorded from neurons. Fig. 1 illustrates the variation in resting potential in amphibian glial cells and neurons when the external [K] surrounding the isolated tissue is varied. The graph shows that at normal [K] the glial membrane potential is not only higher than that in neurons but also much more sensitive to variations in [K]. As $[K]_0$ is increased from 1.5 mEq/l, the glial resting potential decreases 59mV for a ten-fold change in $[K]_0$, as predicted by the Nernst equation, $E = RT/zF \ln [K]_0/[K]_i$. In this range the glial membrane behaves as an accurate potassium electrode. The deviation of the glial resting potential from the predicted slope at low $[K]_0$ would be expected if the glial cell had a low permeability to sodium ions or if potassium leaked out of neurons and glia at low $[K]_0$, keeping the concentration in the cleft system above that in the applied bathing solution. The greater deviation from prediction for neurons presumably reflects the higher resting sodium permeability in these cells. It can be concluded that the ratio of potassium to sodium permeability in glial cells is much greater than that found in neurons under comparable conditions. It is not known, however, to what extent the glial cell is permeable to other ions. The above experiments were conducted in a chloride-free sulfate-Ringer to prevent water movements during the exposure to high [K]. Additional experiments are necessary to determine the permeability of glial cells to anions such as Cl^- and HCO_3^- or cations such as Ca^{++} and H^+. Two additional conclusions follow from the relation between glial membrane potential and external [K]. First, glial cells contain a high $[K]_i$. Thus, when $[K]_0 = [K]_i$ the resting potential will be eliminated. The graph predicts this will occur at a $[K]_0$ of 99 mEq/l. Second, $[K]_i$ appears to remain constant despite changes in $[K]_0$.

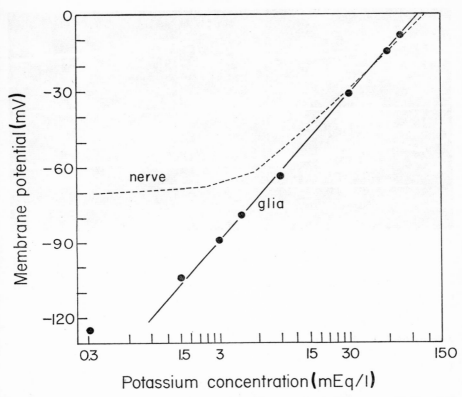

Fig. 1. Relation between membrane potential and external potassium concentration (log scale) for nerve and glia. Solid line has slope of 59 mV, according to the Nernst equation. Points are membrane potentials from glial cells in *Necturus* optic nerve (Kuffler *et al.* 1966). Dashed line is relation found for frog myelinated nerve fibers (Huxley & Stämpfli 1951).

It should be pointed out that as $[K]_i$ is about 100 mEq/l, changes of a few mEq/l would not have been detected.

Another property common to neuroglia is that they respond passively to changes in membrane potential of up to 100mV; there is no regenerative response as found in neurons. In addition, it has been found that currents injected into a glial cell spread passively through the adjacent glial cells. The cells are connected by low electrical resistance pathways. These pathways are presumably in the region where the glial cells are closely apposed and form "gap" junctions with one another.

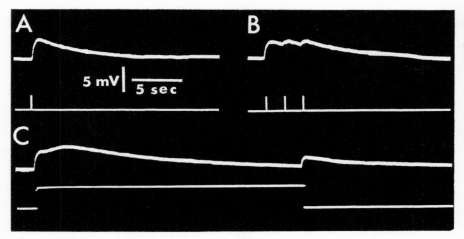

Fig. 2. Effect of neuron activity on glial resting potentials. Light flashes were shone into the eye causing discharge of retinal ganglion cells while recording intracellularly from a glial cell in an optic nerve of an anesthetized *Necturus*. Lower beams monitor currents applied to light bulb. A: single light flash of 100 msec duration sets up transient depolarization. B: same flash repeated three times. C: light stimulus is maintained for 27 sec. The initial glial depolarization declines due to adaptation of neuronal discharges. When the light is turned off an additional depolarization is produced (from Orkand *et al.* 1966).

EFFECT OF NERVE ACTIVITY ON GLIAL MEMBRANE POTENTIAL

Action potentials in neurons of cats (Goldring & Karahashi 1965), amphibia (Orkand *et al.* 1966) and leech (Baylor & Nicholls 1969) produce depolarization of the surrounding glial cells. Fig. 2 illustrates the depolarization of a glial cell in the *Necturus* optic nerve following impulse activity in retinal ganglion cells induced by illumination of the retina. The conclusion that the glial depolarization results from potassium accumulation is supported by the following: First, if the neurons liberate a constant amount of potassium, the logarithmic relation between glial membrane potential and potassium predicts that the depolarization increase in amplitude at low $[K]_o$ and decrease at high $[K]_o$. Orkand *et al.* (1966) found excellent quantitative agreement between the expected changes in glial depolarization at different $[K]_o$ and those actually recorded. Second, it is possible to compare the observed glial depolarization with that expected from (a) the potassium liberated from the active axons, as measured by the efflux of radioactive potassium, (b) the width of the intercellular clefts and (c) the concentration of potassium necessary to depolarize the glial cell by the amount observed. In order for a glial cell in *Necturus* to be depolarized 3mV by a single nerve volley, as observed, the [K] in the clefts would have to be increased by 0.39 mEq/l. If the width of the intercellular clefts is taken as 250 Å, as it often appears in electron micrographs, the required potassium efflux can be calculated in the following way:

width of cleft (cm) × increase in $[K]_o$ (M/cm³) = K liberated per impulse/cm² membrane.

2.5×10^{-6} cm × 0.39×10^{-6} M/cm³ = 0.97×10^{-12} M/cm²

This result compares favorably with the value of about 1×10^{-12} M/cm² of K liberated per impulse in unmyelinated axons found by Keynes & Ritchie (1965).

It appears, therefore, that the glial depolarization is a necessary consequence of the efflux of potassium from active axons and the sensitivity of glial membrane potential to changes in external potassium concentration.

ROLE OF NEUROGLIA IN CONTROL OF INTERCELLULAR POTASSIUM
DURING NEURONAL ACTIVITY

With prolonged repetitive activity in neurons, the $[K]_o$ in the intercellular clefts increases to a point where neuronal signaling is affected (Baylor & Nicholls 1969) and eventually leads to blockage of propagated action potentials (Orkand *et al.* 1966). This raises the question of whether the glial cells exert any control over the intercellular potassium. One possibility is that the glial cells take up potassium when extracellular potassium increases. As the glial cell volume is much greater than the intercellular volume, a small increase in the glial $[K]_i$ would lead to a large decrease in intercellular potassium. Unfortunately, the available experimental data no not provide evidence for or against such an hypothesis. Another possibility is that glial cells act as spatial potassium buffers to redistribute potassium. A possible mechanism for the redistribution is diagrammed in Fig. 3. Trachtenberg & Pollen (1970) consider this redistribution of potassium to be an important function of glial cells. Their analysis is based on the assumption that the glial cell is solely permeable to potassium and is therefore an upper estimate of the role of the glial cells. As indicated above, the permeability of glial cells to most other ions is unknown; the presence of significant permeability to other ions would decrease the buffering of potassium.

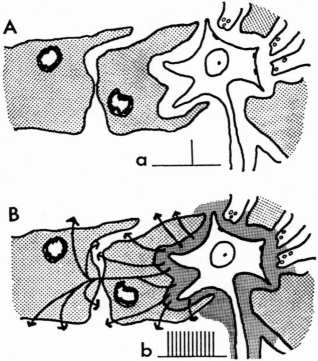

Fig. 3. Diagram of anatomical relations between neurons (clear) and glial cells (cross hatched). A: at rest or with little activity (a) the [K] around glial cells and neurons is uniform and the resting potential of the glial cells is normal. B: during and following a burst of action potentials in the neuron (b) the [K] in the intercellular clefts around the neuron increases (stippled region). The glial membrane apposed to these regions is depolarized causing a potential difference between this portion of glial membrane and portions apposed to normal [K]. The potential difference causes a current (indicated by arrows) which carries potassium from regions of high [K] to those of low [K]. Note current through low resistance "gap junction" between glial cells. Width of intercellular clefts is exaggerated making them relatively larger than they appear in usual electron micrographs.

POTASSIUM COMPOSITION OF INTERCELLULAR FLUID

Since the extracellular spaces between neurons and glial cells are only a few hundred Å wide, it is not possible to obtain directly samples of this fluid for chemical analysis. In the preceding sections it has been shown that the glial membrane behaves as an accurate potassium electrode over a wide range of $[K]_o$. Cohen, Gerschenfeld & Kuffler (1968) used the glial membrane

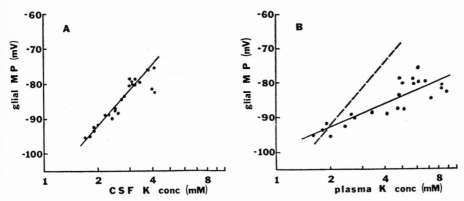

Fig. 4. Relation between glial membrane potential and potassium concentration (log scale) in CSF (A) and in plasma (B). (A) Solid line drawn with slope of 59 mV, according to the Nernst equation. (B) Solid line calculated to fit points (slope of 22 mV) and is significantly different from dashed line with slope of 59 mV (Cohen *et al.* 1968).

potential to measure the intercellular [K] while varying the [K] in the blood and cerebrospinal fluid (CSF). The blood potassium was varied by chronically maintaining *Necturus* in tank water with the potassium concentration raised to 50 or 100 mM. In the course of these experiments the plasma [K] varied from 1.5 to 9 mM whereas the CSF [K] varied from 1.5 to 4 mM. The relation between CSF [K] and plasma [K] had a slope of about 0.3. This indicates that the *Necturus,* like mammals (Bradbury & Kleeman 1967) and the more primitive dogfish (Cserr & Rall 1967) can regulate its CSF [K] to values below those in plasma, though clearly the regulation is not as rigorous as in mammals. The results of the membrane potential measurements as a function of plasma and CSF [K] are shown in Fig. 4. As the glial membrane potential is related to CSF [K] with a slope of about 59 mV, as it is *in vitro,* and to plasma [K] with a slope of about 22 mV, it is apparent that the [K] in the intercellular clefts is similar to that of the CSF and not the plasma. The same conclusion was reached by Fencl, Miller & Pappenheimer (1966) for H^+ and HCO_3^- in their study relating activity in respiratory neurons to the concentration of these ions in blood and CSF.

ROLE OF CHOROID PLEXUS IN ION TRANSPORT

The finding that *Necturus* can maintain CSF [K] below that in plasma raises the question as to the site and mechanism of [K] regulation. Wright &

Table 1.

Na, K, Cl and Ca Fluxes Across the Isolated Choroid Plexus.

	Flux	
	Blood to ventricle	Ventricle to blood
	μ–equiv./cm^2/h $\pm$ S.E.M.	
^{22}Na	5.4 $\pm$ 0.2 (119)	3.8 $\pm$ 0.1 (88)
^{36}Cl	4.8 $\pm$ 0.2 (53)	4.5 $\pm$ 0.2 (44)
^{42}K	0.11 $\pm$ 0.01 (15)*	0.12 $\pm$ 0.01 (24)*
^{45}Ca	0.04 $\pm$ 0.01 (35)	0.02 $\pm$ 0.01 (43)

* In these experiments the K concentration was 3.6 m-equiv./l. Numbers in parentheses give number of determinations. Data from Wright (1970).

Prather (1970) have developed an *in vitro* preparation of the frog choroid plexus, and preliminary results (Wright 1970) are now available which suggest a mechanism for some of the processes involved in the secretion of CSF. The posterior choroid plexus of the bullfrog was set up in an Ussing type chamber so that the potential and flux of radioactive isotopes of Na, K, Ca, and Cl across the epithelium could be measured. Table 1 gives the unidirectional fluxes of ^{22}Na, ^{42}K, ^{36}Cl and ^{45}Ca across the choroid plexus. The only ion to show a net flux is ^{22}Na. The net flux is about 1.6 μ-equiv/ cm/^{2}h from blood to CSF. The net flux of Na was blocked by ouabain (7×10^{-5}M) added to the CSF side or removal of HCO_3^- from the bathing solutions but unaffected by the addition of acetazolamide (5×10^{-3}M). The potential difference across the choroid plexus was less than 0.5mV with identical solutions on either side of the epithelium with or without ouabain or acetazolamide. Thus, sodium transport is electrically silent, presumably coupled either to cation exchange or anion transport in the same direction. The lack of a net transport of K, Ca, or Cl rules out a coupled NaCl pump or a Na-K or Na-Ca exchange. The inhibition of Na transport in HCO_3^- free solution leads to the tentative conclusion that CSF secretion in the bullfrog results from the activity of a sodium bicarbonate pump. These results provide no evidence for chorodial mechanisms regulating K or Ca in the CSF. These functions must be carried out by cells elsewhere in the central nervous system.

REFERENCES

Baylor, D. A. & Nicholls, J. G. (1969) Changes in extracellular potassium concentration produced by neuronal activity in the central nervous system of the leech. *J. Physiol (Lond.) 203,* 555–569.

Bradbury, M. W. B. & Kleemann, C. R. (1967) Stability of the potassium content of cerebrospinal fluid and brain. *Amer. J. Physiol. 213*, 519–528.

Brightman, M. W. (1965) The distribution within the brain of ferritin injected into cerebrospinal fluid compartments. I. Ependymal distribution. *J. Cell Biol. 26*, 99–123.

Brightman, M. W. & Reese, T. S. (1969) Junctions between intimately apposed cell membranes in the vertebrate brain. *J. Cell Biol. 40*, 648–677.

Cohen, M. W., Gerschenfeld, H. M. & Kuffler, S. W. (1968) Ionic environment of neurones and glial cells in the brain of an amphibian. *J. Physiol (Lond.) 197*, 363–380.

Cserr, H. & Rall, D. P. (1967) Regulation of cerebrospinal fluid [K+] in the spiny dogfish, Squallus acanthias. *Comp. Biochem. Physiol. 21*, 431–434.

Dennis, M. & Gerschenfeld, H. M. (1969) Some physiological properties of identified mammalian neuroglial cells. *J. Physiol (Lond.) 203*, 211–222.

Fencl, V., Miller, T. B. & Pappenheimer, J. R. (1966) Studies on the respiratory response to disturbances of acid-base balance, with deductions concerning the ionic composition of cerebral interstitial fluid. *Amer. J. Physiol. 210*, 459–472.

Frankenhaeuser, B. & Hodgkin, A. L. (1956) The after-effects of impulses in the giant nerve fibres of Loligo. *J. Physiol (Lond.) 131*, 341–376.

Goldring, S. & Karahashi, Y. (1965) Intracellular potentials from "idle" cells in cerebral cortex of cat. *Electroenceph. clin. Neurophysiol. 20*, 600–607.

Horstmann, E. & Meves, H. (1959) Die Feinstruktur des molekularen Rindengraues und ihre physiologische Bedeutung. *Z. Zellforsch. 49*, 569–604.

Huxley, A. F. & Stämpfli, R. (1951) Effect of potassium and sodium on resting and action potentials of single myelinated nerve fibres. *J. Physiol. (Lond.) 112*, 496–508.

Keynes, R. D. & Ritchie, J. M. (1965) The movement of labelled ions in mammalian nonmyelinated nerve fibres. *J. Physiol (Lond.) 179*, 333–367.

Kuffler, S. W. & Nicholls, J. G. (1966) The physiology of neuroglial cells. *Ergebn. Physiol. 57*, 1–90.

Kuffler, S. W., Nicholls, J. G. & Orkand, R. K. (1966) Physiological properties of glial cells in the central nervous system of amphibia. *J. Neurophysiol. 29*, 768–787.

Nicholls, J. G. & Kuffler, S. W. (1964) Extracellular space as a pathway for exchange between blood and neurons in central nervous system of leech: The ionic composition of glial cells and neurons. *J. Neurophysiol. 27*, 645–673.

Orkand, R. K., Nicholls, J. G. & Kuffler, S. W. (1966) Effect of nerve impulses on the membrane potential of glial cells in the central nervous system of amphibia. *J. Neurophysiol. 29*, 788–806.

Trachtenberg, M. C. & Pollen, D. A. (1969) Neuroglia: Biophysical properties and physiologic function. *Science 167*, 1248–1251.

Wardell, W. M. (1966) Electrical and pharmacological properties of mammalian neuroglial cells in tissue culture. *Proc. roy. Soc. B. 165*, 326–361.

Wright, E. M. (1970) Ion transport across the frog posterior choroid plexus. *Brain Res. In press.*

Wright, E. M. & Prather, J. W. (1970) The permeability of the frog choroid plexus to nonelectrolytes. *J. Membrane Biol. 2*, 127–149.

DISCUSSION

MINES

The slope of the line relating the CSF-blood potential to arterial pH decreases about 75 per cent after ouabain (Held, Fencl & Pappenheimer 1964). If the sodium-potassium pump in the glial cells was knocked out by ouabain, might there not be a massive efflux of potassium into the interstitial fluid space, which would then cause this shift in the CSF-blood potential difference?

ORKAND

One should then be able to measure a change in the potassium concentration in the CSF, because the intercellular clefts exchange freely with the CSF.

MINES

In amphibians you have shown regulation of several ions in CSF, but do you believe that the sodium-bicarbonate pump has no relation to that?

ORKAND

Yes, in amphibians one has to look elsewhere than in the choroid plexus for the site of the regulation of at least calcium and potassium.

SEVERINGHAUS

Did Dr. Wright keep the pH constant while changing the bicarbonate concentration?

ORKAND

Yes.

RALL

You seem to have shrunk the extracellular space in the brain.

In the dogfish you can also isolate the choroid plexus of the fourth ventricle, but we were never convinced that we did have enough tissue to accu-

Held, D., Fencl. V. & Pappenheimer, J. R. (1964) Electrical potential of cerebrospinal fluid. *J. Neurophysiol.* 27, 942–959.

rately measure ion fluxes (Patlak *et al.* 1966). How big is the chunk of tissue that Dr. Wright is using for flux measurements? I will also mention that in the isolated choroid plexus of the dogfish you get a very reproducible and unquestionable 2 to 3 mV potential difference, positive on the CSF side. It is abolished when you add ouabain to the ventricular side.

ORKAND

The area of the window between the two chambers is 2.7 mm². Regarding the size of the extracellular fluid space: I have only measured the extracellular space once, and I did it with a large series at electronmicrographs and a dart, throwing the dart at the pictures. I counted how many hits I made on the extracellular space, how many I made on neurons, and how many I made on glia (Kuffler *et al.* 1966). This is not such an unreasonable technique as you might think, considering that the artefacts in fixation etc. are possibly of the same order of magnitude as the other artefacts we have discussed this morning.

RALL

Were they frozen?

ORKAND

No, they were fixed with glutaraldehyde.

RALL

I really think that you are about 10 years behind your time.

ORKAND

I am not sure whether I am 10 years behind or 10 years ahead, but let me say why I think the extracellular argument is devoid of physiological interest. The important points are that the channels between the cells permit the movement of even large molecules such as peroxidase (Brightman & Reese

Patlak, C. S., Adamson, R. H., Oppelt, W. W. & Rall, D. P. (1966) Potential difference of the ventricular fluid in vivo and in vitro in the dogfish. *Life Sci. 5*, 2011–2015.
Kuffler, S. W., Nicholls, J. G. & Orkand, R. K. (1966) Physiological properties of glial cells in the central nervous system of amphibia. *J. Neurophysiol. 29*, 768–787.

1969) and that the neurons don't interact electrically except at synapses. The relative volume of the total extracellular space depends on the size of the cellular elements and will vary in different regions of the central nervous system. I know that the gaps between cells are about 300 Å wide, because I know how much potassium comes out of a neuron when it fires, and I know the size of the space that potassium must be dumped into to raise the concentration to a level where it depolarizes the glial cells to a certain extent (Orkand *et al.* 1966).

CAMERON

What was the pH in Dr. Wright's experiments on the isolated choroid plexus? If it were alkaline one might not, by inference from the mammalian situation, be surprised that he did not find much of a potential difference.

ORKAND

The experiments that I saw him do in physiology at UCLA were done using 5 % CO_2 and 25 mMol of bicarbonate, which gives a pH of 7.4. In fact, the potential difference across the frog choroid plexus is insensitive to pH over the range 2.4 to 10.7 (Wright & Prather 1970).

Another point: What one can conclude is that sodium is actively transported with a potential difference across the epithelium.

WELCH

I would like to know the significance of flow ratios when you do have a volume flow.

ORKAND

He was not in a position to measure volume flow. It was a regular frog skin chamber with big volumes on either side.

Brightman, M. W. & Reese, T. S. (1969) Junctions between intimately apposed cell membranes in the vertebrate brain. *J. Cell Biol. 40*, 648–677.

Orkand, R. K., Nicholls, J. G. & Kuffler, S. W. (1966) Effect of nerve impulses on the membrane potential of glial cells in the central nervous system. *J. Neurophysiol. 29*, 788–806.

Wright, E. M. & Prather, J. W. (1970) The permeability of the frog choroid plexus to nonelectrolytes. *J. Membrane Biol. 2*, 127–149.

SEVERINGHAUS

How did he measure bicarbonate flux?

ORKAND

Bicarbonate flux was not measured, but when you remove the bicarbonate the active sodium transport stops.

RALL

The histology of the choroid plexus from a dogfish shows the choroidal epithelium to be largely around the vessels. I am really uncertain as to what sort of membrane Dr. Wright is looking at in his system because it must be remembered that the choroid plexus in vivo separates blood, in the capillaries, and the CSF.

ORKAND

You are correct in the sense that he is not perfusing the choroid plexus through its normal blood supply. The presence of blood vessels and connective tissue adjacent to the epithelium does somewhat restrict diffusion of molecules to and from the base of the cells just as in the in vitro preparation of frog skin, urinary bladder, gall bladder, etc. However, this should not significantly affect the measurement of net fluxes.

Potassium Homeostasis in Cerebrospinal Fluid

M. W. B. Bradbury

Sherrington School of Physiology, St. Thomas's Hospital Medical School, London, S.E.1., England.

GENERAL APPROACH TO CSF HOMEOSTASIS

The title of this symposium implies that homeostasis of both hydrogen and potassium ions occurs in the brain and in its associated fluids. What is meant by the term homeostasis as applied to the concentration of an ion in the cerebrospinal fluid (CSF) or in the interstitial fluid of the brain? The meaning is best defined in simple mathematical terms. In a steady-state it may be anticipated that the concentration of a solute in CSF, C_{csf}, will depend in some measure on the concentration of the solute in blood plasma, C_{pl}. After a disturbance, $\triangle C_{pl}$ has been made in the plasma concentration and been maintained until a new steady-state has been reached; a disturbance $\triangle C_{csf}$ will occur in the CSF concentration. If $\triangle C_{csf} < \triangle C_{pl}$, it may be said that there is homeostasis or a tendency towards stability of the CSF concentration in the face of fluctuation in the blood plasma concentration. If $\triangle C_{csf}$ is infinitely small compared with $\triangle C_{pl}$, the CSF concentration is stable in this situation.

Exchanges of ions across the blood-brain and blood-CSF barriers are slow with half times of hours or even days. Hence steadystates and prolonged steady disturbances are difficult to maintain. Nevertheless, the literature contains unequivocal evidence that homeostasis, as defined above, applies to the cations of potassium, calcium, magnesium and hydrogen in the CSF of mammals and other vertebrates. An early assessment of the situation with respect to calcium was made by Herbert (1933) who stated: "In human cases of hypocalcemia and hypercalcemia, the calcium of the CSF remains relatively constant in spite of very wide variations in serum calcium. The CSF calcium cannot be taken as a measure of the diffusible calcium of serum.

In hyperparathyroidism the diffusible calcium is greater than the CSF calcium, in tetany and in some cases of uraemia the diffusible falls below the CSF calcium". The latter observation that a positive gradient from CSF to plasma at raised plasma concentrations may change to a gradient in the other direction at low plasma concentrations has been confirmed for the other cations mentioned and for bicarbonate in metabolic alkalosis and acidosis. In the cases of bicarbonate (Pappenheimer 1967) and potassium (Bradbury & Kleeman 1967) it is suggestive of the possibility of the active transport of the ion in either direction.

The mechanisms controlling the concentrations of the above four cations in CSF may have features in common. Certainly an understanding of one mechanism might suggest an approach to the elucidation of the other three. Whilst contemporary clinical and physiological interest is less in potassium than in hydrogen ion, potassium is simpler to study in the system. The activity of potassium ion in solution is close to its concentration. Not only is this true of plasma and CSF, but it is likely to be true of intracellular potassium in brain. Thus in squid and in frog muscle, potassium is almost as mobile in an electronic field as in a solution of KCl of similar concentration (Hodgkin & Keynes 1953, Harris 1954). Similarly, intracellular activity measured with a glass electrode (Hinke 1961, Lev 1964) is close to that in KCl. The situation with calcium and magnesium is very different, large fractions being associated with a non-active form with plasma proteins, cell membranes and intracellular particles (Borle 1967, Walser 1967). Interpretation of hydrogen ion changes in CSF is even more difficult since it can be formed by the dissociation of carbonic acid from CO_2 or by the dissociation of organic acids formed in brain. The factors affecting potassium distribution between blood, brain and CSF are therefore likely to be fewer and more easily resolved.

K^+ DISTRIBUTION BETWEEN BLOOD AND CSF

Recent interest in the specific problem of potassium homeostasis stems from the experiments of Bekaert & Demeester (1951 a, b, c). Plasma-K^+ was raised in dogs by the infusion of KCl. It was depressed by injections of insulin and glucose or by treatment with desoxycorticosterone (DOCA). CSF-K^+ was unchanged during 4 hours hyperkalaemia but was slightly lowered from 3.12 to 2.80 mEq/l after 3 hours infusion of insulin and

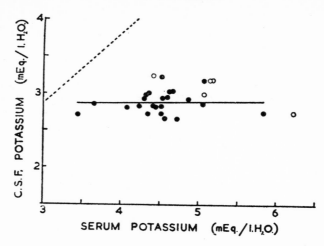

Fig. 1. The relation of lumbar CSF potassium to serum potassium for subjects with normal barriers and subjects with active tuberculous meningitis (0). The continuous line (————————) is the regression line for those with normal barriers; the interrupted line (– – – – – – –) follows the ratio for a dialysate of plasma. (Bradbury *et al. Cli. Sci.*).

glucose. During this period the plasma-K^+ fell from 4.91 to 2.46 mEq/l. There was no fall in CSF-K^+ after 8 days treatment with DOCA, but under these conditions the plasma-K^+ only decreased to 3.83 mEq/l.

Cooper *et al.* (1955) and Bradbury *et al.* (1963) examined lumbar CSF from human patients (Fig. 1). In both studies, CSF-K^+ varied less than plasma K^+ and averaged 2.96 $\pm$ 0.45 mEq/l in the former and 2.88 $\pm$ 0.15 in the latter. Some consistent variation with plasma-K^+ was evident in the former series in which patients with more severe hypo- and hyperkalaemia were present. The limiting K^+ concentrations in plasma were 1.97 and 7.16 mEq/l and in the corresponding CSFs were 2.43 and 3.55 mEq/l. Four patients with acute tuberculous meningitis were present in the second group. Despite high permeabilities of their blood-CSF barriers, as judged from bromide and urea distribution ratios, CSF-K^+ was little raised at 3.06 $\pm$ 0.21. Possibly an active mechanism is overcoming an increased entry of potassium.

Studies on animals allow a degree of control not possible in human subjects and also permit the analysis of brain tissue. Bradbury & Kleeman (1967) induced potassium depletion in rabbits by feeding a potassium free diet. Over three weeks, plasma-K^+ fell from 4.15 $\pm$ 0.27 to 1.58 $\pm$ 0.09 mEq/l.

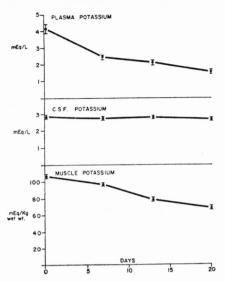

Fig. 2. Variation in plasma, CSF and muscle potassium in rabbits after 7, 13 and 20 days on a K-free diet (Bradbury & Kleeman, *Amer. J. Physiol.*).

CSF-K⁺ was 2.72 ± 0.06 compared with 2.83 ± 0.08 mEq/l in control animals (Fig. 2 and Table 1). Chronic hyperkalaemia was brought about by incorporating solid KCl in the diet. At a plasma-K⁺ of 7.09 ± 0.59, CSF-K⁺ had only risen to 3.02 ± 0.12 mEq/l (Table 1). Thus the control of CSF-K⁺ is rather better in cisternal CSF from the rabbit than in the same fluid from the dog or lumbar fluid from man. Again the CSF is not completely immune to changes in the blood. No measurements were made of CSF pH. Arterial

Table 1. Potassium contents of plasma, CSF, skeletal muscle and brain from rabbits dieted 3 weeks. Water, per cent wet weight, in brackets.

	Plasma mEq/l	CSF mEq/l	Muscle mEq/kg wet wt.	Brain mEq/kg wet wt.	Arterial pH
Control (6)	4.15 ± 0.27	2.83 ± 0.08	111.0 ± 2.7 (75.1)	95.4 ± 1.3 (78.5)	7.41 ± 0.03
Low K (5)	1.58 ± 0.09	2.72 ± 0.06	72.2 ± 2.6 (76.3)	94.5 ± 1.3 (79.1)	7.41 ± 0.02
Low K (5) + KCl infusion	4.45 ± 0.18	2.84 ± 0.05	93.5 ± 4.2 (77.8)	95.5 ± 1.7 (78.9)	7.39 ± 0.02
High K (7)	7.09 ± 0.59	3.02 ± 0.12	109.8 ± 0.9 (77.2)	94.9 ± 0.8 (78.5)	7.29 ± 0.05

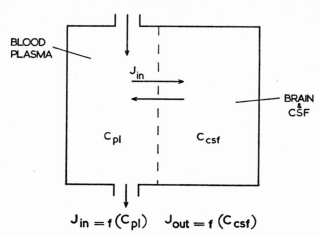

$$J_{in} = f\,(C_{pl}) \qquad J_{out} = f\,(C_{csf})$$

Fig. 3. Model of brain ECF and CSF as a single closed compartment, the concentration, C_{csf}, of a solute which is dependent on C_{pl} and the fluxes, J_{in} and J_{out}.

blood pH was normal after 3 weeks on the low K^+ diet, but the hyperkalaemic animals were moderately acidotic.

Brain potassium was quite unchanged in the above experiments, whereas 35 per cent of skeletal muscle potassium was lost and largely replaced with sodium (Table 1). If potassium can be lost from muscle cells but not from brain cells, which are known to have a high permeability to this ion, homeostasis of the interstitial fluid of the brain can be inferred.

SIMPLE ANALYSIS OF MECHANISM

The concentration of K^+ in CSF must in the steady state depend on a balance between forces causing entry into CSF and those causing its exit. Let us consider a simple model in which CSF and the interstitial fluid of brain together represent a perfectly mixed compartment containing potassium at a concentration of C_{csf} (Fig. 3). The brain cells which cannot in any case contribute to a steady-state situation are disregarded and exchange can only occur with the plasma-K^+ fixed at a concentration of C_{pl}. Influx J_{in} is considered to be solely as a function of C_{pl}, whereas efflux J_{out} is solely a function of C_{csf}. In any steady-state,

$$J_{in} = J_{out} \qquad (1)$$

Similary after a maintained change in plasma-K^+, $\triangle C_{pl}$ resulting in a change of flux $\triangle J$,

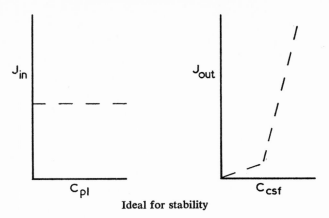

Ideal for stability

Fig. 4. Relations of J_{in} to C_{pl} and J_{out} to C_{csf} which are ideal for homeostasis.

$$\triangle J_{in} = \triangle J_{out} \qquad (2)$$

The presence of homeostasis is indicated by

$$\triangle C_{csf} < \triangle C_{pl} \qquad (3)$$

Hence from (2) and (3)

$$\frac{\triangle J_{in}}{\triangle C_{pl}} < \frac{\triangle J_{out}}{\triangle C_{csf}} \qquad (4)$$

That is to say, if the slopes of the curves relating J_{in} to C_{pl} and J_{out} to C_{cfs} are both positive, then the average slope of the former must be less than that of the latter in the relevant regions. A highly stable CSF will result from a flat slope of the former and a near vertical slope of the latter (Fig. 4).

The situation in the animal is obviously much more complex than in the model. Not only will diffusion and flow occur between several non-homogeneous compartments, but J_{in} may depend on other factors than C_{pl} (similarly for J_{out} and C_{csf}). Nevertheless, it may be anticipated that similar relations will occur *in vivo* and that this might be revealed by a consideration of the [42]K exchanges in the blood-brain CSF system.

[42]K ENTRY INTO BRAIN AND CSF

A near constant concentration of [42]K was maintained in the blood plasma of hypokalaemic, normal and hyperkalaemic rabbits by intravenous infusion

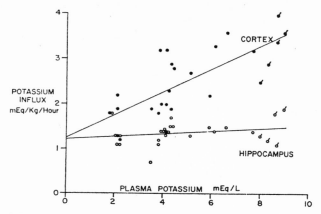

Fig. 5. ^{42}K influx into cerebral cortex and hippocampus of the rabbit as a function of the plasma potassium (Bradbury & Kleeman, *Amer. J. Physiol.*).

of the isotope at a diminishing rate (Bradbury & Kleeman 1967). The activity of ^{42}K in different regions of the brain and CSF was estimated at periods of up to 3 hours after the start of the infusion. Since entry into a given region of brain is slow (half time, about 35 hour) and depends on a single rate constant influx/hour/Kg of brain may be readily calculated. The relation of influx of potassium into brain to C_{pl} appears linear, is not steep and has a large positive intercept when extrapolated to $C_{pl} = 0$ (Fig. 5). The slope of the relation varied for different regions of the brain, the extremes being represented by the hippocampus for which it was almost zero and the cerebral cortex for which it was more pronounced. The intercept was similar for all regions.

The entry of ^{42}K into CSF does not follow first order kinetics (Fig. 6). Presumably for many hours, the brain with its high content of K^+ provides a sink of low specific activity into which ^{42}K can drain, having directly entered from the blood-stream via the choroid plexuses or capillaries close to brain-CSF interphases. The entry of ^{42}K into CSF with time can be described by an equation including two exponential coefficients. The fast rate constant (half time, about 20 min) depends on direct entry of ^{42}K from blood and diffusion from CSF into brain; the slow rate constant (half time, about 35 hour) depends on equilibration of the reservoir of potassium in brain. The direct influx of ^{42}K from blood at different plasma-K^+s into CSF is not readily calculable from our limited and rather variable results. It can,

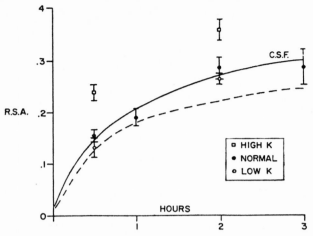

Fig. 6. Penetration of ⁴²K into cisternal CSF of the rabbit expressed as specific activity relative to that in plasma (RSA) against time. The interrupted line is that of RSA = 1 − .81e ⁻·⁰²²ᵗ − 19e ⁻·¹⁹⁶ᵗ and is derived from the rate constants for ⁴²K exchanges between blood and brain, and between CSF and brain (Bradbury & Kleeman, *Amer. J. Physiol.*).

however, be shown mathematically that the rate constants determining this are approximately proportional to the relative specific activities in CSF after the fast phase is virtually complete. Hence an influx into CSF has been calculated on the basis of the relative specific activity of CSF to plasma at 2 hours (Fig. 7). Again the influx increases gradually with plasma-K⁺ and has a large positive intercept, when extrapolated to $C_{pl} = O$.

⁴²K EXIT FROM CSF

The exit of ⁴²K from CSF has been studied during bilateral ventriculo-cisternal perfusion in the anaesthetized rabbit. If the volume flow entering both lateral ventricles and the volume flow leaving the cisterna magna are carefully determined by weighing, the total activity of ⁴²K entering and leaving the system can be assessed. The difference must be ⁴²K left in the animal. After 2 hours perfusion, residual CSF, the whole brain and cervical spinal cord were removed. Lost radioactivity not recoverable in these tissues was assumed to have passed into the bloodstream, either directly across the choroid plexuses or indirectly across the blood-brain barrier, having crossed

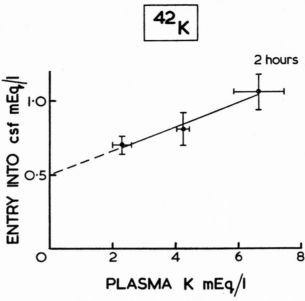

Fig. 7. Influx of ^{42}K into CSF as a function of plasma potassium. The units, mEq/l, have relative but not absolute significance and are derived from the RSA's at 2 hours in Fig. 6.

the ependyma into brain first. The perfusion fluid contained blue dextran (MW 2×10^6). Colorimetry of inflowing and outflowing fluids allowed CSF production and any loss of fluid to be determined. Movements of ^{42}K have been expressed as clearances, that is, radioactivity transferred divided by average radioactivity in the perfusing CSF.

The soundness of the assumption that lost radioactivity represents passage into blood has been discussed in detail (Bradbury & Stulcova 1970). In brief, if no blue dextran enters brain, loss of this solute will represent a residual volume of perfusion fluid which has either passed by bulk flow out of the CSF system or which has been left adherent to the membranes within the cranial cavity after removal of the brain. After exclusion of experiments in which there was an obvious impediment to cisternal drainage and in which this volume was greater than 1.0 ml, the average residual volume was 0.33 ml. If this fluid contained ^{42}K at the same concentration as in the cisternal effluent, it would have resulted in an overestimation of barrier clearances by only 3 μl/min (interrupted line in Fig. 9). However, the ventricular

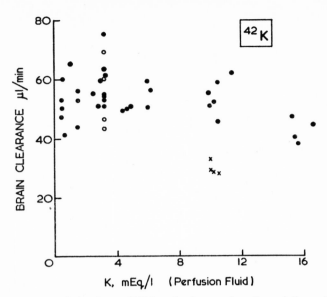

Fig. 8. The clearance of ⁴²K from CSF into brain as a function of the potassium concentration in inflowing CSF during ventriculo-cisternal perfusion. 0 refers to experiments with a low Na fluid and X to experiments in which the fluid contained ouabain 10^{-2} mM.

surfaces of the brain were stained blue, suggesting the loss of some blue dextran by diffusion into this tissue and hence an overestimate of less than 3 μl/min. Further it may be noted that in 7 experiments, the ⁴²K movement from CSF into blood was determined by total body counting of the rabbit carcass after removal of the brain and cervical spinal cord (Fig. 10). Values obtained for K⁺ exit into blood by this method correspond well with those obtained by the difference method.

The clearance of ⁴²K from CSF into brain was independent of K⁺ in the inflowing fluid between 0 and 10 mEq/l (Fig. 8). It was certainly depressed by ouabain 10^{-5}M and probably by 15 mEq/l, K⁺ in the inflowing fluid. Removal of the isotope by brain under these conditions is probably not restricted by cellular uptake (the cells must provide a large sink of low specific activity K⁺) but by the diffusion processes across the ependyma and within the interstitial fluid of brain which must occur before cellular entry can occur. The capacity of the cells adjacent to the ventricles to take up ⁴²K is, of course, likely to be impaired if they are poisoned with ouabain or depolarized by the highest concentration of potassium.

10*

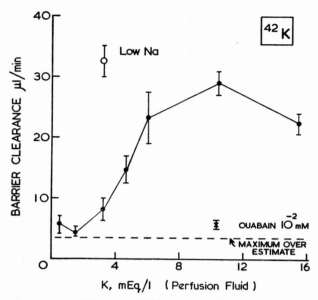

Fig. 9. The clearance of ^{42}K from CSF into blood (barrier clearance) as a function of the potassium concentration in flowing CSF during ventriculo-cisternal perfusion. 0 refers to experiments with a low Na fluid and X to experiments in which the fluid contained ouabain 10^{-2} mM.

Clearance of ^{42}K into blood (barrier clearance) was small, about 9 per cent of the total, when the perfusion fluid contained 2.0 mEq/l of potassium or less (Fig. 9). At levels above this it increased very steeply, reaching a maximum, 37 per cent of total, at 10 mEq/l of K$^+$ in the perfusion fluid (Fig. 9). The increased clearance of ^{42}K at high concentrations of K$^+$ was almost completely inhibited by ouabain 10^{-5}M in the fluid and was stimulated at normal CSF potassium concentrations by perfusion of a fluid in which 85 per cent of the Na$^+$ was replaced with choline. Exit of ^{42}K into blood was also progressively enhanced by concentrations of Rb$^+$ in the fluid of up to 15 mEq/l. Although respiration was sometimes initially stimulated by the high potassium fluids, the arterial pH was not consistently higher in such rabbits and the increased barrier clearance of ^{42}K could not be attributed to this. The barrier clearance of ^{14}C urea was not affected by K$^+$ in the perfusion fluid. The changes observed in the ^{42}K barrier clearance must therefore be specific to potassium and not due to a non-specific cause such as an altering blood flow.

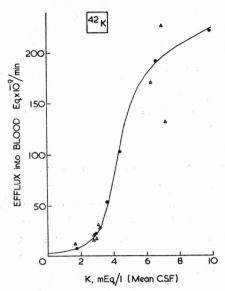

Fig. 10. Relation of efflux of ^{42}K from CSF across the barrier to the mean concentration of potassium in perfusing CSF. $\triangle$'s refer to experiments in which this was determined by total body counting rather than by difference.

The conditions of the experiment provide no proof as to where the exit of ^{42}K into blood occurred. Since the choroid plexuses of the two lateral, the third and the fourth ventricles are all bathed during perfusion, it is likely that these are the site of transport. Another possibility is that ^{42}K having diffused into brain then passes back into blood across the blood-brain barrier.

Certainly the movements of ^{42}K observed probably represent net movement of potassium. Thus increasing CSF-K^+ does not increase ^{42}K influx from blood during ventriculo-cisternal perfusion, as might be anticipated if the increased exit were due to exchange diffusion. This finding also indicates that J_{in} is independent of C_{csf} and provides justification for an application to the results of the theoretical analysis already described. Further, enhancement of ^{42}K exit into blood by perfusion of a low Na fluid or a Rb containing fluid is associated with a substantial fall in the K^+ concentration in the cisternal effluent from the normal value in the inflowing fluid of 2.9 mEq/l. The minimum effluent concentrations were 2.12 mEq/l (low Na perfusion) and 2.41 mEq/l (perfusion containing Rb 10 mEq/l).

Table 2. Evidence that K^+ efflux from CSF to blood is largely due to a Na-K pump.

	Reference:
1) Inhibition by ouabain	Bradbury & Stulcova 1970
2) Enhancement by low Na^+ in CSF	Bradbury & Stulcova 1970
3) Sigmoid relation to K^+ in CSF	Bradbury & Stulcova 1970
4) Enhancement by Rb in CSF	Bradbury, unpublished
5) Lower electrochemical potential of K^+ in CSF than in blood plasma in hyperkalaemia	Bradbury & Kleeman 1967

If it is assumed that the K^+ concentration on the CSF side of the barrier where transport is occurring is the mean of that in the inflowing and outflowing perfusion fluids, values for efflux of potassium into blood may be calculated (Fig. 10). The efflux varies with the mean CSF-K^+ in a sigmoid fashion. The added points ($\triangle$) represent the additional experiments in which barrier clearance and hence efflux were estimated by total body counting of ^{42}K rather than by difference. The sigmoid shape of the relation of influx to K^+ concentration is suggestive that the movement is due to a Na-K pump. Such a relation occurs for active movement of K^+ into r.b.c. although the initial gradient is steeper (Sachs & Welt 1967). A very similar curve denotes the relation between Na^+ efflux, as well as K^+ influx, and the extracellular K^+ concentration for squid axon (Baker *et al.* 1969). Other facts, suggestive that the efflux of ^{42}K into blood is largely due to a Na-K pump, directed for K^+ from CSF to blood, are listed in Table 2. The pump is presumably sited at the CSF-facing membrane of the choroid epithelium. A similar pump might occur at the blood-brain barrier or indeed a pump at the latter site might completely explain the findings.

PREDICTION OF CSF K^+ FROM FLUXES

The ability of the observed influx and efflux relations to cause a stable CSF can now be tested. The relations of Fig. 7 and Fig. 10 have been superimposed in Fig. 11. A small linear efflux component due to the normal bulk flow of CSF has been added to the $J_{out} - C_{csf}$ curve. The relative $J_{in} - C_{pl}$ line was multiplied by a constant factor to make J_{in} equal J_{out} at normal CSF and plasma - K^+ values, namely 2.82 and 4.22 mEq/l. At any value of plasma-K^+ J_{in} must equal J_{out}. Hence at any value of plasma-K^+ a horizontal line (iso-flux) may be used to predict the value of CSF-K^+. The predicted values for CSF in hypokalaemia and hyperkalaemia, namely 2.33

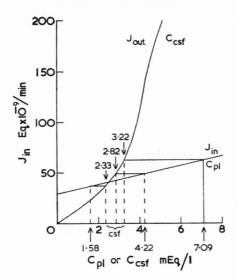

Fig. 11. Superimposition of curves from Fig. 7 and Fig. 10. For adjustments made see text. For a given value of C_{pl}, C_{csf} may be derived by use of the appropriate horizontal line (iso-flux).

and 3.22 mEq/l, are more disparate than the observed values 2.72 and 3.02 mEq/l – but very much closer than the plasma values, 1.58 and 7.09 mEq/l.

A number of simplifications have been made for the purpose of this analysis – in particular the assumption that the CSF represents a single compartment in which perfect mixing occurs. Exchanges with the brain are likely to be a major disturbing factor. In addition, influx and efflux have inevitably not been measured under perfectly symmetrical conditions. It is not surprising therefore that the predicted CSF concentrations do not correspond exactly with the observed values. The findings do, however, give substance to the hypothesis that potassium homeostasis in CSF is due to the basic nature of the transport mechanisms responsible for movement of potassium between blood and CSF. They give no support for, but do not exclude, the presence of a feed-back mechanism involving chemoreceptors sensitive to the K^+ concentration in CSF.

K^+ HOMEOSTASIS IN THE INTERSTITIAL FLUID OF BRAIN

Since potassium can exchange freely across the ependyma, it is unlikely that CSF could be stabilized with respect to K^+, if the interstitial fluid of the brain were not also controlled. A control of the latter fluid might dominate the CSF, but it is unlikely that a controlled CSF could dominate the interstitial fluid of brain. The maintenance of brain K^+ in severe hypokalaemia also favours a primary control of the interstitial fluid of the brain. Such a control mechanism would presumably be sited at the blood-brain barrier. Again the mechanism would seem to partially depend on the relation between J_{in} and C_{pl}, particularly in regions of the brain such as the hippocampus where the slope of the relation is almost zero (Fig. 5). Since potassium is controlled in cerebral cortex and in the layer of subarachnoid CSF over the cortex, it may be surmised that there is an efflux mechanism with a steep dependence on interstitial fluid K^+ at the blood-brain barrier. It might be an Na-K pump of the type demonstrated during ventriculo-cisternal perfusion. Some substance is given to this hypothesis by observations on the partial replacement of body potassium in rabbits by rubidium. The latter ion reaches a much lower degree of replacement, i.e., Rb/ (Rb + K) is about half in brain and CSF than in skeletal muscle and blood plasma (Bradbury *et al.* 1968). There may be a potassium pump, capable of transporting rubidium, at the blood-brain barrier.

CONCLUSIONS

The homeostasis of K^+ in CSF can be largely, if not completely, explained in terms of the relation between J_{in} and C_{pl} and that between J_{out} and C_{csf}. The former process involves a gradual slope for the line relating influx to plasma-K^+, and must be largely energy dependent since it can maintain an appreciable electro-chemical gradient between blood and CSF in hypokalaemia. The latter process with a steep sigmoid gradient is dependent on a Na-K pump, the K^+ movement being directed towards blood. It is not known whether these two processes are entirely independent or occur at the same sites. One site of the Na-K pump, responsible for K^+ efflux from CSF, is probably at the CSF-facing membrane of the cells of the choroid epithelium. There are reasons for supposing that a similar pump must occur at the blood-brain barrier. Indeed the presence of such a pump at the latter site might explain the CSF findings, in the absence of a Na-K pump at the choroid epithelium. The principles involved probably apply to the problems of calcium and magnesium homeostasis in CSF, and possibly to those of hydrogen and bicarbonate ion homeostasis.

REFERENCES

Baker, P. F., Blaustein, M. P., Keynes, R. D., Manil, J., Shaw, T. I. & Steinhardt, R. A. (1969) The ouabain sensitive fluxes of sodium and potassium in squid giant axons. *J. Physiol. (Lond.) 200*, 459–496.

Bekaert, J. & Demeester, G. (1951a) The influence of glucose and insulin upon the potassium concentration of serum and cerebrospinal fluid. *Arch. int. Physiol. 59*, 262–264.

Bekaert, J. & Demeester, G. (1951b) The influence of desoxycorticosterone on potassium concentration in the serum and in the cerebrospinal fluid. *Arch. int. Physiol. 59*, 391–392.

Bekaert, J. & Demeester, G. (1951c) The influence of the infusion of potassium chloride on the cerebrospinal fluid concentration of potassium. *Arćh. int. Physiol. 59*, 393–394.

Borle, A. B. (1967) Membrane transfer of calcium. *Clin. Orthop. 52*, 267–291.

Bradbury, M. W. B., Bagdoyan, H., Berberian, A. & Kleeman, C. R. (1968) Distribution of rubidium and potassium between blood, muscle, CSF and brain in the rabbit. *Proc. Int. Union Physiol. Sci. 7*, 57.

Bradbury, M. W. B. & Kleeman, C. R. (1967) The stability of the potassium content of cerebrospinal fluid and brain. *Amer. J. Physiol. 213*, 519–528.

Bradbury, M. W. B. & Stulcova, B. (1970) Efflux mechanism contributing to the stability of the potassium concentration in cerebrospinal fluid. *J. Physiol. 208*, 415–430.

Cooper, E. S., Lechner, E. & Bellet, S. (1955) Relations between serum and cerebrospinal fluid electrolytes under normal and abnormal conditions. *Amer. J. Med. 18*, 613–621.

Harris, E. J. (1954) Ionophoresis along frog muscle. *J. Physiol. (Lond.) 124*, 248–253.

Herbert, F. K. (1933) The total and diffusible calcium of serum and the calcium of cerebrospinal fluid in human cases of hypocalcaemia and hypercalcemia. *Biochem. J. 27*, 1978–1991.

Hinke, J. A. M. (1961) The measurement of sodium and potassium activities in the squid axon by means of cation selective glass micro-electrodes. *J. Physiol. (Lond.) 156*, 314–335.

Hodgkin, A. L. & Keynes, R. D. (1953) The mobility and diffusion coefficient of potassium in giant axons from sepia. *J. Physiol. (Lond.) 119*, 513–528.

Lev, A. A. (1964) Determination of activity and activity coefficients of potassium and sodium ions in frog muscle fibres. *Nature (Lond.) 201*, 1132–1134.

Pappenheimer, J. R. (1967) The ionic composition of cerebral extracellular fluid and its relation to control of breathing. *Harvey Lect. 61*, 71–94.

Sachs, J. R. & Welt, L. (1967) The concentration dependence of active potassium transport in the human red blood cell. *J. clin. Invest. 46*, 65–76.

Walser, M. (1967) Magnesium metabolism. *Ergebn. Physiol. 59*, 185–341.

The Effect of Acid-Base Changes on K^+ Homeostasis in the CSF

I. R. Cameron

INTRODUCTION

Brain and cerebro-spinal fluid [K+] are remarkably constant; this constancy can be maintained in spite of wide fluctuations in plasma [K+] of acute or chronic duration. This symposium is devoted to the mechanisms which maintain this stability, not only of CSF [K+] but also of CSF pH. There has been no systematic investigation of a possible relation between the mechanisms regulating the concentrations of these ions, that is to say, the control of CSF [K+] has been investigated during prolonged hypo- and hyperkalaemia but there have been no studies of possible exchanges of K+ between blood and CSF or brain and CSF during acidosis and alkalosis. Exchanges of K+ between intra-cellular fluid (ICF) and extra-cellular fluid (ECF) during acidosis and alkalosis have been extensively investigated in other tissues; similar exchanges might well be expected within the compartments of the CNS during acid-base changes. It would be difficult to predict the direction or magnitude of such K+ exchanges for two reasons. First, since the CNS is a complex multicompartmental system, and second, since it has been observed in other tissues that the direction and nature of K+ exchanges may vary from organ to organ.

THE EFFECT OF ACIDOSIS AND ALKALOSIS ON THE DISTRIBUTION OF K+

Exchanges of K+ between ICF and ECF have been investigated during acidosis in skeletal muscle, cardiac muscle and liver. In general, it has been found that a change in the pH gradient between ICF and ECF is accompa-

Dept. of Clinical Physiology, St. Thomas' Hospital, London, S. E. 1., United Kingdon

nied by a change in the distribution of K^+. Early studies on frog sartorius muscle maintained *in vitro* (Fenn & Cobb 1934) indicated that an increase in PCO_2 of the muscle and the incubation fluid produced a loss of K^+ from the tissue. Further experiments with the same preparation (Fenn & Cobb 1935) showed that although K^+ moved out of the muscle into a Ringer solution when the PCO_2 was increased, K^+ movement was in the opposite direction when the muscle was incubated in blood. It was concluded that this occurred because muscle was intermediate in its buffering capacity between Ringer solution and blood and that K^+ moved in the direction of the less buffered compartment. Essentially similar results were established for frog sciatic nerve *in vitro* (Fenn & Gerschman 1950). Later *in vitro* experiments (Fenn, Rogers & Ohr 1958) revealed that there was an increased loss of K^+ from frog muscle, whether the incubating Ringer was made acid by addition of HNO_3 or by equilibration with CO_2.

In the whole animal the findings were considerably more complicated. During inhalation of CO_2 a gradually increasing plasma $[K^+]$ was observed (Young et al. 1954, Ladé & Brown 1963). A similar increase in plasma $[K^+]$ occurred when acidosis was induced by i. v. infusion of HCl (Swan & Pitts 1955, Tobin 1956, Simmons & Avedon 1959). This increase in plasma $[K^+]$ could be accounted for partly by a loss of K^+ from skeletal muscle. This is contrary to the predictions from *in vitro* experiments. Since intra-cellular $[H^+]$ is normally greater than extra-cellular, it is possible during hypercapnia to obtain a change in intra-cellular pH which is relatively greater than extra-cellular, yet in spite of this the ratio H^+_i/H^+_e may decrease and K^+ would shift accordingly from ICF to ECF (Brown & Goott 1963). The situation in the whole animal is further complicated by other factors which may influence the distribution of K^+; for example, during hypercapnia there is a loss of K^+ from liver to blood. This occurs partly in response to an increase in circulating catecholamines, causing an increased mobilization of glucose and the passage of K^+ with glucose into the blood (Fenn & Asano 1956). Cardiac muscle is peculiar in that it has been shown to gain K^+ during respiratory acidosis (Young et al. 1954, Mithoefer et al. 1968). It is clear, therefore, that the increase in plasma $[K^+]$ observed in acidosis is the result of complex and varying processes; nevertheless it is clearly established that in these tissues a change in the pH gradient between ICF and ECF will cause a redistribution of K^+. During respiratory acidosis an increase in CSF $[K^+]$ has been demonstrated (Saunier et al. 1966, 1967). It is possible that such changes in CSF

[K$^+$] may occur secondarily to changes in the pH gradient between one or more of the CNS compartments. Such exchanges are likely to be complex, since they may take place between brain ICF and ECF (resulting eventually in changes in CSF [K$^+$]), between blood and brain, or lastly, between blood and CSF.

This paper describes the changes in CSF [K$^+$] during acute acidosis and alkalosis in anaesthetized dogs and rabbits and the results of experiments designed to investigate the cause of the observed changes in CSF [K$^+$]. The view will be presented that exchanges of K$^+$ between brain ICF and ECF may occur during respiratory acidosis and alkalosis, and that such exchanges may account for the observed shifts in CSF [K$^+$].

THE EFFECT OF ACIDOSIS AND ALKALOIS ON CSF [K$^+$] IN ANAESTHETIZED DOGS

The effect of respiratory acidosis and alkalosis and of metabolic acidosis on CSF [K$^+$] was investigated in anaesthetized dogs. Acidosis was induced in 2 groups of dogs by inhalation of 10 % CO_2 or by i. v. infusion of 0.3N HCl; the infusion rate of HCl was arranged so that the fall in arterial pH was approximately matched to that in the CO_2 group (see Fig. 1). End-tidal PCO_2 was monitored and metabolic acidosis induced at constant PCO_2. Respiratory alkalosis was produced in a further group by hyperventilation to an end-tidal PCO_2 of approximately 20 mm Hg. CSF was sampled via a needle indwelling in the cistern and arterial blood from a femoral artery cannula. All experiments lasted 4 hr; control samples of blood and CSF were withdrawn at the beginning and end of a 1 hr control period. CO_2 inhalation, hyperventilation or acid infusion continued for a 2 hr period; final samples were obtained 1 hr after the end of this period. All results have been expressed as the difference between a given measurement and the mean of the 2 control measurements. Each group contained 6–8 dogs.

During respiratory acidosis the mean ($\pm$ S. E. of mean) fall in CSF pH after 2 hr was 0.17 $\pm$ 0.02 pH unit, whereas the mean fall in the group infused with HCl was only 0.07 $\pm$ 0.02 pH unit (see Fig. 1). It is apparent, therefore, that even when respiratory compensation is prevented by controlled ventilation, there is marked homeostasis of CSF pH during metabolic acidosis. After 2 hr hyperventilation CSF pH rose 0.17 $\pm$ 0.006 pH unit.

The changes in CSF [K$^+$] during respiratory acidosis and alkalosis are shown in Fig. 2. After 2 hr CO_2 inhalation CSF [K$^+$] increased 0.34 $\pm$ 0.06

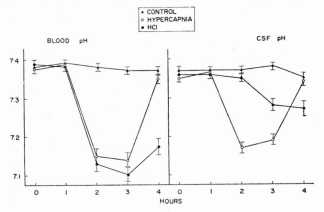

Fig. 1. Arterial and CSF pH in anaesthetized dogs during metabolic (i.v. infusion 0.3 N HCl) and respiratory acidosis (inhalation of 10 % CO_2) compared with control animals. Acidosis was induced between hr 1–3. Vertical lines represent ± S. E. of mean.

mEq/kg H_2O; this rise is statistically significant (p < 0.005) when compared with the changes in CSF [K^+] in controls at the same time. After 2 hr hyperventilation CSF [K^+] fell 0.1 mEq/kg H_2O, a fall which is also statistically significant when compared to control (p < 0.005). As will be seen from Fig. 2, there was a small increase (0.06 mEq/kg H_2O) in CSF [K^+] in control experiments; the cause for this is not readily apparent. It may be that repeated sampling of CSF hastens the appearance of newly formed CSF at the cistern; such newly formed fluid has, in the cat, a [K^+] some 0.6 mEq greater than that of cisternal fluid (Ames *et al.* 1964). It may be concluded from these experiments that during acute respiratory acidosis and alkalosis there are changes in CSF [K^+]. When acidosis was induced by infusion of 0.3N HCl, the mean rise in CSF [K^+] after 2 hr was 0.02 ± 0.036 mEq/kg H_2O; this rise was not statistically significant when compared to controls (p < 0.4).

Three possible mechanisms could account for the observed changes in CSF [K^+]; in respiratory acidosis the increase in CSF [K^+] might be due to:

(1) An increased entry of K^+ into CSF from blood.
(2) Decreased transport of K^+ out of CSF into blood.
(3) Exchange of K^+ between brain ICF and ECF; these exchanges would be seen eventually as changes in CSF [K^+].

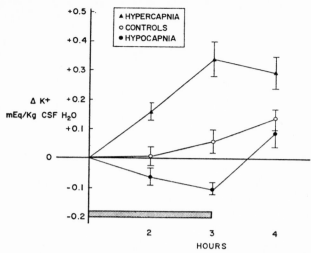

Fig. 2. The changes in CSF [K⁺] during respiratory acidosis and alkalosis compared with those in control dogs. Duration of 10 % CO_2 inhalation or hyperventilation is indicated by the shaded bar. Vertical lines represent ± S. E. of mean.

Since CSF and blood pH were measured simultaneously with CSF and blood [K⁺], it is possible to examine these results for any relation between the CSF-blood pH and [K⁺] gradient; no simple relation has been found for the 3 situations investigated. It may be possible, however, to relate the observed changes in CSF [K⁺] more simply to changes in CSF pH. During respiratory acidosis and alkalosis, CSF pH moves either in an acid or alkaline direction respectively; during metabolic acidosis the change in CSF pH was small and correspondingly there was no significant change in CSF [K⁺].

During respiratory acidosis, plasma [K⁺] rose 0.62 ± 0.17 mEq/kg H_2O and during respiratory alkalosis, plasma [K⁺] fell 0.25 ± 0.11 mEq/kg H_2O. CSF and plasma [K⁺] changed, therefore, in the same direction. In view of the known stability of CSF [K⁺] in the face of wide fluctuations in plasma [K⁺], it is unlikely that these small variations would influence CSF [K⁺]. It has been shown, however, that during hypercapnia the apparent permeability of the blood-brain barrier may be increased (Cameron *et al.* 1970); the possibility of an increased entry of K⁺ into CSF during respiratory acidosis has been investigated by examining the entry of ⁴²K into the CSF of anaesthetized rabbits.

THE ENTRY OF ^{42}K INTO CSF OF RABBITS DURING RESPIRATORY ACIDOSIS

CSF [K$^+$] was measured before and after 2 hr inhalation of 10 % CO_2 in a group of anaesthetized rabbits; there was a small rise in CSF [K$^+$] (0.3 mEq/kg H_2O) which was probably significant when compared with the change observed in air-breathing controls ($p < 0.05$). It appears, therefore, that similar changes occur in CSF [K$^+$] during respiratory acidosis in dogs and rabbits. In order to examine the entry of K$^+$ into CSF during hypercapnia, ^{42}K was infused i. v. into control and hypercapnic rabbits so as to maintain an approximately constant activity in plasma. CSF was sampled in groups of rabbits maintained for ½, 1 and 2 hr; both [K$^+$] and ^{42}K activity were measured in CSF and plasma, and hence the specific activity for each fluid was calculated; finally from the specific activities of the 2 fluids the ratio of specific activities (RSA $= \dfrac{\text{sp. activity CSF}}{\text{sp. activity plasma}}$) was obtained. The mean RSA for each group of rabbits was calculated and the values for control and hypercapnic rabbits compared.

In these experiments plasma [K$^+$] contains a high proportion of labelled K$^+$; K$^+$ entering CSF from plasma will come, therefore, from a source of high ^{42}K activity. An increased entry of K$^+$ into CSF would be accompanied by an increase in CSF specific activity and an increase in RSA of the hypercapnic rabbits compared with controls. If, on the other hand, the increased [K$^+$] in hypercapnia were due to a decreased passage of K$^+$ out of CSF, or, to exchanges with brain ICF K$^+$ (primarily a source of unlabelled K$^+$) the RSA obtained in the hypercapnic rabbits might be expected to be decreased when compared with controls.

Fig. 3 shows the RSA's obtained in groups of control and hypercapnic rabbits maintained for ½, 1 and 2 hr. The entry of ^{42}K into CSF cannot be described by a simple expression; results such as those in Fig. 3 are the result of 2 processes. First, the entry of ^{42}K from blood via the choroid plexus and brain capillaries and second, exchange of ^{42}K between CSF and brain intra-cellular K$^+$ which will act as a large "sink" for labelled K$^+$. The fast phase, which is dependent largely on the entry of ^{42}K into CSF from blood, will be effectively complete in the 2 hr experiments shown in Fig. 3. There was no statistically significant difference in RSA between the CO_2 and control groups at any time. If significance were to be attached to these results, the RSA's in the hypercapnic rabbits were always less than

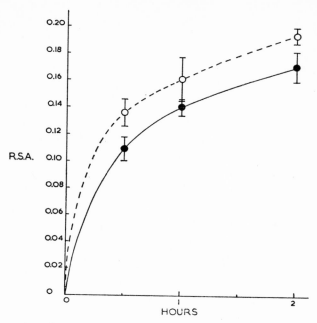

Fig. 3. The entry of ^{42}K into CSF of anaesthetized rabbits expressed as RSA plotted against time (RSA $= \dfrac{\text{sp. activity } ^{42}K \text{ in CSF}}{\text{sp. activity } ^{42}K \text{ in plasma}}$). Open circles represent control, air-breathing rabbits, closed circles represent rabbits breathing 10 % CO_2. Each result is the mean from 6–8 rabbits. Vertical bars indicate $\pm$ S. E. of mean.

those in the control animals. These experiments are not entirely conclusive, since the small changes observed in CSF [K^+] in respiratory acidosis and alkalosis could be accounted for by very small changes in the passage of K^+ into or out of CSF. It is possible that such small changes might be lost in the scatter of the results shown in Fig. 3. It is concluded that these findings do not support the hypothesis that an increased entry of K^+ into CSF from blood could account for the observed increase in CSF [K^+] in hypercapnia; if anything, they would support the possibility either of exchanges between brain intra-cellular K^+ and CSF or of diminished transport of K^+ out of CSF.

EFFECT OF ACIDOSIS AND ALKALOSIS ON THE INTRA-CELLULAR [K$^+$] OF FROG
BRAIN IN VITRO

The experiments so far described have been complicated by the attempt to
investigate exchanges in a multi-compartment system *in vivo*. Although the
presence of changes in CSF [K$^+$] with respiratory acidosis and alkalosis can
be adequately established, the contribution to these changes of exchanges
between brain and CSF and between blood and CSF or brain cannot be
separated. An *in vitro* preparation of frog brain has been used to examine
exchanges between brain and an incubating medium. It has been assumed
that in this situation, changes in the electrolyte content of the incubating
medium will correspond to those occurring in CSF *in vivo* and that this
medium will, like CSF, be in equilibrium with brain ECF. In such a simplified preparation there will be no exchanges between blood and brain or
between blood and CSF. The experiments are further simplified since the
choroid plexus is removed during the preparation of the brain for incubation.

The frog brains were removed and incubated as described by Bradbury
et al. (1968). All experiments were performed at room temperature (23–
25° C). The pH of the incubation fluid was altered either by equilibration
at varying PCO$_2$ or by altering the [HCO$_3^-$]. In this way brains were incubated either at constant [HCO$_3^-$] and varying PCO$_2$ (respiratory acidosis
and alkalosis), or at constant PCO$_2$ and varying [HCO$_3^-$] (metabolic acidosis
and alkalosis). The electrolyte contents both of the medium and an aqueous
extract of brain were measured after 2 hr incubation. The extra-cellular
space (ECS) of brain was measured using ^{35}SO$_4$ as an extra-cellular marker.
It has been shown (Bradbury *et al.* 1968) that such ECS measurements with
^{35}SO$_4$ agree closely with measurements using sucrose and insulin. This preparation was found to maintain constant values for tissue electrolytes and
ECS over 3 hr of incubation, thus confirming previous findings (Zadunaisky
& Curran 1963, Chiarandini & Zadunaisky 1966, Bradbury *et al.* 1968). In
particular there was no loss of K$^+$ by the tissue during 3 hr of control incubation. It would appear, therefore, that this preparation is capable of maintaining electrolyte homeostasis *in vitro* and is suitable for examining electrolyte shifts.

Frog brain, incubated *in vitro,* has been used to examine the hypothesis
that, as in other tissues, changes in ECF pH, and therefore to some extent
of ICF pH, will induce exchanges of K$^+$ between ICF and ECF. Such ex-

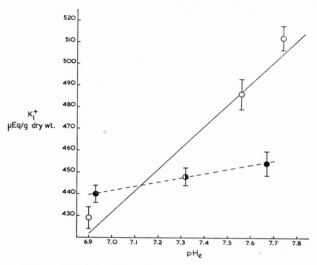

Fig. 4. The variation of intra-cellular [K⁺] (K^+_i) of frog brain *in vitro* with changes in pH of the incubating fluid (pH_e). Respiratory alkalosis and acidosis (changes in PCO_2 at constant extra-cellular [HCO_3^-] are represented by closed circles, metabolic acidosis and alkalosis (changes in extra-cellular [HCO_3^-] at constant PCO_2) by open circles. Calculated regression lines have been drawn through the points for metabolic and respiratory changes. The control point, ◑ (PCO_2, 35 mm Hg; [HCO_3^-] 25 mM) is common to both lines. From the slope of the line for respiratory changes in pH_e, K^+_i will change 18.3 μEq/g dry wt/pH unit, (r = 0.99) and in metabolic acidosis and alkalosis K^+_i varies 97.7 μEq/ g dry wt/pH unit, (r = 0.96).

changes of K⁺ would be deduced from measurements both of intra-cellular [K⁺] ([K⁺]ᵢ) and the [K⁺] of the incubating fluid ([K⁺]ₑ). The results of these experiments are shown in Fig. 4. Each point represents the mean result from at least 9 brains. [K⁺]ᵢ has been measured as μEq/g dry wt brain; it has been necessary to record brain [K⁺] as a function of dry wt since it was found that movement of K⁺ between ICF and ECF was accompanied by exchanges of water; concentration changes of K⁺ were thereby minimized. It will be seen that during incubation in a medium of varying PCO_2, there was a fall in [K⁺]ᵢ in respiratory acidosis and an increase in respiratory alkalosis. During metabolic acidosis and alkalosis, however, quantitatively much greater shifts in [K⁺]ᵢ were observed, although acidosis was again accompanied by a fall in [K⁺]ᵢ and alkalosis by an increase. Regression lines calculated by the method of least squares have been drawn through the points for respiratory and metabolic changes. From the slope of the line for respiratory alterations of extra-cellular pH (pH$_e$), [K$^+$]$_i$ was found to change 18.3 μEq/g dry wt/pH unit (r $=$ 0.99), whereas in metabolic alkalosis and acidosis [K$^+$]$_i$ changed 97.7 μEq/g dry wt/pH unit (r $=$ 0.96). In each case a rise in [K$^+$]$_i$ was accompanied by a fall in [K$^+$]$_e$ and a fall in [K$^+$]$_i$ by a rise in [K$^+$]$_e$. It is concluded that frog brain incubated *in vitro* looses K$^+$ when equilibrated in an acid medium and tends to gain K$^+$ in a medium of alkaline pH. Such changes vary considerably in magnitude depending on the method of varying pH$_e$, relatively small shifts of K$^+$ accompaying changes in PCO$_2$ but much greater exchanges occurring when the [HCO$^-_3$] of the medium was altered. The explanation for such a discrepancy is not immediately obvious but may be explicable in terms of a varying pH gradient between brain ICF and ECF in the two different methods of changing pH$_e$, that is to say, when PCO$_2$ is changed alterations will occur both in ICF and ECF pH. When extra-cellular [HCO$^-_3$] is varied it would be expected that greater changes will occur in the pH of ECF than in that of ICF (Adler *et al.* 1965).

CONCLUSION

The results of these *in vitro* experiments support the hypothesis formed from *in vivo* studies. When CSF pH is changed, and by presumption brain ECF pH, there is an exchange of K$^+$ between brain ICF and ECF. Such changes in brain ECF [K$^+$] are eventually reflected in the changes which are seen in CSF [K$^+$] and correspond to the changes measured in the incubating fluid *in vitro*. It is important to note that changes occurred *in vitro* when extra-cellular pH was altered by varying PCO$_2$ or [HCO$^-_3$]; *in vivo* changes in CSF [K$^+$] occurred only in respiratory acidosis and alkalosis. It is only, however, in respiratory acidosis and alkalosis that significant changes in CSF pH are seen in the intact animal. During acute metabolic acidosis and alkalosis CSF pH is maintained within narrow limits. Since the compartment which is composed of brain ICF, brain ECF and CSF is protected during metabolic acidosis and alkalosis by the function of the blood-brain and blood-CSF barriers, little or no change in pH occurs in this compartment, and consequently no exchanges of K$^+$ between brain ICF and ECF are provoked.

ACKLOWLEDGEMENTS

The author would like to thank Dr. C. R. Kleeman for many invaluable discussions and suggestions. This work was undertaken at the Cedars-Sinai Medical Center, Los Angeles, California, while the author was supported by a U. S. Public Health Service Postdoctoral Fellowship (No. FOSTW 1457–01). This work was supported by U. S. Public Health Service Research Grant No. NB 05905–05.

REFERENCES

Adler, S., Roy, A. & Relman, A. S. (1965) Intracellular acid-base regulation. 1. The response of muscle cells to changes in CO_2 tension or extracellular bicarbonate concentration. *J. clin. Invest. 44*, 8–20.

Ames, A. III, Sakanoue, M. & Endo, S. (1964) Na, K, Ca, Mg and Cl concentrations in choroid plexus fluid and cisternal fluid compared with plasma ultrafiltrate. *J. Neurophysiol. 27*, 672–681.

Bradbury, M. W. B., Villamil, M. & Kleeman, C. R. (1968) Extracellular fluid, ionic distribution and exchange in isolated frog brain. *Amer. J. Physiol. 214*, 643–651.

Brown, E. B., Jr. & Goott, B. (1963) Intracellular hydrogen ion changes and potassium movement. *Amer. J. Physiol. 204*, 765–770.

Cameron, I. R., Davson, H. & Segal, M. B. (1970) The effect of hypercapnia on the blood-brain barrier to sucrose in the rabbit. *Yale J. Biol. Med. 42*, 241–247.

Chiarandini, D. J. & Zadunaisky, J. A. (1966) Exchange of sodium in the isolated brain of the frog. *Exp. Neurol. 15*, 319–328.

Fenn, W. O. & Asano, T. (1956) Effects of carbon dioxide inhalation on potassium liberation from the liver. *Amer. J. Physiol. 185*, 567–576.

Fenn, W. O. & Cobb, D. M. (1934) The potassium equilibrium in muscle. *J. gen. Physiol. 17*, 629–656.

Fenn, W. O. & Cobb, D. M. (1935) Evidence for a potassium shift from plasma to muscles in response to an increased carbon dioxide tension. *Amer. J. Physiol. 112*, 41–55.

Fenn, W. O. & Gerschman, R. (1950) The loss of potassium from frog nerves in anoxia and other conditions. *J. gen. Physiol. 33*, 195–203.

Fenn, W. O., Rogers, T. A. & Ohr, E. A. (1958) Muscle electrolytes in acid and alkaline solutions. *Amer. J. Physiol. 194*, 373–378.

Ladé, R. I. & Brown, E. B. Jr. (1963) Movement of potassium between muscle and blood in response to respiratory acidosis. *Amer. J. Physiol. 204*, 761–764.

Mithoefer, J. C., Kazemi, H., Holford, F. D. & Friedman, I. (1968) Myocardial potassium exchange during respiratory acidosis: the interaction of carbon dioxide and sympatho-adrenal discharge. *Resp. Physiol. 5*, 91–107.

Saunier, C., Schibi, M. & Colas, T. (1967) Équilibre acido-basique et électrolytique du sang et du liquide céphalo-rachidien au cours de l'hypercapnie aiguë expérimentale chez le chien. *Bull. Physio-Pathol. Resp. 3*, 303–354.

Saunier, C., Schibi, M., Reichart, E. & Colas, T. (1966) Hypercapnie aiguë expérimentale chez le chien: variations précoces du potassium dans le plasma artériel et le
liquide céphalorachidien. *C. R. Soc. Biol. (Paris) 160,* 1049–1053.

Simmons, D. H. & Avedon, M. (1959) Acid-base alterations and plasma potassium
concentration. *Amer. J. Physiol. 197,* 319–326.

Swan, R. C. & Pitts, R. F. (1955) Neutralization of infused acid by nephrectomized
dogs. *J. clin. Invest. 34,* 205–212.

Tobin, R. B. (1956) Plasma, extracellular and muscle electrolyte responses to acute
metabolic acidosis. *Amer. J. Physiol. 186,* 131–138.

Young, W. G. Jr., Sealy, W. C. & Harris, J. S. (1954) The role of intracellular and
extracellular electrolytes in the cardiac arrhythmias produced by prolonged hypercapnia. *Surgery 36,* 636–647.

Zadunaisky, J. A. & Curran, P. F. (1963) Sodium fluxes in isolated frog brain. *Amer.
J. Physiol. 205,* 949–956.

e

DISCUSSION

SØRENSEN

Dr. Cameron, you only examined shortlasting respiratory acidosis. If the increase in CSF potassium, which you observed, was due only to an exchange between intra- and extracellular fluid, would you then expect a change in CSF potassium in the chronic state?

CAMERON

I would not expect changes in the chronic state. There are some results on chronic respiratory acidosis from Saunier *et al.* (1969), but I think they are difficult to interpret because they compared one group of patients with long-term respiratory acidosis with normal people. It is very difficult to get significance in that situation.

SØRENSEN

They are, however, important experiments in order to examine if there is any interference between the hydrogen ion concentration, and the mechanism which maintains the CSF potassium concentration constant.

CAMERON

Yes, and this was in fact what the experiments were primarily set up to look at.

SIESJÖ

Bleich, Berkman & Schwartz (1964) studied dogs for periods of up to 5 days, and found that the potassium concentration in the CSF during chronic hypercapnia was the same as in the control group.

CAMERON

I suspect that they did not compare the CSF potassium concentrations in each dog during the experiment and because of the very small changes which

Saunier, C., Aug-Laxenaire, M. C., Schibi, M. & Sadoul, P. (1969) Acid-base and electrolyte equilibrium of arterial blood and cerebrospinal fluid in respiratory insufficiency. *Respiration 26,* 81–101.
Bleich, H. L., Berkman, P. M. & Schwartz, W. B. (1964) The response of cerebrospinal fluid composition to sustained hypercapnia. *J. clin. Invest. 43,* 11–16.

we find it is very difficult to get significance with such an experimental design.

BROWN

It's nice to find that the brain, like skeletal muscle, fits the notion that the ratio between intracellular and extracellular potassium concentration changes in the same direction as the ratio between intracellular and extracellular hydrogen ion concentration. Several years ago I tried to measure arterio-venous differences for potassium across the brain during hypercapnia but I could not detect a difference; recognizing that the difference could have been there, but it could have been much too small to detect. We could demonstrate a difference in potassium concentration across skeletal muscle indicating that the rise in potassium concentration in plasma and extracellular fluid is partially due to efflux from skeletal muscle although it may be due to other sources as well, in particular the liver (Lade & Brown 1963, Gonzalaz, Hojo & Brown 1968). We followed the plasma potassium concentration in rats breathing 10 % CO_2 for up to 20 days and the extracellular potassium which increased initially, after about 24 hours went back down. The ratio between the intracellular and extracellular potassium concentrations went back to its normal value and at the same time I think the ratio between intracellular and extracellular hydrogen ion concentration was restored to normal (Martin *et al.* 1967). I would expect that, given time, you would find the whole thing reversed in the CSF as well.

WEYNE

You mentioned the possibility of an increased permeability of the blood-brain barrier during hypercapnia. Has such an increase been demonstrated with 10 % CO_2 or are higher concentrations needed?

Lade, R. I. & Brown, E. B. Jr. (1963) Movement of potassium between muscle and blood in response to respiratory acidosis. *Amer. J. Physiol. 204,* 761–764.

Gonzales, N. C., Hojo, T. & Brown, E. B. Jr. (1968) Myocardial potassium uptake with constant arterial potassium concentration. *J. appl. Physiol. 24,* 498–502.

Martin, E. D., Scamman, F. L., Attebery, B. A. & Brown, E. B. Jr. (1967) Time-related adjustments in acid-base status of extracellular and intracellular fluid in chronic respiratory acidosis. USAF School of Aerospace Medicine, Brooks Air Force Base, Texas. *SAM-TR-* 67–116.

CAMERON

It has not been demonstrated with an inspired CO_2 concentration of 10 % (Cutler & Barlow 1966); higher concentrations have always been necessary. In our experiments (Cameron, Davson & Segal 1970) we used 18 % CO_2 to demonstrate an increased permeability of the blood-brain barrier to sucrose in rabbits.

PLUM

Lending, Slobody & Mestern (1961) using I[131] labelled albumin did show increased permeability of the blood-CSF barrier in puppies given inhalations with CO_2 concentrations of 7 % in 21 % oxygen.

AMES

In the experiments that we did on newly formed choroid plexus fluid during hypercapnia and hyperventilation, the pH in plasma varied from 7.00 with hypercapnia to 7.86 with hyperventilation, but the concentration of potassium in the newly formed fluid only changed from 3.69 $\pm$ 0.2 (SEM) to 3.54 $\pm$ 0.2 (SEM), which was not a significant change.

CAMERON

This agrees with the suggestion that the changes in CSF potassium concentration during hypercapnia are due to exchange between intracellular and extracellular fluid.

DAVSON

What is the position with regard to the hydrogen ion concentration in muscle? Conway thought that the distribution of hydrogen ions followed the electrochemical potential difference for potassium, but other people have claimed

Cutler, R. W. P. & Barlow, C. F. (1966) The effect of hypercapnia on brain permeability to protein. *Arch. Neurol. 14,* 54–63.

Cameron, I. R., Davson, H. & Segal, M. B. (1970) The effect of hypercapnia on the blood-brain barrier permeability to sucrose in the rabbit. *Yale J. Biol. Med. 42,* 241–247.

Lending, M., Slobody, L. B. & Mestern, J. (1961) Effects of hyperoxia, hypercapnia, and hypoxia on blood-cerebrospinal fluid barrier. *Amer. J. Physiol. 200,* 959–962.

Ames, A., III, Higashi, K. & Nesbett, F. B. (1965) Effects of Pco_2, acetazolamide and ouabain on volume and composition of choroid plexus fluid. *J. Physiol. (Lond.) 181,* 516–524.

that the pH inside the muscle fiber is not as acidic as we can expect from the potassium distribution. Does the ratio between intracellular and extracellular hydrogen ion concentration follow the potassium ratio?

BROWN

We are still in the state of trying to decide what the real answer is here. Dr. Carter et al. (1967) by direct measurements have come up with intracellular pH values which fit Conway's idea, but no one else gets this. All other techniques give a pH value about one pH unit higher (Waddell & Butler 1959, Brown & Gott 1963).

WADDELL

The gradient for potassium and for hydrogen ions does shift together under all experimental conditions. In addition the sodium gradient apparently does too.

LASSEN

Is there any strong interrelation between acid-base balance and potassium homeostasis in the brain? In your experiments the changes in pH were rather drastic but the potassium changes were actually minimal. We also heard that during prolonged CO_2 exposure the cerebrospinal fluid potassium concentration comes back to normal.

Would the glial or neural environment be changed much by the demonstrated changes in potassium concentration?

CAMERON

I am looking at changes in bulk CSF. The exchange may occur between intracellular and extracellular fluid in the brain. I don't know what the concentration changes are in the intercellular clefts; I believe that they may be larger than those in CSF. Whether this has any functional significance

Carter, N. W. ,Rector, F. C., Jr., Campion, D. S. & Seldin, D. W. (1967) Measurement of intracellular pH of skeletal muscle with pH-sensitive glass microelectrodes. *J. clin. Invest.* 46, 920–933.

Waddell, W. J. & Butler, T. C. (1959) Calculation of intracellular pH from the distribution of 5,5-dimethyl-2,4-oxazolidinedione (DMO). Application to skeletal muscle of the dog. *J. clin. Invest.* 38, 720–729.

Brown, E. B., Jr. & Gott, B. (1963) Intracellular hydrogen ion changes and potassium movement. *Amer. J. Physiol.* 204, 765–770.

I don't know, but if you double the potassium concentration in ventriculo-cisternal perfusion fluid then you do see physiological effects on the respiratory and cardiovascular systems (Leusen 1949).

BROWN

I assume that in your *in vitro* experiments the frog brain was bathed in a balanced Ringer solution through which you bubbled CO_2. It would be interesting to see whether you would get the same result if you repeated the experiments using blood instead of saline. In Dr. Fenn's experiments he first bathed the sartorius muscle in saline and found that the potassium moved in one direction (Fenn & Cobb 1934). He wrote a paper on these experiments but later he repeated the experiment using blood, and found that potassium moved in the other direction (Fenn & Cobb 1935). He again wrote a paper and indicated the difference. Therefore you can always find a paper of Dr. Fenn's that you can refer to and support the direction of movement that you find. His explanation was that in the case of saline the tissue was better buffered than the saline whereas in the case of the blood, the blood was better buffered than the tissue. This was assumed to account for the difference in the direction of potassium movements.

SIESJÖ

Would you speculate about the possible significance of a change in CSF-plasma potential on the potassium distribution between CSF and plasma?

CAMERON

I have calculated the electrochemical gradients for potassium. I didn't bring them up because the electrochemical gradients are small, the changes are small, and there is a large scatter.

Leusen, I. (1949) The influence of calcium, potassium, and magnesium ions in cere-brospinal fluid on vasomotor system. *J. Physiol. (Lond.) 110*, 319–329.

Fenn, W. O. & Cobb, D. M. (1934) The potassium equilibrium in muscle. *J. gen. Physiol. 17*, 629–634.

Fenn, W. O. & Cobb, D. M. (1935) Evidence for potassium shift from plasma to muscles in response to an increased carbon dioxide tension. *Amer. J. Physiol. 112*, 41–48.

DAVSON

I would like to congratulate Dr. Bradbury on demonstrating so nicely that there is a control mechanism which accelerates potassium extrusion from CSF when the potassium concentration raises, which is an unusual situation. Have you done any studies where you replaced potassium with rubidium?

BRADBURY

Increasing the rubidium at a normal potassium concentration in the perfusing CSF turns on the mechanism for moving K^{42}, i. e. the barrier clearance of K^{42} is raised by increasing rubidium instead of potassium. Under these circumstances the absolute potassium concentration is reduced, which might perhaps give some substance to the suggestion that one might be measuring net fluxes and not just the K^{42} flux. I would like to add that the potential in acute experiments seems to be such that the potassium distribution requires that in hypokalemia one would have to hypothesize active transport into CSF, whereas in hyperkalemia one would have to hypothesize active transport out of CSF.

Proton Veils and the Three Cornered Stat

J. W. Severinghaus

In the full course of this Symposium we shall consider nine or more mechanisms which contribute to stability of the hydrogen ion concentration in brain ECF. The two most important mechanisms are sufficiently well-established as to require only passing comment: the kidney and the respiratory medullary surface hydrogen ion chemoreceptors. Both act externally to the system, altering the composition of blood. At the other extreme are at least four mechanisms operating primarily within cells to handle protons, and thereby in part affect extracellular pH. These will be discussed tomorrow and also are only acknowledged here: the enzymatic control of carbonic acid generated by metabolism; the stimulus to lactic acid formation by alkalosis; the buffering of protons by intracellular proteins; and the active transport of hydrogen out of cells which somehow keeps intracellular pH at least one unit more alkaline than electrochemical equilibrium with its strongly negative internal potential.

Between these extremes lie three phenomena, candidates for the role of extracellular pH regulators, which I have called the three cornered stat. They merit our intense interest, not only because they bear directly on ECF pH regulation, but because each is poorly understood and begging for study. These are vasomotor control of tissue carbonic and lactic acids, the electrical potential between ECF and blood, and the endothelial surface charge.

Cerebral arterioles constrict when their ECF pH rises. The resulting fall of local CBF raises Pco_2 and H^+ and eventually lowers Po_2 enough to increase local lactic concentration, depending on blood oxygen supply. These locally produced hydrogen ions then redilate the arteriole and increase local CBF, carrying away the CO_2 and some lactic acid, and perhaps permit the reoxygenated cells to consume some lactic acid. This cycle forms an

Cardiovascular Research Institute, University of California Medical Center, San Francisco, California 94122, USA.

effective negative feedback regulator, with ECF pH as the regulated variable. At normal steady state, the arterioles may be regarded as more than half constricted, since flow can be more than doubled by hypercapnia. We may regard this constriction as being due to a pH of 7.32, the normal ECF value. ECF pH without this constriction would trend toward the more alkaline blood pH of 7.40. We shall discuss on Saturday what proportion of this gradient is lactic acid, the evidence I know suggesting about 5–10 per cent, the remainder, of course, carbonic acid. Cerebral arterioles may be observed to open and close with a normal period of about 20 seconds. Tissue Po_2 as recorded with implanted platinum microelectrodes shows cycles of similar period. We should consider the relationship of this cyclic phenomenon to the arteriolar pH stat, and investigate whether the period and duty cycle are functions of ECF pH. We may predict that this mechanism will be ineffective in systemic acidosis, but effective in systemic alkalosis and in local tissue acidosis and alkalosis. During my sabbatical here six years ago I observed essentially complete pH restoration on rabbit cortical surface while holding blood pH at 7.7 and Pco_2 at 20 torr, and hopefully after this meeting I may understand the meaning and mechanism of it.

The second corner of the stat is the electrical potential generated across the blood brain barrier by still undetermined mechanisms. The positive potential in CSF rises some 30–40 mv per pH unit fall in arterial blood, tending to drive H^+ out and HCO_3^- in to brain ECF from blood in acidosis. If this mechanism is the only force operating across the blood brain barrier in severe acidosis, we may expect the calculated transbarrier electrochemical potential gradients of H^+ and HCO_3^- to approach zero in acidosis, and evidence to date supports this. We need to discover the generator of this potential and study its energetics. Ouabain, the pump handle of the Ussing school, essentially destroys the EMF-pH relationship, whether injected into CSF or perfused through the blood stream (with the aid of cardiac bypass), which suggests we begin our search in the endothelial sodium transport. Dr. Ussing once told me he thought cells pump sodium as a poor substitute for hydrogen. Perhaps the observed potential dependence upon arterial pH is indeed induced by the diffusion of H^+ from blood into endothelial cells, being partially stopped by the resulting potential, while the sodium-hydrogen pump keeps intracellular pH stable by swapping potassium for H^+ instead of Na^+. Assuming the pump is neutral, and busy handling H^+, the inward leaking Na^+ will also contribute toward the positivity seen on the brain side of the barrier. Presumably the endothelial cell rapidly reaches a new steady state with slightly more H^+ and Na^+ inside and a reduced potential across its blood surface.

The third corner of our stat must be credited to Gurtner, Davies & Riley (*Fed. Proc. 29*, 134, 1970). It has to do with the effect of endothelial surface negativity on the distribution of weak acids and bases, and was first noticed in the lung where a non-ventilated lobe was observed to have a Pco_2 as much as 30 torr higher than mixed venous blood. The concept is that, as blood is spread out over a large capillary surface, a rapid translocation of H^+ occurs toward the negative charges on the endothelium. H^+ can diffuse much faster than anions, not only because it is smaller, but because proton-water exchange permits a relay race type of movement (more than "faciliated diffusion"). The excess H^+ near the surface reacts with local HCO_3^-, lowering its concentration and increasing H_2CO_3. The concentrations available for diffusion into and across endothelium are thus not those of mean capillary blood. In the case of the brain, the relevant HCO_3^- concentration in capillary plasma is thus lower than predicted from analysis of either tissue Pco_2 and blood buffer base, or from mixed venous blood. Furthermore, the newly formed HCO_3^- in brain capillary red cells is inhibited from diffusing to the endothelial wall by the surface charges. Thus, both by attracting H^+ and repelling HCO_3^-, the endothelial charge reduces the relevant HCO_3^- available for diffusion into brain ECF, and may account for part of the normally observed electrochemical gradient of about —9 mv or 28 per cent less in CSF than would be expected with a potential of $+4$ mv in ECF. If so, a relatively small role may be assigned to lactic acid production in establishing the HCO_3^- distribution in normoxia.

It thus seems that each corner of the stat has its domain of dominance: vasoconstriction in alkalosis, the transbarrier potential in acidosis, and the endothelial surface charge at normal pH. Yet no mechanism operates alone in a system with nine or more proton veils.

Distribution of H^+ and HCO_3^- in Cerebral Fluids

V. Fencl

In the normal acid-base balance, the cerebrospinal fluid (CSF) is more acid than plasma. This applies to all mammalian species that have been studied. CSF pH, as in any compartment of the body fluids, follows the ratio of the local concentration of the molecular CO_2 (Pco_2), and of bicarbonate, the conjugate base of the "carbonic acid" (Henderson-Hasselbalch equation).

The concentrations of bicarbonate in CSF in various mammalian species in the normal acid-base balance are shown in Table 1. In all the species listed, CSF bicarbonate is lower than what would correspond to the ultrafiltrate of arterial or capillary plasma. Simultaneous measurements in the lumbar and in the cisternal CSF show that in humans the concentrations of bicarbonate are the same in the two regions (Bradley & Semple 1962, van Heijst *et al.* 1966). This seems to apply to the normal acid-base condition, and also to steady acid-base disturbances, when $[HCO_3^-]$ in CSF is changed.

Pco_2 in CSF reflects the tension in the adjacent tissues and is normally some 8 to 10 mm Hg higher than Pco_2 in arterial blood. During steady-state distribution of the respiratory gases in the cerebral fluids, Pco_2 in the intracranial CSF will reflect the average CO_2 tension in the brain (Bradley & Semple 1962, Pontén & Siesjö 1966). On the other hand, in the lumbar region, CSF Pco_2 will reflect the tissue Pco_2 prevailing in that region. The very careful measurements of van Heijst *et al.* (1966) suggest that, in normal man in steady state of gas exchange, lumbar CSF Pco_2 is somewhat higher than in the simultaneously taken sample of cisternal CSF. There is essentially no buffering for CO_2 in CSF; therefore, CSF pH is appreciably affected by changes in CSF Pco_2. This, of course, poses serious technical problems

Department of Physiology, Harvard Medical School, 25 Shattuck Street, Boston, Mass. 02115, U. S. A.

Table 1. Distribution of bicarbonate between blood and CSF in normal
acid-base balance.

	[HCO$_3^-$], mE/kg H$_2$O Blood plasma		CSF	Ratio CSF/capillary plasma
	arterial	capillary		
Rat (1)	31	33	28	0.85
Rabbit (2)	25	27	22	0.81
Dog (3)	26	28	23.5	0.84
Goat (4)	28	30	22	0.73
Sheep (5)	30	32	23	0.72
Fetal lamb (5)..........	28	30	25	0.83
Man (6)	26	28	24	0.86

(1) Pontén & Siesjö (1967); (2) Davson (1967); (3) Bleich *et al.* (1964); (4) Pappenheimer *et al.* (1965); (5) Hodson *et al.* (1968); (6) Mitchell *et al.* (1965).

in direct measurements of pH in anaerobic samples of CSF. Also, it is conceivable that pH measured in lumbar samples from humans gives values slightly different from what obtains to the intracranial CSF (van Heijst *et al.* 1966).

In my discussion I shall not go into the mechanisms which determine the concentration gradients of bicarbonate between plasma and CSF. I shall rather concentrate on presenting in descriptive terms the variations of pH, Pco$_2$, and bicarbonate in the cerebral fluids and in blood during the various types of acid-base imbalance. First of all, I should like to say a few words about the relationship between CSF in the cerebral cavities (cerebral ventricles and subarachnoid space) and in the interstitial fluid in the brain (cISF). In experiments with perfusions of the ventriculo-cisternal system with various abnormal concentrations of HCO$_3^-$ and Cl$^-$, we observed that both these anions exchanged across the ependyma, in proportion to their concentration gradients imposed by the composition of the perfusate (Fig. 1). The transependymal fluxes of HCO$_3^-$ and Cl$^-$ reached zero values when the concentrations in the perfusate were equal to those spontaneously present in the cavity fluid (CSF). This applied to the normal acid-base balance and also to various degrees of stable metabolic acidosis and alkalosis. We concluded that (a) HCO$_3^-$ and Cl$^-$ can exchange by diffusion between CSF and cISF across the ependyma and the pial surface; (b) in the steady acid-base conditions studied, there was no concentration gradient between CSF and cISF for HCO$_3^-$ and Cl$^-$ (Fencl *et al.* 1966). If this observation

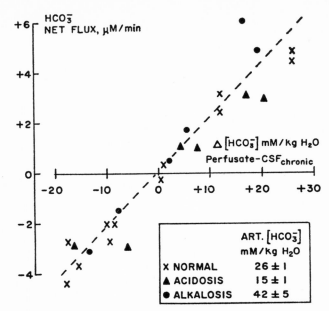

Fig. 1. Net transependymal fluxes of bicarbonate in normal goats, and in chronic stable metabolic acidosis and alkalosis, during ventriculo-cisternal perfusions with artifical CSF of abnormal [HCO$_3^-$] and [Cl$^-$]. From Fencl *et al.* 1966.

can be generalised one would infer that, in steady state of an acid-base condition, CSF in the cerebral cavities and cISF approximate in terms of [HCO$_3^-$], [Cl$^-$], and also in pH, since the CO$_2$ tension in both fluids is determined by the brain tissue. It would also follow from the diffusiveness of HCO$_3^-$ and Cl$^-$ between the two compartments of cerebral fluids that, during transients in acute acid-base disturbances, the relationship between CSF and cISF would be very complex indeed; the rate of turnover of the two fluids is different, and so is the rate of equilibration of molecular CO$_2$ and of ions between the two compartments. Therefore, during the transient states of acute acid-base disbalance, the composition of CSF sampled from the large cavities will not give any clues to the composition of cISF (the "paradoxical shifts" in CSF pH during acute metabolic acidosis and alkalosis are extreme examples of such transient imbalance between CSF and cISF).

In long-term abnormalities of acid-base balance, CSF pH is said to be remarkably stable, although pH in blood may vary appreciably (Mitchell *et al.* 1965). Fig. 2 shows the ranges of pH values in blood and in CSF

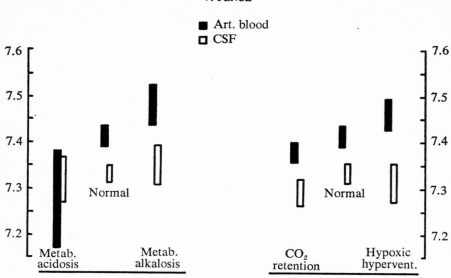

Fig. 2. Range of pH values in chronic acid-base disturbances. Compiled human data. For references see Mitchell *et al.* 1965.

reported in various acid-base disturbances in humans. In steady acid-base imbalance of "metabolic" origin, blood pH may vary remarkably indeed, and CSF pH varies much less. Note that in severe chronic metabolic acidosis, CSF may become less acid than blood. Similarly, in respiratory alkalosis accompanying chronic hypoxia, CSF pH changes very little. On the other hand, with chronic CO_2 retention, CSF pH seems to decrease as much as it does in blood. Although there is a rather wide scatter of the data on CSF pH, one would suspect that the efficiency of stabilising CSF pH varies with the various types of chronic acid-base disturbances.

Let us now analyze how the two determinants of the CSF pH, bicarbonate and P_{CO_2}, vary in the various types of acid-base imbalance, keeping in mind that in a stable condition, our conclusions would probably also apply to cISF.

Fig. 3 shows how CSF bicarbonate varies with the changes produced in blood bicarbonate by "metabolic" acid-base disturbances in humans. The plot fits a straight line and the slope of the line is about 0.4, i.e., about 40 per cent of the change produced in blood bicarbonate concentration by metabolic acidosis or alkalosis is reflected in the change in CSF bicarbonate.

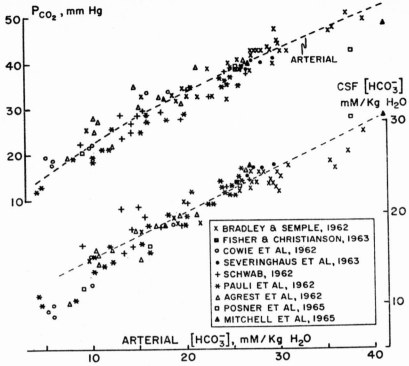

Fig. 3. [HCO₃⁻] in blood and in CSF in patients with chronic metabolic acidosis and alkalosis. Compiled data, from Fencl *et al.* 1966.

In well pronounced stable metabolic acidosis, CSF bicarbonate is higher than in blood plasma.

Analogous data in chronic acid-base disturbances of "respiratory" origin are shown in Fig. 4. Here again, variations in CSF bicarbonate concentration are correlated with changes in blood bicarbonate in humans, in this case produced by chronic CO_2 retention or by chronic hyperventilation due to hypoxia (high altitude). Again, the plot follows a straight line. From Fig. 5 it can be seen that the slopes of the plots of the human data shown in Figs. 3 and 4 differ significantly. In acid-base imbalances of the "respiratory" type, almost ⅔ of the change in blood bicarbonate concentration is reflected in the CSF bicarbonate, as opposed to only 40 per cent in the "metabolic" disturbances. In other mammalian species this difference between the two types of acid-base imbalance is also very obvious (Fig. 6).

12*

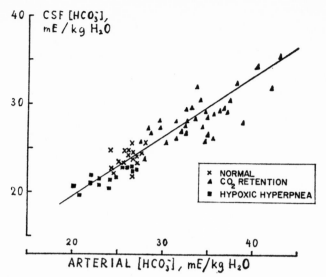

Fig. 4. [HCO$_3$] in arterial plasma and in CSF in patients with chronic CO$_2$ retention and with hypoxic hyperpnea. Compilation of data from Bühlmann *et al.* 1963, Fisher & Christianson 1963, van Heijst *et al.* 1965, 1966, Huang & Lyons 1966, Manfredi 1962, Merwarth *et al.* 1961, Mitchell *et al.* 1965, Pauli *et al.* 1962, Posner *et al.* 1965, Saunier *et al.* 1965, Schwab 1962a, b, Severinghaus *et al.* 1963, Severinghaus & Carceleń 1964.

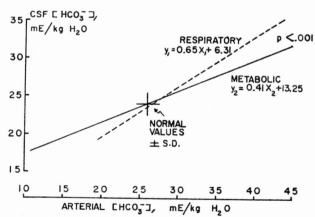

Fig. 5. Relationship between the concentration of bicarbonate in CSF and in arterial plasma in chronic acid-base disturbances of respiratory and metabolic origin in humans. Data on respiratory disturbances from Fig. 4, on metabolic disturbances from Fencl *et al.* 1969.

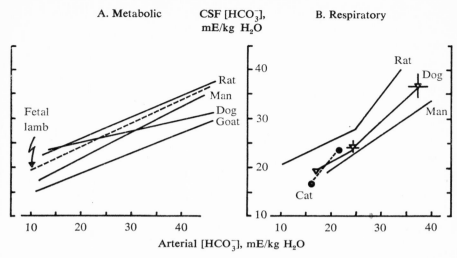

Fig. 6. Distribution of bicarbonate between blood and CSF in acid-base disturbances in various mammalian species. Data from Bleich *et al.* 1964, Fencl *et al.* 1969, Hodson *et al.* 1968, Leusen 1965, Pontén 1966, Pontén & Siesjö 1967, Swanson & Rosengren 1962; data on dogs in metabolic acidosis and alkalosis: Nesbakken, Nornes & Fencl, (unpublished observations); human data on respiratory acidosis and alkalosis from Fig. 3.

Without going into the detailed mechanisms which determine these peculiar and variable relationships between bicarbonate in blood and in CSF, let me just point out that the concentration of bicarbonate in CSF probably depends on several factors: (a) bicarbonate concentration in blood plasma; (b) the complex processes at the blood-brain barrier (BBB), including the variable electric potential between blood and CSF; (c) the variable rate of lactate production by the brain; (d) possibly also the buffering of CO_2 by the brain tissue (with subsequent diffusional exchange of bicarbonate and chloride between cISF and CSF ?) (Table 2). Dr. Messeter and Dr. Sørensen will present quantitative evaluations of the various factors which influence $[HCO_3^-]$ in CSF, and I expect that we shall have some lively discussion on that later on.

What determines the tension of CO_2 in the brain and in the intracranial CSF? The average P_{CO_2} in the brain tissue results from the concentration of the molecular CO_2 in the incoming arterial blood, Pa_{CO_2}, plus the local increment in P_{CO_2} in the brain, $\triangle P_{CO_2}$ (brain). (Table 2). In the steady state of gas exchange, Pa_{CO_2} is a function of the ratio $\dot{V}_{CO_2}$ (whole body) / $\dot{V}_A$ or,

Table 2.

$$pH(csf) = pK'(csf) + \frac{[HCO_3^-]\,(csf)}{Sco_2(csf) \cdot Pco_2(csf)}$$

$[HCO^-]\,(csf) = f$ $\begin{bmatrix} [HCO_3^-]\ (arterial) \\ (Blood\text{-}Brain\ Barrier) \\ (Cerebral\ lactate\ production) \\ (Cerebral\ buffering\ for\ CO_2 \end{bmatrix}$

$Pco_2\,(csf) = f$ $\begin{bmatrix} Pa_{CO_2} \\ \\ \triangle Pco_2\ (brain) \end{bmatrix}$ $\longleftarrow \quad \dfrac{\dot{V}co_2\ (whole\ body)}{\dot{V}_A}$

$\longleftarrow \quad \dfrac{\dot{V}co_2\ (brain)}{C.\ B.\ F.}$

at a constant $\dot{V}co_2$ (at rest), $Paco_2$ is a simple reciprocal function of the effective pulmonary ventilation ($\dot{V}_A$). The increment in Pco_2, going from the arterial inflow into the brain to the Pco_2 at the tissue level ($\triangle Pco_2$), is a function of the ratio (cerebral $\dot{V}co_2$) / (cerebral blood flow, C.B.F.) or, since the volume of CO_2 produced by the brain is constant, the increment in Pco_2 is a simple reciprocal function of C.B.F.

Let us now analyze how the two determinants, $\dot{V}_A$ and C.B.F. operate in the various types of acid-base disturbances. Firstly, in steady metabolic acidosis and alkalosis, the resting effective pulmonary ventilation ($\dot{V}_A$) is largely (Mitchell et al. 1965) or perhaps even exclusively (Fencl et al. 1966, 1969) determined by the pH in CSF (or cISF). The cerebral vascular resistance and C.B.F. are regulated by the pH in cISF in the close vicinity of the cerebral arterioles (Fencl et al. 1969). This means that, e.g., any decrement in the concentration of bicarbonate in cISF in metabolic acidosis would tend to reduce the cerebral-tissue Pco_2 by increasing both the effective pulmonary ventilation and the perfusion of the brain with blood. And conversely, an increment in bicarbonate in cISF during metabolic alkalosis, by its effect on $\dot{V}_A$ and C.B.F., would tend to increase the cerebral-tissue Pco_2. Therefore, the regulation of $\dot{V}_A$ and of C.B.F. can be viewed as an additional homeostatic system which serves in stabilising pH in the brain, acting in concert with those mechanisms at the BBB which protect the cerebral fluids from mirroring the full extent of a loss or gain in bicarbonate, occurring in blood. This dual defense of CSF pH in metabolic acidosis and alkalosis is very efficient. It has been estimated that in humans, the variation in [H^+] in CSF is reduced to only 1/10 of that occurring in blood in chronic metabolic acidosis and alkalosis (Fencl *et al.* 1969). On the other hand, in chronic CO_2 retention resulting from lung disease, the regulatory loop for Pa_{CO_2} is obliterated by the pulmonary pathology, and C.B.F. is not increased (Schneiberg *et al.* 1953), possibly due to the build-up of a high bicarbonate concentration in cISF (cf. Fig. 4). This would suggest why the defense of a stable CSF pH appears much less efficient than in the "metabolic" acid-base disorders. Finally, in hypoxic hyperventilation, the primary acid-base disorder is the loss of molecular CO_2 shared by all body stores of CO_2, including the cerebral fluids. C.B.F. is not reduced (Severinghaus *et al.* 1966), in spite of the abnormally low Pa_{CO_2}. Therefore, the mechanisms which in hypoxic hyperpnea maintain the stability of CSF pH would solely depend on adjusting the concentration of bicarbonate in the cerebral fluids to the decreased concentration of molecular CO_2 (active transport of H^+ at the BBB?; increased influx of lactate into cISF?). I trust that we shall hear on this particular problem from Dr. Sørensen and from Dr. Severinghaus.

In summary, I have tried to point out that there are two basic mechanisms which can be called upon to stabilise the acidity of the cerebral fluids during chronic disturbances of acid-base balance: Firstly, the mechanisms which determine the distribution of bicarbonate between blood and CSF. These include the poorly understood processes at the blood-brain barrier and possibly other local factors in the brain. Secondly, the modification of the concentration of the molecular CO_2 in the cerebral fluids, produced by readjusting the effective pulmonary ventilation and the cerebral blood flow. Finally, in the various types of acid-base disturbances, the efficiency of the two mechanisms varies.

REFERENCES

Agrest, A., Roehr, E. & Ruiz-Guñazu, A. (1962) Säure-Basen-Gleichgewicht des Liquor cerebrospinalis und des arteriellen Blutes bei Niereninsuffizienz. *Klin. Wschr. 40,* 1045–1048.

Bleich, H. L., Berkman, P. M. & Schwartz, W. B. (1964) The response of cerebrospinal fluid composition to sustained hypercapnia. *J. clin. Invest. 43,* 11–16.

Bradley, R. D. & Semple, S. J. G. (1962) A comparison of certain acid-base characteristics of arterial blood, jugular venous blood and cerebrospinal fluid in man, and the effect on them of some acute and chronic acid-base disturbances. *J. Physiol. (Lond.) 160,* 381–391.

Cowie, J., Lambie, A. T. & Robson, J. S. (1962) The influence of extracorporeal dialysis on the acid-base composition of blood and cerebrospinal fluid. *Clin. Sci. 23,* 397–404.

Bühlmann, A., Scheitlin, W. & Rossier, P. H. (1963) Die Beziehungen zwischen Blut und Liquor cerebrospinalis bei Störungen des Säure-Basen-Gleichgewichtes. *Schweiz. med. Wschr. 93,* 427–432.

Davson, H. (1967) *Physiology of the Cerebrospinal Fluid.* J. & A. Churchill, London.

Fencl, V., Miller, T. B. & Pappenheimer, J. R. (1966) Studies on the respiratory response to disturbances of acid-base balance, with deductions concerning the ionic composition of cerebral interstitial fluid. *Amer. J. Physiol. 210,* 459–472.

Fencl, V., Vale, J. R. & Broch, J. A. (1969) Respiration and cerebral blood flow in metabolic acidosis and alkalosis in humans. *J. appl. Physiol. 27,* 67–76.

Fisher, V. J. & Christianson, L. C. (1963) Cerebrospinal fluid acid-base balance during a changing ventilatory state in man. *J. appl. Physiol. 18,* 712–716.

van Heijst, A. N. P., Maas, A. H. J. & Visser, B. F. (1965) L'équilibre acido-basique dans le sang et le liquide céphalo-rachidien dans l'hypercapnie chronique. *Bull. Physio-Path. resp. 1,* 169–179.

van Heijst, A. N. P., Maas, A. H. J. & Visser, B. F. (1966) Comparison of the acid-base balance in cisternal and lumbar cerebrospinal fluid. *Pflügers Arch. ges. Physiol. 287,* 242–246.

Hodson, W. A., Fenner, A., Brumley, G., Chernick, V. & Avery, M. E. (1968) Cerebrospinal fluid and blood acid-base relationships in fetal and neonatal lambs and pregnant ewes. *Resp. Physiol. 4,* 322–332.

Huang, C. T. & Lyons, H. A. (1966) The maintenance of acid-base balance between cerebrospinal fluid and arterial blood in patients with chronic respiratory disorders. *Clin. Sci. 31,* 273–284.

Leusen, I. R. (1965) Aspects of the acid-base balance between blood and cerebrospinal fluid. In: *Cerebrospinal Fluid and the Regulation of Ventilation,* ed. Brooks, C. McC., Kao, F. F. & Lloyd, B. B. Blackwell, Oxford.

Manfredi, F. (1962) Acid-base relations between serum and cerebrospinal fluid in man under normal and abnormal conditions. *J. Lab. clin. Med. 59,* 128–136.

Merwarth, C. R., Sieker, H. D. & Manfredi, F. (1961) Acid-base relations between blood and cerebrospinal fluid in normal subjects and patients with respiratory insufficiency. *New Engl. J. Med. 265,* 310–313.

Mitchell, R. A., Carman, C. T., Severinghaus, J. W., Richardson, B. W., Singer, M. M. & Shnider, S. (1965) Stability of cerebrospinal fluid pH in chronic acid-base disturbances in blood. *J. appl. Physiol. 20,* 443–452.

Pappenheimer, J. R., Fencl, V., Heisey, S. R. & Held, D. (1965) Role of cerebral fluids in control of respiration as studied in unanesthetized goats. *Amer. J. Physiol. 208,* 436–450.

Pauli, H. G., Vorburger, C. & Reubi, F. (1962) Chronic derangements of cerebrospinal fluid acid-base components in man. *J. appl. Physiol. 17,* 993–998.

Pontén, U. (1966) Consecutive acid-base changes in blood, brain tissue and cerebrospinal fluid during respiratory acidosis and baseosis. *Acta neurol. scand. 42,* 455–471.

Pontén, U. & Siesjö, B. K. (1966) Gradients of CO$_2$ tension in the brain. *Acta physiol. scand. 67*, 129–140.

Pontén, U. & Siesjö, B. K. (1967) Acid-base relations in arterial blood and cerebrospinal fluid of unanesthetized rats. *Acta physiol. scand. 71*, 89–95.

Posner, J. B., Swanson, A. G. & Plum, F. (1965) Acid-base balance in cerebrospinal fluid. *Arch. Neurol. 12*, 479–496.

Saunier, C., Reichart, E., Schibi, M., Aug, M.-C. & Rouch, Y. (1965) L'équilibre acids-basique du liquide céphalo-rachidien au cours de l'hypercapnie. *Bull. Physio-Path. resp. 1*, 181–202.

Schneiberg, P., Blackburn, I., Saslaw, M., Rich, M. & Baum, G. (1953) Cerebral circulation and metabolism in pulmonary emphysema and fibrosis with observations on the effect of mild exercise. *J. clin. Invest. 32*, 720–728.

Schwab, M. (1962a) Das Säure-Basen-Gleichgewicht im arteriellen Blut und Liquor cerebrospinalis bei chronischer Niereninsuffizienz. *Klin. Wschr. 40*, 765–772.

Schwab, M. (1962b) Das Säure-Basen-Gleichgewicht im arteriellen Blut und Liquor cerebrospinalis bei Herzinsuffizienz und Cor pulmonale und seine Beeinflussung durch Carboanhydrase-Hemmung. *Klin. Wschr. 40*, 1233–1245.

Severinghaus, J. W. & Carceleń, B. (1964) Cerebrospinal fluid in man native to high altitude. *J. appl. Physiol. 19*, 319–321.

Severinghaus, J. W., Chiodi, H., Eger, E. I., Branstater, B. B. & Hornbein, T. F. (1966) Cerebral blood flow at high altitude. *Circulat. Res. 19*, 274–282.

Severinghaus, J. W. & Lassen, N. (1967) Step hypocapnia to separate arterial from tissue P$_{CO_2}$ in the regulation of cerebral blood flow. *Circulat. Res. 20*, 272–278.

Severinghaus, J. W., Mitchell, R. A., Richardson, B. W. & Singer, M. M. (1963) Respiratory control at high altitude suggesting active transport regulation of CSF pH. *J. appl. Physiol. 18*, 1155–1166.

Swanson, A. G. & Rosengren, H. (1962) Cerebrospinal fluid buffering during acute experimental respiratory acidosis. *J. appl. Physiol. 17*, 812–814.

DISCUSSION

MAREN

In hyperventilation how good is the pH regulating mechanism?

FENCL

The measurements of CSF pH in chronic hyperventilation show that, in this condition, the mechanisms defending the CSF pH operate quite efficiently; however, pH seems to be singlehandedly defended by the mechanisms which lower the CSF bicarbonate concentration, because the lowering of CSF Pco_2 which results from hyperventilation certainly does not help in stabilizing CSF pH.

SEVERINGHAUS

It does seem that CSF pH regulation during hyperventilation occurs sooner and perhaps more completely if hypoxia is also present. Eger *et al.* (1968) determined the amount of left shift of the hyperoxic CO_2 response curve, which is believed to be a reasonable index of CSF HCO_3^-, in volunteers who were hyperventilated for 8 hours. After hyperventilating with air, the shift was only about 15 per cent complete; that is, CSF $[HCO_3^-]$ reduction presumably was only 15 per cent of that amount needed to afford complete pH regulation. When they were hyperventilated with a hypoxic gas mixture, the shift and presumed $[HCO_3^-]$ reduction were about 40 per cent complete.

SIESJÖ

Dr. Severinghaus, I want to challenge the proposition that changes in the cerebral blood flow will have any significant effect on the regulation of the CSF pH. In a normal state, Pco_2 in cisternal CSF is approximately 6 to 6.5 mm Hg higher than it is in arterial blood. If, during marked hyperventilation, you wait for 10 to 15 minutes you find the Pco_2 in CSF to be about 7 to 8 mm Hg higher than in the arterial blood. The regulation by CBF should therefore be working by increasing the difference between Pco_2 in arterial blood and CSF by about 1.5 mm Hg. This is not any appreciable regulation, when compared to the other factors operating.

Eger, E. L., Kellogg, R. H., Mines, A. H., Limo-Ostos, M., Morril, C. G., & Kent, D. W. (1968) Influence of CO_2 on ventilatory acclimatization to altitude *J. appl. Physiol. 24,* 601–615.

DISCUSSION 187

SEVERINGHAUS

If the cerebral blood flow falls with hyperventilation, as we know it does, then the tissue oxygen tension will fall. I think we can agree on that. We know that even at rest at sea level we have a certain amount of anaerobic metabolism and that this is contributing hydrogen ions to the CSF. When flow falls, and therefore Po_2 falls, there will be more lactic acid generation, both because of a lower oxygen tension and because there is an independent stimulation of anaerobic metabolism by alkalosis. So for several reasons there will be more hydrogen ion generated if flow falls.

SIESJÖ

I agree to that. However, the lactic acid produced as a result of alkalosis must surely be unrelated to a fall in flow. My point was that the CO_2 tension changes due to a change in flow are so small that they would make rather insufficient contributions.

SKINHØJ

May I show a table which demonstrates the clinical consequences of the subject which we are discussing.

Chronic metabolic acidosis.

Patient no.	Arterial blood						CBF ml/100 g/min.
	Pco_2 mm Hg	HCO_3^- mEq/l	pH	Pco_2 mm Hg	HCO_3^- mEq/l	pH	
1	26.1	13.4	2.341	34.1	14.9	7.301	47
2	30.0	15.0	7.333	38.1	17.5	7.298	49
3	24.3	9.7	7.209	31.5	12.3	7.229	140
4	21.8	7.5	7.069	23.5	10.8	7.298	73
5	29.3	10.4	7.198	33.1	14.5	7.278	152

Chronic hypercapnia.

6	47.7	31.2	7.420	53.0	25.0	7.310	48
7	63.5	43.5	7.441	69.5	32.1	7.307	47
8	59.1	35.5	7.401	69.1	31.6	7.296	51
9	59.2	40.0	7.443	63.5	29.6	7.304	50
10	62.1	33.7	7.349	69.2	30.6	7.281	98

11	86.0	33.0	7.214	92.1	35.4	7.221	150
12	65.1	34.9	7.346	69.0	31.0	7.279	92
13	73.7	40.0	7.363	83.3	32.9	7.232	34

Normal values: 35–43 23–28 7.35–7.45 42–50 20–26 7.29–7.33 42–57

This table illustrates that CSF pH is kept closer to normal than plasma pH is during clinical disturbances in the blood acid-base balance.

During these conditions cerebral blood flow (CBF) does not correlate with arterial Pco_2 if CSF pH is close to the normal value. However, when CSF pH decreases CBF increases, which supports our earlier suggestion that the cerebral vascular resistance is determined by the pH in brain interstitial fluid.

BRADBURY

Dr. Severinghaus: Would you expand a little more on the theory of Gürtner *et al.* You made the suggestion, that there is maldistribution of substances between two compartments, due to the negative charge on the membrane. This would seem to suggest that the system is not taking up its position of maximum entropy.

SEVERINGHAUS

A capillary bed has much more surface area than the aorta. As the blood is distributed over a larger surface, positive charges will be translocated toward the negative by charged endothelium. Protons are capable of moving more rapidly than the anions. Therefore transiently the surface of the blood in the capillary has an excessive hydrogen ion concentration. These hydrogen ions react with bicarbonate and form carbonic acid locally against the surface wall of the capillary. The carbonic acid concentration adjacent to endothelial surface will then be higher than in the middle of the blood column in the capillary. Gürtner *et al.* suggest that CO_2 is then evolved near the surface, and reaches diffusion equilibrium with the adjacent alveoli. My interpretation is that carbonic acid at the surface equilibrates with the endothelium and in the tissue, carbonic acid concentration is in equilibrium with CO_2. I suspect it may not necessarily be in equilibrium with CO_2 in the capillary plasma.

WADDELL

You are saying that there is an area of low pH on the surface of the capillary, and that this increases the concentration of the unionized form of the weak acid. Why do you propose an increase in the concentration of the unionized form, instead of a decrease in the concentration of the ionized form? With free permeability to the unionized form, the unionized form would exist in the same concentration in all locations.

SEVERINGHAUS

You suggest that the processes that occur in the capillary wall are a decrease in the concentration of for example the bicarbonate ion and increase in the concentration of carbonic acid. I think they both occur and I didn't mean to exclude either one. That species which is in equilibrium with CO_2 of course is carbonic acid, and if its concentration is increased in the endothelium wall outside the capillary then the P_{CO_2} will be increased.

WADDELL

But there is an instantaneous equilibrium between carbonic acid and bicarbonate.

SEVERINGHAUS

But there are more hydrogen ions in the vicinity because of the translocation. The relative fall of HCO_3^- is negligible. One may calculate that, in order to raise plasma P_{CO_2} by 10 per cent, the H^+ concentration must rise 4×10^{-9} M, (+ 10 per cent) while the HCO_3^- concentration will fall only .12 mM (0.5 per cent). Furthermore, the absence of carbonic anhydrase in plasma permits doubt that P_{CO_2} reaches equilibrium with the new H_2CO_3, so the number of HCO_3^- ions reacting may be even less, H_2CO_3 being less than 1 per cent of the dissolved CO_2.

WADDELL

With instantaneous equilibrium I don't see how one can say that one is higher and the other is lower. It seems more likely to me that the less diffusible species would maintain the concentration gradient.

Electrochemical Gradients for H^+ and HCO_3^- Between Blood and CSF During Sustained Acid-Base Changes

K. Messeter & B. K. Siesjö

It is now well-known that the extracellular pH in the brain shows very small deviations from the normal values in most chronic plasma acid-base disturbances. The deviations seem especially small in nonrespiratory acid-base changes and in chronic hypocapnia (Bradley & Sample 1962, Schwab 1962, Mitchell *et al.* 1965, Fencl *et al.* 1966), while a somewhat larger shift is observed in chronic hypercapnia (Bühlman *et al.* 1963, see also Bleich *et al.* 1964).

It is only natural that the stability of the CSF pH has led to speculations about the mechanisms which are responsible for what appears to be a homeostatic regulation. Although the same type of factors probably operate in nonrespiratory and in respiratory acid-base disturbances, the problems can be phrased somewhat differently. Thus, which are the mechanisms responsible for the large changes in the CSF bicarbonate concentrations during chronic respiratory acidosis and alkalosis? Further, which are the mechanisms responsible for the fact that a given change in the plasma bicarbonate concentration during nonrespiratory acidosis or alkalosis is accompanied by a much smaller change in the CSF bicarbonate concentration?

It seems well-established that the H^+ and HCO_3^- ions are not passively distributed in the electrical field between CSF and plasma (Held *et al.* 1964). Thus, in spite of the fact that the CSF is normally electrically positive to plasma, the CSF HCO_3^- concentration is lower. This nonequilibrium distribution of H^+ and HCO_3^- implies that there is a net force acting on the ions which we can calculated according to the following equations:

Research Dept. 4, E-Blocket, University Hospital, S-220 05 Lund 5, Sweden.

$$\triangle\mu_{H^+} = 61.5 \ (pH_{pl} - pH_{CSF}) + E$$

$$\triangle\mu_{HCO_3^-} = 61.5 \log \frac{(HCO_3^-)_{CSF}}{(HCO_3^-)_{pl}} - E$$

where $\triangle\mu$ represents an electrochemical potential difference (in mV) and E the CSF/plasma p. d. (also in mV). In the normocapnic situation the net $\triangle\mu_{H^+}$ is usually around 5–10 mV (Severinghaus et al. 1963, Held et al. 1964).

The presence of a net electrochemical potential difference for an ion is often equated with an "active" transport of the ion, and, if we can assume that no other unbalanced passive forces exist (see Ussing 1960), it is thus logical to assume that H⁺ are actively transported into the CSF (see Severinghaus et al. 1963, Fencl et al. 1966).

With the stability of the CSF pH in mind, the existing $\triangle\mu$ led to the further assumption that the hypothetical transport of H⁺ ions serves a regulatory function in maintaining the CSF pH constant whenever there is a tendency for it to change. However, when Kjällquist & Siesjö (1968) and Kjällquist (1970) calculated the $\triangle\mu_{H^+}$ and $\triangle\mu_{HCO_3^-}$ values in sustained nonrespiratory acid-base changes in the rat, very small deviations from the control values were found. In respiratory acidosis the $\triangle\mu_{H^+}$ values even appeared to increase, suggesting that the mechanism which is responsible for the excess of H⁺ in the CSF in the control state had increased its "pumping" of H⁺ into the already acid CSF. These facts did not seem to fit with the presence of a H⁺ transport which purposefully kept the CSF pH constant, and the hypothesis was advanced that most of the stability of the CSF pH could be explained by passive factors (Siesjö & Kjällquist 1970).

METHODS

In order to gain further information on the factors which regulate the CSF pH, we have studied the electrochemical gradients for H⁺ and HCO₃⁻ in acute and chronic hypercapnia in rats. Acute hypercapnia was induced by the administration of about 10% CO_2 to rats anaesthetized with 70% N_2O, or with 0.7% halothane. These rats were studied after 5, 15 or 45 min, respectively. "Chronic" hypercapnia was induced by exposing unanaesthetized animals to the same gas mixture in a Perspex box which was heated to avoid hypothermia. During the last 45 min of the exposure periods the animals were anaesthetized, curarized and artificially ventilated. All animals were mechanically hyperventilated so as to give an arterial CO_2 tension close to that obtained in the unanaesthetized animals.

The electrical potential difference between the CSF and plasma was measured between a catheter in the external jugular vein, and a glass pipette introduced into the cisterna magna (Kjällquist 1970). Both the catheter and the pipette were filled with 3 M KCl in 3% agar, and the exposed atlanto-occipital membrane was covered with paraffin oil before the puncture. Since leakage of CSF around the tip of the pipette was found to lower the recorded potential, all experiments with visible CSF leakage were discarded. In addition, potential differences which varied more than 2 mV during the recording period (5–10 min) were also rejected.

Repeated plasma pH and pCO_2 values were measured on samples anaerobically drawn from one femoral artery, and the plasma bicarbonate concentrations were calculated from these data. Mean capillary HCO_3^- concentrations were calculated as previously described from the laboratory, and the pH values were correspondingly corrected (see Kjällquist 1970). The CSF bicarbonate was calculated from the total CO_2 content, determined with a micro-diffusion technique.

THE CSF/PLASMA D.C. POTENTIAL DIFFERENCES

In order to allow a calculation of electrochemical potential differences in all the hypercapnic groups, the CSF/plasma potential differences were measured in groups of animals exposed to 10% CO_2 for 5, 15 and 45 min, and for 3, 24 and 48 hrs. However, in order to facilitate an analysis of $\triangle E/\triangle pH$ changes, the p. d. was measured also after 5, 15 and 45 min of hyperventilation. In addition, the 45 min material included both normocapnia and extreme hypocapnia, thus allowing a study of the CSF/plasma p. d. over an extended pH range.

Fig. 1 shows that, at 45 min, the CSF/plasma p. d. varied linearly with the plasma pH, giving a slope ($\triangle E/\triangle pH$) of 27 mV/pH unit. An identical slope was obtained at 15 min but at 5 min a significantly larger $\triangle E/\triangle pH$ slope was obtained. However, the biological significance of this finding is unclear due to the non-steady state conditions.

Fig. 2 shows the mean p. d. values obtained in all groups exposed to 10% CO_2 except the 5 min group. The values have been compared to a regression line calculated from all acute experiments, including the hypocapnic groups.

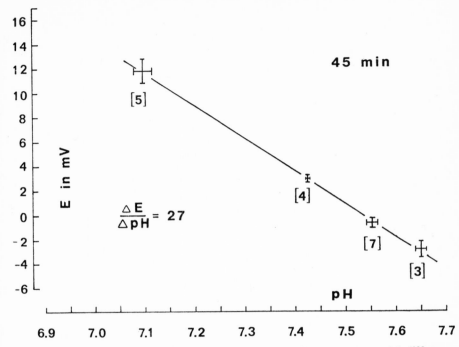

Fig. 1. The relation between the plasma pH and the CSF/plasma potential difference in anaesthetized rats exposed to four different CO_2 tensions. The figures within parantheses indicate number of experiments. Means ± s. e. In all groups the exposure time was limited to 45 min. The figure shows a linear relationship between the plasma pH and the potential difference with a slope of 27 mV/pH unit.

The results strongly indicate that the changes in the CSF/plasma p. d. during respiratory acidosis were entirely determined by the changes in the plasma pH, and they show that neither the plasma pH nor the CSF/plasma p. d. returned to normal values in "chronic" hypercapnia.

THE CSF AND PLASMA BICARBONATE CONCENTRATIONS

Fig. 3 illustrates the gradual increase in the calculated CSF and capillary HCO_3^- concentrations, as well as the gradual return of the corresponding pH values towards normocapnic levels, during the continuous state of hypercapnia (cf. Bleich *et al.* 1964). At all exposure periods studied, the bicarbonate concentrations in the CSF exceeded the plasma bicarbonate concentration.

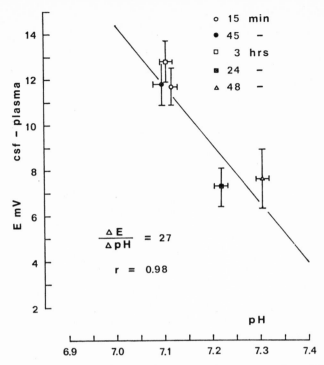

Fig. 2. CSF/plasma potential differences in groups of rats exposed to 10% CO_2. The line of regression was calculated from all acute experiments, including animals exposed to 6–12% CO_2, as well as normocapnic and hypocapnic groups. The change in the p. d. during acute and sustained respiratory acidosis seemed to be entirely determined by the plasma pH. Means ± s. e.

However, the CSF bicarbonate never increased to values which gave a normalization of the CSF pH, a finding which has been confirmed with 72 hrs of hypercapnia.

ELECTROCHEMICAL GRADIENTS

Having information about the bicarbonate concentrations in the CSF and in the plasma water, as well as the corresponding CSF/plasma potential differences, electrochemical potential differences could be calculated.

Fig. 4 shows both the CSF/plasma potential differences, and the mean $\triangle\mu_{HCO_3^-}$ values during the continuous hypercapnia. In the acute phases (5,

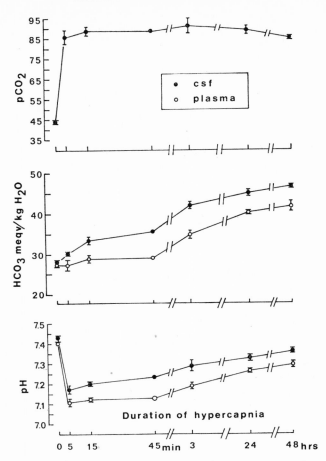

Fig. 3. Tissue CO_2 tensions, CSF and plasma bicarbonate concentrations, as well as CSF and plasma pH values, of rats exposed to about 10% CO_2 for various times. Means ± s. e. The figure illustrates the gradual increase in both the plasma and the CSF pH due to the gradually increasing bicarbonate concentrations. Neither the plasma pH, nor the CSF pH was normalized in the "chronic" groups.

15 and 45 min) there were large increases in the $\triangle\mu_{HCO_3^-}$ values, mostly due to the markedly increased CSF/plasma p. d. However, in the chronic states, when the d. c. potentials were still above normocapnic levels, the $\triangle\mu_{HCO_3^-}$ values had either returned to the control values or were only moderately increased.

13*

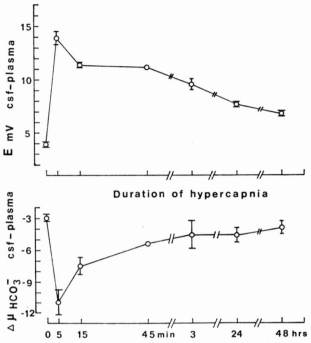

Fig. 4. The relation between the duration of hypercapnia and the CSF/plasma potential differences, as well as the calculated $\triangle\mu\ _{HCO_3^-}$. The potential differences were obtained by calculating each value from the mean line of regression (see Fig. 3), using the capillary pH from each individual experiment. The $\triangle\mu\ _{HCO_3^-}$ was calculated according to the equation

$$\triangle\mu\ _{HCO_3^-} = 61.5\ \log\ \frac{(HCO_3^-)\ _{CSF}}{(HCO_3^-)\ _{pl}} - E$$

The figure shows large increases in both the p. d. and in the $\triangle\mu_{HCO_3^-}$ during acute hypercapnia. In the chronic groups the d. c. potential differences were still elevated but the $\triangle\mu_{HCO_3^-}$ values had returned towards the control values.

DISCUSSION

The present experiments seem to established three things. Firstly, the CSF/ plasma p. d. is linearly related to the plasma pH changes in acute and chronic respiratory acidosis. Secondly, the CSF/plasma p. d. is not only increased when the plasma pH decreases during acute respiratory acidosis, but remains elevated in chronic hypercapnia as long as the plasma pH is acid. Thirdly, the net electrochemical potential difference for HCO_3^- increases acutely with the electrical potential and returns toward normal values in sustained hypercapnia.

When we try to interpret these findings in terms of "regulatory" mechanisms, we are bound to introduce assumptions which may not be very well-justified. However, one conclusion seems immediately justified. Thus, provided we assume that the CSF/plasma p. d. will influence the distribution of H^+ and HCO_3^- between CSF and plasma, the gradual increase in the CSF bicarbonate concentration (and thereby the gradual "regulation" of the CSF pH) can be entirely explained by purely passive factors, i.e., by the momentary increase in the CSF/plasma p. d. and by the gradual increase in the plasma bicarbonate concentration. As long as these factors can be made responsible for the near-normalization of the CSF pH, we are evidently not entitled to assume that an active H^+ transport is involved.

It is more difficult to interpret the significance of the net $\triangle\mu$ values in chronic hypercapnia. Thus, if we assume that the net $\triangle\mu_{HCO_3^-}$ in the control state is caused by an active transport of H^+ from plasma to CSF, we seem to be forced to conclude that this transport goes on unchanged, or even that it increases, in chronic hypercapnia. However, we can also start with the assumption that the net $\triangle\mu_{HCO_3^-}$ in the control state is not caused by active transport of H^+ between CSF and plasma but by an outflux of acid from the cells. Then the present results would require an unchanged or increased outflux of H^+ in the chronic hypercapnic state. Some of our results, to be reported later in this Symposium (Siesjö & Messeter 1971) appear at first sight to be compatible with such an interpretation. However, at steady state there ought to be an equally large passive influx of H^+ into the cells, and it is difficult to understand how such a state could be compatible with a *net* acidification of the extracellular fluids.

The fact that available evidence cannot confirm the presence of a "purposeful" H^+ ion transport between plasma and CSF during respiratory acidosis does not exclude that the hypothetical transport mechanisms help to regulate the CSF pH to constancy in nonrespiratory acid-base disturbances. Thus, if such a transport of H^+ is triggered by the CO_2 tension (or by the plasma HCO_3^- concentration, see Mines & Sørensen 1971), the rate of "pumping" would increase and decrease in nonrespiratory alkalosis and acidosis, respectively. According to Kjällquist's results, sustained nonrespiratory acid-base changes in rats were associated with $\triangle\mu_{HCO_3^-}$ changes which did not exceed 2 mV (Kjällquist 1970). These results raise the question whether or not the changes in the CSF/plasma p. d. are sufficient to explain the fact that there are much smaller changes in the CSF bicarbonate concentration than in the plasma bicarbonate concentration. It is presently difficult to evaluate the importance of a hypothetical H^+ transport, since the analysis requires knowledge of the CSF/plasma p. d. in chronic nonrespiratory acidosis and alkalosis. Kjällquist's results definitely suggest that the changes in the CSF/plasma p. d. are upheld in sustained acid-base changes. However, since Held *et al.* (1964) have reported $\triangle E/\triangle pH$ changes as high as 43 mV/pH unit under acute nonrespiratory acidosis and alkalosis in dogs, it will evidently be necessary to measure the potential changes in the same animal species as we use for measuring the CSF and plasma acid-base parameters.

SUMMARY

The net electrochemical potential differences $(\triangle \mu)$ for H^+ and HCO_3^- between CSF and plasma are usually interpreted to indicate an active transport of the ions. The remarkable stability of the CSF pH in various chronic acid-base disturbances has led to the further assumption that this hypothetical transport serves as a purposeful regulating mechanism which comes into action whenever there is a tendency for the CSF pH to change.

There are reasons to doubt that there exists a H^+ or HCO_3^- transport between plasma and CSF with the complex functions involved. In the first instance, the excess acidity in the CSF could be due to an outflux of H^+ ions from the CNS cells. Secondly, the existing $\triangle \mu$ for H^+ and HCO_3^- ions could be the result of a coupling to another energy-dependent process which is not triggered by the H^+ or HCO_3^- activities.

It has previously been reported from our laboratory that the $\triangle \mu_{HCO_3^-}$ and $\triangle \mu_{H+}$ show very small changes in sustained nonrespiratory alkalosis and acidosis in the rat. In the experiments presented here we have evaluated the electrochemical potential differences in both acute and chronic hypercapnia. The results show large increases in the $\triangle \mu$ values in acute respiratory acidosis, whereas in the chronic situations the calculated $\triangle \mu$ values were very close to those found in normocapnia. These findings do not seem to fit the assumption of a H^+ transport which purposefully keeps the CSF pH constant. It is suggested that most of the stabiliy of the CSF pH can be explained by passive mechanisms, i. e., mechanisms which are unrelated to active transport of H^+ or HCO_3^-.

ACKNOWLEDGMENTS

Supported by the Swedish Medical Research Council (Project B70–14X–263–06 and B70–40X–2179–02), by the Swedish Bank Tercentary Fund, by Carl-Bertel Nathhorst's Vetenskapliga Stiftelse and by PHS Research Grant No. R01 NB07838–01 from NIH.

REFERENCES

Bleich, H. L., Berkman, P. M. & Schwartz, W. B. (1964) The response of cerebrospinal fluid composition to sustained hypercapnia. *J. clin. Invest. 43*, 11–16.

Bradley, R. D. & Semple, S. J. G. (1962) A comparison of certain acid-base characteristics of arterial blood, jugular venous blood and cerebrospinal fluid in man, and the effect on them of some acute and chronic acid-base disturbances. *J. Physiol. 160*, 381–391.

Bühlman, A., Scheitlin, W. & Rossier, P. H. (1963) Die Beziehungen zwischen Blut und Liquor cerebrospinalis bei Störungen des Säure-Basen-Gleichgewichtes. *Schweiz. med. Wschr. 93*, 427–432.

Fencl, V., Miller, T. B. & Pappenheimer, J. R. (1966) Studies on the respiratory response to disturbances of acid-base balance, with deductions concerning the ionic composition of cerebral interstitial fluid. *Amer. J. Physiol. 210*, 459–472.

Held, D. R., Fencl, V. & Pappenheimer, J. R. (1964) Electrical potential of cerebrospinal fluid. *J. Neurophysiol. 27*, 942–959.

Kjällquist, Å. & Siesjö, B. K. (1968) Regulation of CSF pH: influence of the CSF/plasma potential. In *CBF & CSF*, ed. Ingvar, D. H., Lassen, N. A., Siesjö, B. K. & Skinhøj, E. *Scand. J. clin. Lab. Invest.*, Suppl. 102, 1, C.

Kjällquist, Å. (1970) The CSF/blood potential in sustained acid-base changes in the rat. With calculations of electrochemical potential differences for H^+ and HCO_3^-. *Acta physiol. scand. 78*, 85–93.

Mines, A. H. & Sørensen, S. C. (1971) Changes in the electrochemical potential difference for HCO_3^- between blood and cerebrospinal fluid and in cerebrospinal fluid lactate concentration during isocarbic hypoxia. *Acta physiol. scand.* In press.

Mitchell, R. A., Carman, C. T., Severinghaus, J. W., Richardson, B. W., Singer, M. M. & Shnider, S. (1965) Stability of cerebrospinal fluid pH in chronic acid-base disturbances in blood. *J. appl. Physiol. 20* 443–452.

Schwab, M. (1962) Das Säure-Basen-Gleichgewicht im arteriellen Blut und Liquor cerebrospinalis bei chronischer Niereninsuffiziens. *Klin. Wschr. 40*, 765–773.

Severinghaus, J. W., Mitchell, R. A., Richardson, B. W. & Singer, M. M. (1963) Respiratory control at high altitude suggesting active transport regulation of CSF pH. *J. appl. Physiol. 18*, 1155–1166.

Siesjö, B. K. & Kjällquist, Å. (1969) A new theory for the regulation of the extracellular pH in the brain. *Scand. J. clin. Lab. Invest.* 24, 1–9.

Siesjö, B. K. & Messeter, K. (1970) Factors determining intracellular pH. In *Ion Homeostasis of the Brain*, ed. Siesjö, B. K. & Sørensen, S. C. (Alfded Benzon Symposium III). Munksgaard, Copenhagen.

Ussing, H. H. (1960) The alkali metal ions in isolated systems and tissues. In *Handbuch der Experimentellen Pharmakologie*, ed. Eichler, O. & Farah, A., pp. 1–195. Springer-Verlag.

DISCUSSION

SØRENSEN

Kjällquist (1970) calculated $\triangle\mu$ values on the basis of a non-linear relationship between E and plasma pH. Have you recalculated the $\triangle\mu$ values during metabolic acidosis and alkalosis on the basis of your results which show a linear relationship between E and pH in rats?

MESSETER

No, because we have only measured the potential in respiratory acidosis.

SEVERINGHAUS

Did you calculate the electrochemical potential for the hydrogen ion in chronic respiratory acidosis?

MESSETER

Yes, they are approximately the same as the electrochemical potential differences for bicarbonate but with opposite sign.

SEVERINGHAUS

Did they go towards zero?

MESSETER

Yes, but it should then be stressed that they were close to zero from the beginning, i. e. in the normocapnic control state.

PLUM

Experimental acute respiratory acidosis is really very different from any clinical example. In acute experiments bicarbonate is higher in CSF than it is in blood whereas in the chronic states of human respiratory acidosis bicarbonate is lower in CSF than it is in blood. Did you give bicarbonate, or do you know data which show what happens if you give bicarbonate so as to mimic the clinical experience of chronic hypercapnic acidosis, where

Kjällquist, Å. (1970) The CSF/blood potential in sustained acid-base changes in the rat. With calculation of electrochemical potential differences for H+ and HCO3. *Acta physiol. scand. 78*, 85–93.

about 6/10 of the change in the bicarbonate concentration in plasma is reflected in CSF.

FENCL

There are some data on the combined effect of metabolic and respiratory acid-base disturbances on CSF [HCO_3^-]. If you administer bicarbonate and let the system go its way, i. e. allow the regulation of respiration to set the Pco_2, you will get the relationship between blood and CSF bicarbonate that I showed in my paper, i. e. an increase in CSF [HCO_3^-] amounting to some 30 to 40 per cent (depending on the animal species) of the increase in blood bicarbonate. However, if on top of the metabolic alkalosis you give CO_2 to inhale, then for any blood [HCO_3^-] you will get a much higher CSF bicarbonate (Adaro et al. 1969). Similarly, we have observed in anesthetized dogs (Nesbakken, Nornes & Fencl, unpublished) that if you keep blood bicarbonate (Adaro *et al.* 1969). Similarly, we have observed in anesthetized dogs at 40 mm Hg, then CSF bicarbonate won't be lowered as much as it is when you let the system go its way, i. e. when the regulation of pulmonary ventilation lowers the Pco_2 in response to the metabolic acidosis.

SIESJÖ

To Dr. Plum: It is questionable if you can call 72 hrs CO_2 administration to rats *acute* hypercapnia. I think I can at least partly answer your question about changes in the plasma bicarbonate concentration. We induced hypercapnia for 6 hours in two groups of rats (Siesjö & Pontén 1966). In one group sodium bicarbonate was given to keep plasma pH constant, in the other ammonium chloride was administered so that the plasma bicarbonate did not change. The CSF bicarbonate increased also in the latter group but not as much as in the group with constant plasma pH, in which there was a large increase in the plasma bicarbonate.

A short comment to those who ask about the relevance of the electrical potential in calculating $\triangle \mu$ values in acid-base changes. When an electrochemical potential difference for H^+ and HCO^- is found in the normal state,

Adaro, F. V. M., Roehr, E. E., Viola, A. R. & Wymerszberg de Obrutzky, C. (1969) Acid-base equilibrium between blood and cerebrospinal fluid in acute hypercapnia. *J. appl. Physiol. 27,* 271–275.

Siesjö, B. K. & Pontén, U. (1966) Factors affecting the cerebrospinal fluid bicarbonate concentration. *Experientia (Basel) 22,* 611.

this is used as an argument for the presence of an active transport of hydrogen ions into the CSF, so we can't see the reason for not using the same argument in a changed acid-base state, where you have changed the electrical potential. Either you have to discard the potential argument when you look upon the distribution of hydrogen and bicarbonate ions in the first place, or you have to use them in both situations.

SØRENSEN
Several clinical studies have shown that the CSF bicarbonate does not rise as much as the blood bicarbonate during chronic respiratory acidosis, but in many of these studies the patients are probably hypoxic and hypoxia per se does have an effect on the distribution of H^+ and HCO_3^- between blood and CSF (Mines & Sørensen 1971).

PLUM
It's hard to believe that this is just hypoxia although the data in the literature give too little about oxygen tension in patients with chronic respiratory acidosis to be sure. We studied a patient with obesity hypoventilation, delivering low-flow (28 %) oxygen for four days between two cisternal punctures and did not succeed in raising the CSF bicarbonate to a level that equalled or exceeded the blood value:

TR 50° +	Cisternal CSF 21/3/69	Arterial blood 21/3/69	Cisternal 25/3/69	Arterial 25/3/69
pH	7.30	7.34	7.265	7.31
Pco_2 (mmHg)	60	64	71	73
HCO_3 (mEq/l)	29.4	34	32	36.9
Po_2 (mmHg)		46		64

However, one observation is hardly sufficient to permit conclusions. Dr. Siesjö, is the electrical potential difference in chronic hypercapnia the same as you got here in the acute experiment?

SIESJÖ
The electrical potential difference is lower in chronic than in acute hyper-

Mines, A. H. & Sørensen, S. C. (1971) Changes in the electrochemical potential difference for HCO_3^- between blood and cerebrospinal fluid and in cerebrospinal fluid lactate concentration during isocarbic hypoxia. *Acta physiol. scand.* In press.

capnia, since it follows the plasma pH when this is modified by renal mechanics.

LOESCHCKE

It is necessary to differentiate between ion exchanges in plexus fluid and in brain capillary fluid. Plexus fluid must be assumed to be at a low Pco_2 close to the arterial Pco_2 but it equilibrates later with brain tissue. In the capillaries Pco_2 is close to tissue Pco_2 during the time of the production of the fluid. I am asking which site of the ion exchange you are talking about. On the surface of the choroid plexus there is a quick shift of bicarbonate in metabolic acidosis and alkalosis (Loeschcke & Sugioka 1969). This was measured with a small glass electrode sitting on the choroid plexus.

DAVSON

You described an increase in bicarbonate concentration in CSF during hypercapnia with increased bicarbonate concentration in the plasma. Does that imply that the extra bicarbonate has really come from the plasma? All these neural and glial cells, could they not be making some bicarbonate?

SIESJÖ

This does not seem to be the case since the brain intracellular fluids gain bicarbonate continuously during the first few days of a hypercapnia. In other words, we have evidence that the bicarbonate is going from the extracellular to the intracellular fluids. Dr. Loeschcke, we don't know where the exchanges occur since we are looking at the ionic concentrations in cisternal CSF.

SØRENSEN

There may be a redistribution of bicarbonate within the brain in the acute phase, but because it is an open system, in the steady state we only have to consider the distribution between blood and the brain extracellular fluid.

SEVERINGHAUS

My own view would be that in respiratory acidosis these differences are approaching zero, and this would be appropriate for pH regulation. I think

Loeschcke, H. H. & Sugioka, K. (1969) pH of cerebrospinal fluid in the cisterna magna and on the surface of the choroid plexus of the 4th ventricle and its effect on ventilation in experimental disturbances of acid-base balance. Transient and steady states. *Pflügers Arch. ges. Physiol. 312*, 161–188.

the more important situation is alkalosis. The table shows calculated electrochemical potential differences for H$^+$ and HCO$_3^-$ in respiratory and metabolic alkalosis.

Table 1. *Electrochemical potentials for CSF ions in* mV

Condition of dogs		No.	Time	EMF, CSF–blood	H$^+$	HCO$_3^-$	Na$^+$	K$^+$	Cl$^-$
Normal pentobarbital		19	—	+4	+7.3	− 8.3	−2.6	−5.5	−1.5
NaHCO$_3$ I.V.	pH=7.70	3	3 hr	+0.5	+15	−17	−4	+1	+6
	P$_{CO2}$=38	6		+2.7	+12	−15	−2	−1	+4
	HCO$_3^-$=48	9		+2.9	+12	−14	−3	0	+3
Hyperventilation	pH=7.70	15*	3 hr	−1	+ 6.4	−8.7	−3	−6	+2
and NaHCO$_3$ I.V.	P$_{CO2}$=20		6–10	+2	+ 9.4	−11.6	−1	−1	+0.5
	HCO$_3^-$=24								
NH$_4$Cl orally,	pH=7.32	3	3 days	+3	−0.3	− 1.2	+1		
awake normal	P$_{CO2}$=33		(assumed)						
NH$_4$Cl orally,	pH=7.33	3	3 days	+3	−1.3	− 4.8	+1		
awake, denervated	P$_{CO2}$=43		(assumed)						

* 3 for Na$^+$, K$^+$, Cl$^-$ and EMF

In three dogs, made alkalotic at constant P$_{CO2}$, the electrochemical potential difference was +12 mV at the end of 9 hours of continuous alkalosis compared to +7 mV at the beginning. The electrochemical potential differences for chloride are not significantly different from zero. The electrochemical potential of CSF HCO$_3^-$ increased from +8 mV to +14 mV. The CSF-blood potential difference was +2.9 at the end of 9 hours of alkalosis. Therefore in metabolic alkalosis the electrochemical potential differences for both H$^+$ and HCO$_3^-$ increased and they seemed to be stable between 6 and 9 hours. A similar increase in HCO$_3^-$ electrochemical potential difference was seen in respiratory alkalosis. Therefore in both situation the disequilibrium increased.

Siesjö
Dr. Messeter has a number of measurements on hyperventilation but we can't find those large $\triangle\mu$ differences, nor could Kjällquist (1970) find those large differences in the electrochemical potential differences in sustained metabolic acid-base changes.

Kjällquist, Å. (1970) The CSF/blood potential in sustained acid-base changes in the rat. With calculations of electrochemical potential differences for H$^+$ and HCO$_3^-$. *Acta physiol scand. 78,* 85–93.

Factors Regulating $[H^+]$ and $[HCO_3^-]$ in Brain Extracellular Fluid

Søren Claus Sørensen

As we have already heard from Dr. Fencl (this symposium), it is a characteristic of the brain extracellular fluid that its pH changes very little even during extreme changes in blood acid-base composition. The effect of changes in $[H^+]$ on ventilation is at least partly responsible for the stability of $[H^+]$ because it provides a negative feed-back mechanism which minimizes the $[H^+]$ changes in brain extracellular fluid. However, in the steady state the $[H^+]$ and $[HCO_3^-]$ in brain extracellular fluid must be examined in terms of the distribution of these ions between blood and CSF in order to evaluate if the distribution reflects a passive distribution of the ions or if it is necessary to invoke other mechanisms, e.g. changes in the rate of active ion transport.

In the mammal $[H^+]$ is normally higher and $[HCO_3^-]$ is lower in CSF than blood despite the existence of a slightly positive DC-potential in CSF relative to blood (Held *et al.* 1964). This electrochemical disequilibrium for the two ions indicates that maintenance of the steady state ion distribution requires energy either through an active transport of the particular ions or by "coupling" to another process. Another "process" could either be an active transport of another ion or a metabolic production of H^+ by the brain. The distribution of H^+ and HCO_3^- between blood and brain extracellular fluid may be expressed in terms of the electrochemical potential differences* for the two ions:

Institute of Medical Physiology B, University of Copenhagen, 30 Juliane Mariesvej, DK-2300 Copenhagen Ø, Denmark.
* The electrochemical potential difference is most frequently defined as $\triangle\mu = zEF + RT \ln C_1/C_2$ with the dimension of work (Joule/Mol) (Ussing 1960, Davson 1964). The definition used here expresses the electrochemical potential difference with the dimension of Joule/Colomb = Volt, which is equal to the difference between the measured potential (E) and the equilibrium potential for the ion ($RT/F \ln C_1/C_2$) (Katz 1966).

$$\Delta\mu_{H^+} = E + 61\ (pH_{plasma} - pH_{CSF})$$

$$\Delta\mu_{HCO_3^-} = E + 61\ \log\frac{[HCO_3^-]_{plasma}}{[HCO_3^-]_{CSF}}$$

In the dog $\Delta\mu_{H^+}$ and $\Delta\mu_{HCO_3^-}$ is about 7 to 8 mV, when using the DC-potential E measured between cisternal CSF and jugular venous blood with $HgCl_2$–KCl electrodes.

The problems we shall try to evaluate are:

(1) What causes the electrochemical disequilibrium for H^+ and HCO_3^- that exists normally?

(2) What factors affect the distribution of these two ions during acid-base changes and during hypoxia?

The electrochemical disequilibrium under "normal" conditions may be explained either by an active ion transport or by a metabolic H^+ source in the brain. It is not possible to distinguish between these two possibilities but by analyzing the H^+ and HCO_3^- distribution between blood and CSF during altered experimental conditions we may gain insight into the basis for the electrochemical disequilibrium that exists normally. The DC-potential between blood and CSF increases when blood pH is lowered (Held *et al.* 1964, Kjällquist 1970, Sørensen & Severinghaus 1970), so when calculating the $\Delta\mu$ values during acid-base changes we must assume that the DC-potential can be measured correctly during the particular experimental conditions.

The question whether changes in blood acid-base composition affect the electrochemical potential differences ($\Delta\mu$) for H^+ and HCO_3^- may be assessed by simultaneously measuring the concentration differences and the electrical potential between CSF and blood and from this calculate $\Delta\mu$ for the two ions. Few data permitting calculation are available. We may, however, use another approach to examine the behaviour of $\Delta\mu_{H^+}$ and $\Delta\mu_{HCO_3^-}$ during blood acid-base changes. If $\Delta\mu_{H^+}$ and $\Delta\mu_{HCO_3^-}$ were to remain constant during changes in blood acid-base composition, the distribution of H^+ and HCO_3^- between CSF and blood would be determined solely by changes in the DC-potential between CSF and blood; the more the potential increases when plasma $[H^+]$ is increased the less would be the change in CSF $[H^+]$. The relation between the $[H^+]$ in plasma and CSF respectively would be a unique function of the potential changes. By examining the relationship between $[H^+]$ and $[HCO_3^-]$ in blood and CSF, we may therefore evaluate

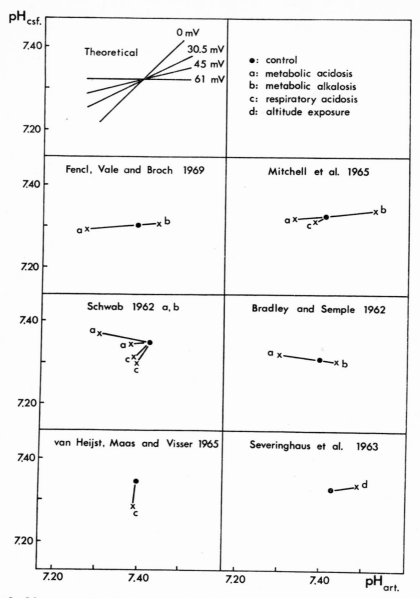

Fig. 1. Measured pH values in CSF and plasma during clinical and experimental chronic blood acid-base changes in humans. The theoretical curves show the predicted relationship for different relations between E and plasma pH if $\triangle\mu_H^+$ remain constant during blood acid-base changes.

whether the attenuation of the effect of changes in plasma [HCO$_3^-$] and [H$^+$] on the CSF concentrations of these ions is explained solely by the concomitant changes in the CSF-blood potential. Fig. 1 describes the relationship between pH$_{CSF}$ and pH$_{plasma}$ during clinical and experimental blood acid-base changes in humans. The lines in the upper left corner describe the predicted relationship if $\triangle\mu$ $_H{}^+$ remained constant while the CSF potential changed as much per pH unit as indicated on each particular line. The fact that corresponding values for pH$_{CSF}$ and pH$_{plasma}$ do not fall along any particular line suggests that the attenuation of the effect of pH$_{plasma}$ and pH$_{CSF}$ is not explained only by the changes in the DC-potential between CSF and blood. The validity of this conclusion only requires that the pH measurements by different authors are comparable within the particular study, but it does not require that the absolute pH values are comparable between the different studies.

Since there are no data available from humans on the effect of plasma pH changes on the DC-potential between CSF and blood, we shall calculate the $\triangle\mu$ values, assuming a relation between plasma pH and potential similar to the one which has been found in dogs. If we try to correlate the $\triangle\mu$ values calculated in this way with different parameters in blood and CSF, we may obtain suggestions about what may change the $\triangle\mu$ values for H$^+$ and HCO$_3^-$ between CSF and blood. If we find the same correlations as in species where both concentration differences and potential differences have been measured, this supports the conclusion.

The obvious analysis to perform is to examine the relation between changes in blood and CSF acid-base composition and the calculated $\triangle\mu$ values during these conditions. Figs. 2 and 3 show how the calculated $\triangle\mu$ values for H$^+$ correlate with different parameters. It is apparent from these plots that only Pco$_2$ and [HCO$_3^-$] in plasma and CSF are positively correlated with changes in the calculated $\triangle\mu$ values, although there is an exception in subjects acclimatized to high altitude. The latter group of subjects are however also hypoxic.

Before examining the reason for the exception during hypoxia, we may try to distinguish between the correlations suggested above, realizing that the correlations are based on very shaky assumptions regarding the potential difference.

We examined in anesthetized dogs the effect of lowering [HCO$_3^-$]$_{plasma}$ while Pco$_2$ was kept constant on the [H$^+$] and [HCO] in cisternal CSF

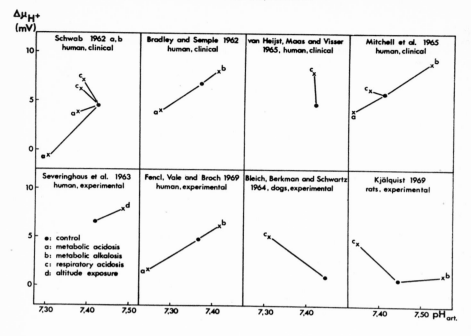

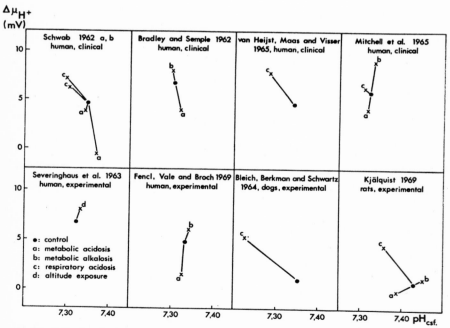

Fig. 2. Calculated changes in $\triangle\mu_{H^+}$ during various clinical and experimental chronic blood acid-base changes in humans and animals plotted as a function of measured pH values in plasma and CSF.

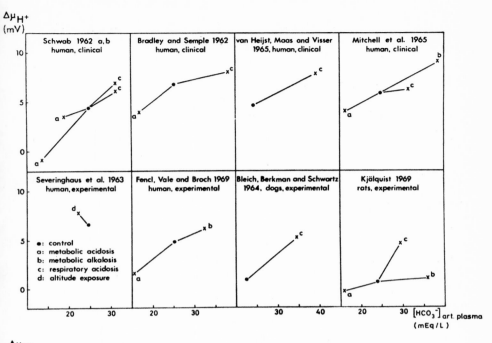

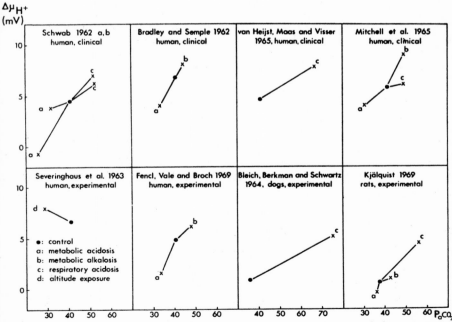

Fig. 3. Calculated changes in $\triangle\mu_{H^+}$ during various clinical and experimental chronic blood acid-base changes in humans and animals plotted as a function of measured arterial Pco_2 and $[HCO_3^-]$ values.

14*

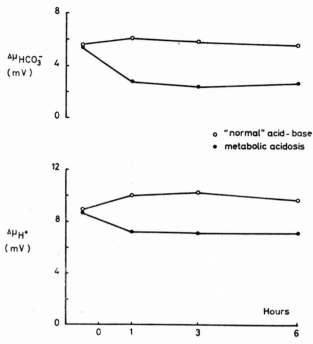

Fig. 4. Calculated electrochemical potential differences ($\triangle\mu$) for H^+ and HCO_3^- between blood and CSF during "normal" acid-base and metabolic acidosis experiments in dog. The $\triangle\mu$ values are calculated assuming that the potential difference CSF-blood increases 30.5 mV/pH unit. (From Mines, Morrill & Sørensen 1971).

(Mines, Morrill & Sørensen 1971). From these results we calculated the effect of changes in [HCO_3^-] in plasma (and CSF) on the $\triangle\mu_{H^+}$ and $\triangle\mu_{HCO_3^-}$ using the potential values obtained by Held *et al.* (1964). Fig. 4 shows that there are differences in $\triangle\mu_{H^+}$ and $\triangle\mu_{HCO_3^-}$ between the acidotic and the control dogs but the differences are small. Since the validity of the assumptions about the potentials are critical, we calculated how much the potential had to change in acidosis in order to explain the observed distribution of H^+ and HCO_3^- without invoking a change in $\triangle\mu_{H^+}$ and $\triangle\mu_{HCO_3^-}$. Fig. 5 shows the distribution of H^+ and HCO_3^- between plasma and CSF after six hours in control experiments and in acidosis experiments, respectively. The numbers on the interconnecting lines show how much the potential had to change per unit change in plasma pH if that alone should explain the attenuation of the effect of changes in plasma [H^+] and [HCO_3^-] on CSF

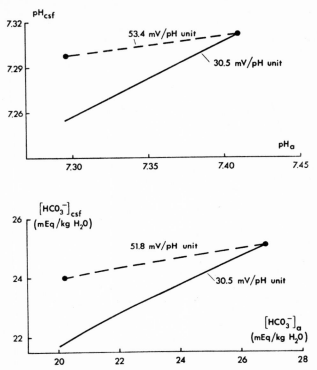

Fig. 5. Arterial pH and [HCO₃⁻] and CSF pH and [HCO₃⁻] during metabolic acidosis and during normal acid-base experiments in dogs. The solid points depict the 6 hour values in the two types of experiments. The solid line depicts the predicted relationship between the two parameters if $\triangle\mu_{H^+}$ and $\triangle\mu_{HCO_3}$ stayed constant while the potential difference CSF-blood increase 30.5 mV pH unit. The broken lines describe the relationship between the two parameters if $\triangle\mu_{H^+}$ and $\triangle\mu_{HCO_3^-}$ stayed constant, while the potential difference CSF-blood increased as much as denoted on the respective figures. (From Mines, Morrill & Sørensen 1971).

[H⁺] and [HCO₃⁻]. These numbers are larger than have ever been found in mammals, which we interpret as an indication that $\triangle\mu_{H^+}$ and $\triangle\mu_{HCO_3^-}$ are affected by changes in [HCO₃⁻]$_{plasma}$ and/or [HCO₃⁻]$_{CSF}$ although we cannot exclude that they are also affected by Pco₂, as suggested by Kjällquist (1970).

The inverse relation between the calculated $\triangle\mu_{H^+}$ and $\triangle\mu_{HCO_3^-}$ and the different parameters when hypoxia is superimposed suggests that hypoxia per se might have an effect on $\triangle\mu_{H^+}$ and $\triangle\mu_{HCO_3^-}$, presumably through an effect on H⁺ production in the brain. We examined this by exposing anesthetized dogs to hypoxia for six hours while keeping their blood acid-

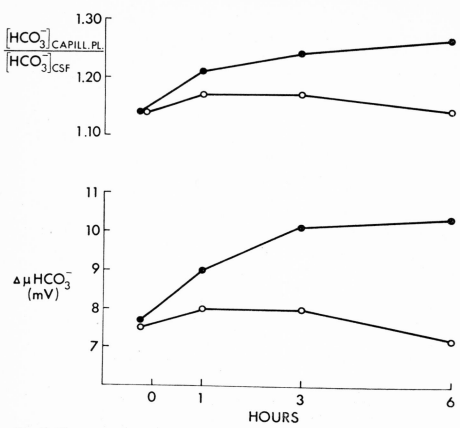

Fig. 6. Changes in the ratio between [HCO$_3^-$] in brain capillary plasma and CSF and in the calculated $\triangle\mu_{HCO_3}$ between CSF and blood in dogs during normoxia and six hours hypoxia with constant arterial pH, Pco$_2$, and [HCO$_3$]. (From Mines & Sørensen 1971).

base composition ([H$^+$], [HCO$_3^-$], and Pco$_2$) constant (Mines & Sørensen 1971). From the changes in CSF acid-base parameters we calculated the changes in $\triangle\mu_{HCO_3^-}$ assuming that the potential difference between CSF and blood did not change during the experiments. The latter point was substantiated in other experiments (Sørensen & Severinghaus 1970). The calculated $\triangle\mu_{HCO_3^-}$ increased during hypoxia as shown in Fig. 6, which we postulate is due to an increased H$^+$ production in the brain during hypoxia.

From the effect of various experimental conditions on the calculated $\triangle\mu$ values for H$^+$ and HCO$_3^-$ we suggest that $\triangle\mu$ for these ions is affected both by changes in acid-base composition ([HCO$_3^-$] in plasma and/or CSF, and perhaps by Pco$_2$) and by changes in the state of oxygenation.

In the beginning I posed the question whether from an analysis of the data obtained during altered blood acid-base conditions and during hypoxia we could determine what causes the electrochemical disequilibrium for H$^+$ and HCO$_3^-$ between blood and CSF during normoxia with normal blood acid-base conditions. Since we suggest that both acid-base changes (presumably through an effect on active ion transport) and hypoxia (presumably through a change in the rate of anaerobic glycolysis) may change the calculated $\triangle\mu$ values, it is difficult to assess how much each of these two mechanisms contributes to the maintenance of an electrochemical disequilibrium in the normal state. The small increase in $\triangle\mu$ during hypoxia compared with a several fold increase in brain anaerobic glycolysis in man during a similar degree of hypoxia (Cohen *et al.* 1967) suggests that the H$^+$ production in the normoxic brain is too small to explain the electrochemical disequilibrium in normoxia. Therefore another process is probably involved, presumably an active ion transport.

As already stated several times, this attempt to determine which factors affect the distribution of H$^+$ and HCO$_3^-$ between blood and CSF is based on a number of assumptions about the DC-potential between CSF and blood, and these assumptions may be erroneous. I must, however, emphasize that the attenuation of the effect of "metabolic" changes in plasma [HCO$_3^-$] and [H$^+$] on CSF [HCO$_3^-$] and [H$^+$] can be explained either by changes in the electrical potential between brain extracellular fluid and blood at the site of ionic exchange or by a change in the rate of an active ion transport between the two compartments. If the rate of active ion transport actually changes when blood acid-base composition changes, it is tempting to question whether such a mechanism would serve a useful purpose. During "metabolic" blood acid-base derangements the changes in $\triangle\mu$ for H$^+$ and HCO$_3^-$ would accentuate the effect of the potential changes on CSF acid-base parameters, but the quantitative importance of such a mechanism may be trivial compared to the effect of the potential changes. During chronic respiratory acidosis, the change in $\triangle\mu$ may, however, be essential in preventing a continuing rise in Pco$_2$. With chronic hypercapnia, renal bicarbonate reabsorption restores arterial pH toward normal. If we assume that the CSF-blood potential is solely a function of plasma pH, it too will return toward normal. In the absence of a change in active transport (i.e. a constant $\triangle\mu$), the $[H^+]$ in CSF must also decrease toward normal, diminishing the central drive to ventilation and permitting Pco_2 to increase further. Pco_2 would continue to rise until renal HCO_3^- reabsorption failed to maintain a normal plasma $[H^+]$ or until some other ventilatory stimulus, such as hypoxia, supervened. Thus a possible change in active transport, i.e. an increase in $\triangle\mu$, provides a possible mechanism for preventing the continual rise of Pco_2.

REFERENCES

Bleich, H. L., Berkman, P. M. & Schwartz, W. B. (1964) The response of cerebrospinal fluid composition to sustained hypercapnia. *J. clin. Invest. 43*, 11–16.
Bradley, R. D. & Semple, S. J. G. (1962) A comparison of certain acid-base characteristics of arterial blood, jugular venous blood and cerebrospinal fluid in man, and the effect on them of some acute and chronic acid-base disturbances. *J. Physiol. (Lond.) 160*, 381–391.
Cohen, P. J., Alexander, S. C., Smith, T. C., Reivich, M. & Wollman, H. (1967) Effects of hypoxia and normocarbia on cerebral blood flow and metabolism in conscious man. *J. appl. Physiol. 23*, 183–189.
Davson, H. (1964) *General Physiology*, p. 1166. J. A. Churchill, London.
Fencl, V., Vale, J. R. & Broch, J. A. (1969) Respiration, cerebral blood flow, and composition of cerebral fluids during steady metabolic acidosis and alkalosis in humans. *J. appl. Physiol. 27*, 67–76.
Held, D. R., Fencl, V. & Pappenheimer, J. R. (1964) Electrical potential of cerebrospinal fluid. *J. Neurophysiol. 27*, 942–959.
Katz, B. (1966) *Nerve, Muscle and Synapse*, p. 191. McGraw-Hill, New York.
Kjällquist, Å. (1970) The CSF/blood potential in sustained acid-base changes in the rat. With calculations of electrochemical potential differences for H^+ and HCO_3. *Acta physiol. scand. 78*, 85–93.
Mines, A. H., Morrill, C. G. & Sørensen, S. C. (1971) The effect of isocarbic metabolic acidosis in blood on $[H^+]$ and $[HCO_3]$ in CSF with deduction about the regulation of active transport of H^+/HCO_3 between blood and CSF. *Acta physiol. scand.* In press.
Mines, A. H. & Sørensen, S. C. (1971) Changes in the electrochemical potential difference for HCO_3 between blood and cerebrospinal fluid and in CSF lactate concentration during isocarbic hypoxia. *Acta physiol. scand.* In press.
Mitchell, R. A., Carman, C. T., Severinghaus, J. W., Richardson, B. W., Singer, M. M. & Schneider, S. (1965) Stability of cerebrospinal fluid pH in chronic acid-base disturbances in blood. *J. appl. Physiol. 20*, 443–452.
Schwab, M. (1962 a) Das Säure-Basen-Gleichgewicht im arteriellen Blut and Liquor cerebrospinalis bei Herzinsuffizienz und Cor pulmonale und seine Beeinflussung durch Carboanhydrase-Hemmung. *Klin. Wschr. 40*, 1233–1245.

Severinghaus, J. W., Mitchell, R. A., Richardson, B. W. & Siner, M. M. (1963) Respiratory control at high altitude suggesting active transport regulation of CSF pH. *J. appl. Physiol. 18,* 1155–1166.

Sørensen, S. C., & Severinghaus, J. W. (1970) The effect of cerebrospinal acidosis on the CSF-blood potential difference. *Amer. J. Physiol. 219,* 68–71.

Ussing, H. H. (1960) The alkali metal ions in isolated systems and tissues. *Handb. exptl. Pharmakol. 13,* 1–195.

Van Heijst, A. N. P., Maas, A. H. & Visser, B. F. (1964) L'équilibre acido-basique dans le sang et le liquide cephalorachidien dans l'hypercapnie chronique. *Entret. Physio-Pathol. Respir.,* Nancy.

DISCUSSION

MINES

Dr. Sørensen and I have worked together for about two years to obtain some
of those data he just showed. I'm sure he won't mind if I show you what
happens to those data if one allows them to grow up in San Francisco instead
of transplanting them to Copenhagen. I want to do this for two reasons:
Firstly because I am not yet convinced that these data indicate the existence
of active transport, and secondly because I would like to emphasize how
much our conclusions depend upon our assumptions, especially in this calculation. I would like first to give you the results as I calculate them, then to
show you why those results differ from the ones Dr. Sørensen just showed
you. We maintained dogs normoxic for 6 hours. Some were kept in normal
acid-base status, some were kept in metabolic acidosis, some in respiratory
acidosis, and some in metabolic alkalosis. The $\triangle\mu_{HCO_3^-}$ (CSF-blood) at the
end of 6 hours for these groups were respectively, -8.7 ± 0.6, $-8.5 \pm 0,3$,
-8.6 ± 0.5, and -8.5 ± 0.5 mV, showing absolutely no difference between
the groups. To calculate $\triangle\mu_{HCO^-}$ Dr. Sørensen and I have both used the

$$\triangle\mu_{HCO_3^-} = 61.5 \log \frac{[HCO_3^-]_{csf}}{[HCO_3^-]_{blood}} - E_{csf\text{-}blood}$$

equation and we have both treated the first part of the equation, 61.5 log
ratio of the concentrations, identically. Although we both have used the
data of Held et al. (1964) to calculate E from our arterial pH's, the results
we get depend on how these data are used. Their data show two lines relating
E to the arterial pH, one in metabolic acidosis and alkalosis, and one in
respiratory acidosis and alkalosis with a common intercept (E $=$ O mV) at
$pH_a = 7.52$. The metabolic states' line has a slope of about 43 mV/pH
unit, and the respiratory states' line has a slope of about 32 mV/pH unit.
I have used their data exactly as it was published. Dr. Sørensen has rightly
argued that it doesn't make any sense to talk about a pH of 7.4 in either
a respiratory or a metabolic state of acid-base balance. So, he has used pH
7.4 and E $=$ 4 mV as the common intercept of the two lines, which will
make all of his calculations of E in metabolic states lower, and in respiratory

Held, D. R., Fencl, V. & Pappenheimer, J. R. (1964) Electrical potential of cerebrospinal fluid. *J. Neurophysiol. 27*, 942–959.

states higher than mine. Thus, his calculations of $\triangle\mu_{HCO_3^-}$ in metabolic acidosis are lower and in respiratory acidoses are higher than mine. It is a very small difference in assumptions which leads to a large difference in conclusions.

CAMERON

If one were to examine the relation between the potential, and the difference between CSF pH and arterial pH, the relation might be changed.

Tschirgi & Taylor (1958), who measured the brain surface to jugular venous blood potential difference, showed that when they plotted the potential difference during metabolic and respiratory acid-base changes against the difference between CSF and blood pH, it became a single relation.

SEVERINGHAUS

There is no other evidence that the relationship is in any way affected by the CSF pH. It seems to be a unique function of arterial pH independent of CSF pH under either one of the two conditions.

SØRENSEN

I showed a graph yesterday on the effect of severe hypoxia on the relationship between plasma pH and the potential (E). In those experiments (Sørensen & Severinghaus 1970) we induced a cerebral acidosis by hypoxia. A change in CSF pH of about 0.2 pH unit did not affect the relationship between E and plasma pH. We kept plasma bicarbonate normal while plasma pH was changed by changing Pco_2.

FENCL

I think that the evidence against the influence of CSF pH (or cerebral ISF pH) on the potential is rather strong: Dr. Sørensen has shown the lack of effect of cerebral acidosis on the potential, and with Held & Pappenheimer (1964) we have shown that the potential is not affected by ventriculo-

Tschirgi, R. D. & Taylor, J. L. (1958) Slowly changing bioelectric potentials associated with the blood-brain barrier. *Amer. J. Physiol. 195,* 7–22.

Sørensen, S. C. & Severinghaus, J. W. (1970) The effect of cerebral acidosis on the CSF-blood potential difference. *Amer. J. Physiol. 219,* 68–71.

Held, D. R., Fencl, V. & Pappenheimer (1964) Electrical potential of cerebrospinal fluid. *J. Neurophysiol. 27,* 942–959.

cisternal perfusions with abnormally low or high concentrations of bicarbonate. I should like to comment on the difference between metabolic and respiratory acid-base disturbances in the slopes of the plots of CSF potential versus arterial pH. If the CSF potential is, as many believe, a diffusion potential of H^+ occurring at the membrane which separates blood from CSF (or cerebral ISF) then, perhaps, we were wrong in plotting the potential against the pH in the arterial blood. What the membrane sees is not the arterial pH but something close to the pH in the capillary blood. I wonder whether the lines for metabolic and respiratory acid-base disturbances would coincide if the potential were plotted against pH in cerebral capillary blood. In acute respiratory acid-base disturbances, pH in cerebral capillary blood varies less than does arterial pH.

SEVERINGHAUS

That may in fact explain the difference between the two slopes during metabolic and respiratory acid-base changes. Because of the increase in cerebral blood flow, the capillary pH changes less with respiratory acidosis than does the arterial pH.

ORKAND

Can any of the changes in the potential be related to the distribution of divalent cations such as calcium? How does the pH affect the concentration of ionic calcium?

STEN-KNUDSEN

I am puzzled when you say that you are calculating electrochemical potential of a single ion because one has difficulties in interpreting a potential difference which is between two fluids of different composition and also in order to calculate the activity coefficient of that single ion, and that is not accessible. Do you just assume that the activities are equal on both sides?

SØRENSEN

In a sense we are measuring activity by measuring pH with a glass electrode, but it is true with bicarbonate that we don't know the activity, because we are measuring concentration.

STEN-KNUDSEN

I have my doubt about the bicarbonate, but pH measurements are operational of course.

SØRENSEN

The calculated values are used together all the time, and we are inferring equally well from one or the other, but we reach the same conclusions about the distribution of the ions, whether we look at the hydrogen ions or the bicarbonate ions.

LOESCHCKE

If you have two ions which are not in electrochemical equilibrium, it is not necessary to conclude that each of these ions is actively transported. Consider a model of the system, in which sodium is being actively transported and there is a bias of the membrane for chloride against bicarbonate, and you will just have the same results.

SØRENSEN

The maintenance of an electrochemical potential difference requires the expenditure of energy, whatever the link between the active transport of one particular ion and the disequilibrium for another ion is. I am not claiming that it is a pumping of hydrogen ions or bicarbonate. I have no reason to think so.

LASSEN

I was impressed by Dr. Sørensen's finding that severe hypoxia did not change the potential. This suggested to me that the source of this potential is not the brain but the choroid plexus. The newly formed fluid at the choroid plexus is not likely, at least not in hypoxia, to be like that of the bulk fluid or of the brain surface. It is likely to have less acid at that particular site than bulk CSF. So I therefore think that you are comparing incomparable things. The spinal fluid you should be using for your calculation is not the one you sample. The whole thing is perhaps happening at the choroid plexus and in that case you should examine what the choroid plexus makes.

SØRENSEN

I am not correlating the potential difference with anything in the cerebrospinal fluid, but in order to asses how much cerebral acidosis we got we sampled cerebrospinal and found that CSF bicarbonate went down from about 25 mEq/l to about 20 mEq/l during hypoxia. At any given Pco_2 we could calculate the decrease in CSF pH. This is however only a minimal value for the change in interstitial fluid pH because in the brain tissue the bicarbonate presumably is lower, because we are dealing with a non-steady state situation, and the sink action of CSF means that the bicarbonate concentration in interstitial fluid was lower. We just wanted to be sure that we had a pronounced acidosis in brain at that time.

KJÄLLQUIST

I have seen many times, when I stopped the pump while measuring the potential differences that there first is a slight positive rise in the potential difference, followed by a marked negative shift down to -10 mV to -20 mV. It lasts for several hours after the animal is dead. Have you seen such a negative shift?

SØRENSEN

Yes, we have seen the same.

SIESJÖ

The fact that the CSF pH is more acid than the plasma, in spite of the positive potential, could be interpreted to mean that the hydrogen ion is being actively transported, but this is not necessarily so. Thus, when we say that the $\triangle \mu$ in the steady state situation is due to an active transport, this is a working hypothesis. We further know that pH of the CSF is stable in chronic acid-base changes, and the second question comes up if the assumed active transport of H^+ and HCO_3^- is involved in keeping the CSF pH constant. We have recently challenged this hypothesis and suggested that since the electrochemical potential differences seem to stay relatively constant in various chronic acid-base conditions we should start discussing passive factors, including the electrical potential (Siesjö & Kjällquist 1969). Now, if there is an active transport regulation of the CSF pH, could we agree that this has relatively little importance in keeping the CSF pH constant in chronic acid-base changes?

LOESCHCKE

It might be necessary to say that it has never been proved that the effect of hydrogen ion concentration on the potential arises on the choroid plexus.

Siesjö, B. K. & Kjällquist, Å. (1969) A new theory for the regulation of the extracellular pH in the brain. *Scand. J. clin. Lab. Invest.* 24, 1–9.

Therefore it is quite possible that it comes from somewhere else. The other way around, there is no doubt, of course, that the potential has an influence on the exchange in the plexus.

MAREN

I want to come back to Dr. Lassen's question. I would like to know what the acid-base composition is in freshly formed fluids. We have a very good model for this, the eye. The posterior chamber, where the fluid is freshly formed, has a bicarbonate concentration about 10 mMol greater than that of the anterior chamber (Becker 1955). The secondary changes therefore are very important. It seems that if we are going to talk about hydrogen ion excess in CSF we have to know whether this is related to CSF formation.

AMES

We did not measure pH or Pco_2 in newly formed choroid plexus fluid, but we did get an indirect estimate of the bicarbonate from calculations based on the balance of charge. By adding up the concentrations of Na^+, K^+, Ca^{++}, and Mg^{++} and then subtracting the concentration of Cl^- and a figure of 4 mEq/kg H_2O for the sum of the minor anions, we obtained a difference of 25 mEq/kg H_2O which we took to be an indication of bicarbonate concentration (Ames et al. 1964). In another series of experiments, the comparable figure was 22 mEq/kg H_2O (Ames et al. 1965). In the first study, cisterna magna fluid sampled simultaneously gave a calculated $[HCO_3^-]$ of 18 mEq/kg H_2O. The fall of 7 mEq between choroid plexus fluid and cisterna magna was statistically highly significant. If this does indeed represent a fall in $[HCO_3^-]$ (a fall of this magnitude in the minor anions seems relatively unlikely), it may be concluded that the newly formed choroid plexus fluid had a pH about 0.15 unit higher than the cisterna magna fluid.

SEVERINGHAUS

Did the bicarbonate concentration come out the same as the plasma filtrate?

Becker, B. (1955) The effects of the carbonic anhydrase inhibitor, acetazolamide, on the composition of the aqueous humor. *Amer. J. Ophthal. 40,* 129.

Ames, A., III, Sakanoue, M. & Endo, S. (1964) Na, K, Ca, Mg, and Cl concentrations in choroid plexus fluid and cisternal fluid compared with plasma ultrafiltrate. *J. Neurophysiol. 27,* 672–681.

Ames, A., III, Higashi, K. & Nesbett, F. B. (1965) Effects of Pco_2, acetazolamide and ouabain on volume and composition of choroid plexus fluid. *J. Physiol. (Lond.). 181,* 516–524.

AMES

In the only experiments we have done in which choroid plexus fluid [HCO_3^-] was calculated and plasma [HCO_3^-] measured on the same animals the values, respectively, were 22 and 18 mEq/kg H_2O. Thus the choroid plexus fluid had about 3 mEq/kg H_2O more HCO_3^-, by calculation, than expected in a plasma ultrafiltrate from these animals.

SØRENSEN

Dr. Maren, we have thought of the eye as an analogy. We did some experiments to see if there was any effect of plasma pH changes on the potential, and we were not able to demonstrate anything but a very minor effect.

Dr. Siesjö, I agree that the possible changes in the rate of an active transport of H^+ or HCO_3^- is rather unimportant, in terms of maintaining pH stability. As a matter of fact the effect of such a transport, if it works in the way we propose, then during respiratory acidosis, the $\triangle \mu$ changes are such as to keep the pH in CSF away from normal. That was the reason I made my last point, because the only reason why I can see that such a mechanism should exist is that it could be a very essential mechanism to prevent the spiraling up of the Pco_2 during respiratory acidosis.

BRADBURY

As Dr. Crone pointed out, the surface area of the blood-brain barrier is probably about 5,000 times the area of the choroid plexus. The implication of this is that it is likely that the blood-brain barrier plays the predominant role in giving rise to this potential. Since your measurements were in fact of CSF, couldn't many of these small changes in $\triangle \mu$ in fact be due to small discrepancies in concentrations of either hydrogen ion or bicarbonate between CSF and the fluid next to the blood-brain barrier.

SØRENSEN

It might well be that we are fooling ourselves by measuring CSF concentrations under these particular circumstances. On the other hand, because I don't believe in surface measurements on the brain this is our best try.

DAVSON

Would it not be more profitable to give up studying the pH and the bicarbonate and go back to chloride, because there is an inverse relationship between chloride and bicarbonate concentrations. There is presumably an active transport of chloride and the active transport of chloride is going to act on the transport of hydrogen ions and bicarbonate. So it seems to me a pity that chloride has been forgotten for so long.

SEVERINGHAUS

We started with the assumption that there was an active transport of chloride, but the electrical potential is essentially sufficient to explain the steady state differences for chloride.

DAVSON

Only under unique conditions, I should say, and certainly not in all species. In hypochloremia you find that the chloride concentration in the cerebrospinal fluid remains at a high level, suggesting a homeostatic control as with potassium and other cations.

SEVERINGHAUS

Was the electrical potential measured under those circumstances?

DAVSON

No.

SEVERINGHAUS

In the normal state the chloride ratio between CSF and plasma is 1.16. When you calculate the electrochemical potential it is exactly balanced by 4 mV.

DAVSON

Yes, but your earlier slides showed dogs with large changes in chloride distribution which were apparently not reflected in changes in potential.

MAREN

I would like to support Dr. Davson from the point of view of phylogeny because as far as I know the only stable ionic characteristic through the entire vertebrate kingdom is the chloride excess. I am not even sure that there is a hydrogen excess in all species. For instance the cat and dogfish do not show it (discussed in Maren, this symposium). Tentatively I would reject the idea that the CSF is necessarily acid, but I know very well that it does have a chloride excess in every vertebrate that has been studied.

SEVERINGHAUS

It has a chloride excess in terms of mEq/l. It does not have a chloride excess in terms of electrochemical potential.

MAREN

The calculation doesn't come out precisely in mammals; I think there is a difference in what is demanded and what is found in these ratios, and you can inhibit the transport of chloride from the plasma into the CSF with acetazolamide with no change in potential. Furthermore in the dogfish the potential is negative in CSF, and there is a typical chloride excess (Hogben et al. 1960).

AMES

I wonder if one might make an argument for chloride transport from measurements of isotope movements. The permeability for chloride of the overall blood-CSF barrier is quite low, about the same as that for sodium (Sweet et al. 1956), so it seems likely that the passive permeability of the choroid plexus for chloride is also low. Consequently, if one invokes only a sodium pump as a means of bulk formation, one would expect an appreciable positive potential on the CSF side. Since this is not observed, one might predict that there is also an active transport of chloride. If sodium and chloride are both transported (and if the membrane is sufficiently permeable to bicarbonate, OH^-, or H^+) the CSF [HCO_3^-] would be determined, secondarily, by the relative rates of the sodium and chloride pumps.

FENCL

In reference to Dr. Davson's question, I should like to project a slide showing data on simultaneous measurements of chloride and bicarbonate in CSF in

Hogben, C. A. M., Wistrand, P. & Maren, T. H. (1960) Role of active transport of chloride in formation of dogfish cerebrospinal fluid. Amer. J. Physiol. 199, 124–126.
Sweet, W. H., Brownell, G. L., Scholl, J. A., Bowsher, D. R., Benda, P. & Stickley, E. E. (1956) The formation, flow and absorption of cerebrospinal fluid; newer concepts based on studies with isotopes. Res. Publ. Ass. nerv. ment. Dis. 34, 101–159.

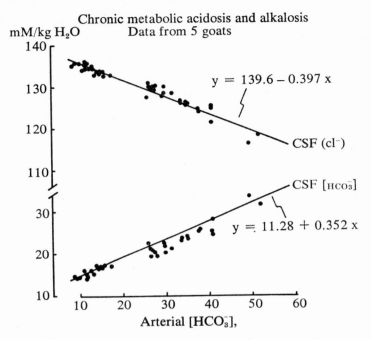

Chronic metabolic acidosis and alkalosis
mM/kg H₂O   Data from 5 goats

$$y = 139.6 - 0.397\,x$$

CSF (cl⁻)

CSF [HCO₃⁻]

$$y = 11.28 + 0.352\,x$$

Arterial [HCO₃⁻],

steady metabolic acidosis and alkalosis produced in goats by administration of ammonium chloride and sodium bicarbonate, respectively (data taken from Fencl *et al.* 1966). On the abscissa is the bicarbonate concentration in blood, and the ordinates are the concentrations of bicarbonate and chloride in CSF. You can see that the slopes of the two plots are reciprocal and that the variations in CSF [HCO₃⁻] and [Cl⁻] go one for one. We also tried to calculate the electrochemical potential of Cl⁻ in CSF versus capillary plasma and, in our estimation, they did vary, from about −15 mV in severe metabolic acidosis to +5 mV in metabolic alkalosis.

SIESJÖ
Dr. Davson, another difficulty in inferring bicarbonate changes from chloride measurements is the fact that lactate becomes an important anion in hyperventilation and in hypoxia. Dr. Maren, when it comes to studying the excess acidity in CSF, there definitely is a pitfall and that is that many

Fencl, V., Miller, T. B. & Pappenheimer, J. R. (1966) Studies on the respiratory response to disturbances of acid-base balance, with deductions concerning the ionic composition of cerebral interstitial fluid. *Amer. J. Physiol. 210,* 459–472.

anesthetic procedures will give rise to a plasma acidosis, so you have to be very careful when studying the relation between pH in CSF and pH in blood.

SØRENSEN

Dr. Welch, when you measured the electrical potentials across the choroid plexus (Welch and Sadler 1965), is it possible that you actually measured potentials generated across the blood-brain barrier, despite the fact that your electrodes were placed at the location of the choroid plexus?

WELCH

Yes, because the CSF electrode was not electrically insulated from the brain interstitial fluid.

LOESCHCKE

There is some potential remaining after isolation of the choroid plexus (Schöne & Loeschcke 1969).

COHEN

Dr. Severinghaus, you remarked that there is a difference in the return to normal of CSF pH during hyperventilation, depending on whether it is accompanied by hypoxia or by normoxia. During hyperventilation a good deal of the lactate production can be minimized by oxygen breathing either at ambient pressures or at hyperbaric conditions. Do we have any knowledge of the adaptation of CSF pH to hyperventilation when hyperbaric conditions are in existence and lactate production is reduced?

PLUM

We measured CSF lactate concentration at the end of 5 to 6 hours of hyperventilation to a Pco_2 of 10 mm Hg at three different inspired oxygen concentrations. With 10 % inspired oxygen concentration the lactate concentration in CSF was 11.5 mEq/l, with 20 % oxygen it was 7.64 mEq/l, and with oxygen breathing at three atmospheres it dropped to 4.29 mEq/l

Welch, K. & Sadler, K. (1965) Electrical potentials of choroid plexus of the rabbit. *J. Neurosurg. 22*, 344–349.

Schöne, H. & Loeschcke, H. H. (1969) Bestandspotentiale am Plexus chorioideus des 4. Ventrikels von Katze und Kaninchen in vitro. *Pflügers Arch. Europ. J. Physiol. 304*, 195–209.

in CSF. Brain lactate concentrations were measured in the last two groups and were slightly higher than CSF in both (Plum & Posner 1967, Plum *et al.* 1968).

SEVERINGHAUS

Is there any evidence that the tissue Po_2 under three atmospheres of oxygen is hyperoxic?

PLUM

We didn't measure tissue Po_2 but cerebral venous blood Po_2 was between 50 and 60 mm Hg in the torcular outflow.

COHEN

Was there any difference between hyperventilation with a normal oxygen tension and hyperventilation at hyperbaric conditions in the returns of CSF pH to normal? If we could minimize lactate formation during hyperventilation we might have some idea of how much bicarbonate secretion independently might contribute.

PLUM

The alkaline CSF pH came back towards normal less rapidly in the oxygenated dogs, but was not significantly different between the groups at atmospheric oxygen and hyperbaric oxygen levels.

SEVERINGHAUS

Dr. Morley Singer and I (unpublished) hyperventilated dogs with oxygen while keeping plasma bicarbonate constant. I was looking at that time for evidence of active transport. The fall in CSF bicarbonate was rather small. After about six hours the CSF bicarbonate fell about 2 mEq/l compared to the plasma, and at this time the rise in lactate concentration was about 2 mEq/l. At that time I discounted the relationship between the two. In the light of subsequent events I think it is quite likely that the small decrease in bicarbonate, which did occur, was due to lactate formation caused both by alkalosis and by increased anaerobic metabolism.

Plum, F. & Posner, J. B. (1967) Blood and cerebrospinal fluid lactate during hyperventilation. *Amer. J. Physiol. 212,* 864–870.

Plum, F., Posner, J. B. & Smith, W. W. (1968) Effect of hyperbaric-hyperoxic hyperventilation on blood, brain and CSF lactate. *Amer. J. Physiol. 215,* 1240–1244.

MINES

Wouldn't you expect that the bicarbonate would fall due to the decreased potential across the CSF-blood barrier?

SEVERINGHAUS

I hoped so.

MINES

Why do you attribute its fall only to the increased anaerobic metabolism? You have both the lactate and the potential, which tend to decrease the bicarbonate concentration in CSF.

SEVERINGHAUS

The electrical potential in CSF did not in fact fall enough to reverse its normal attraction for HCO_3^-, but the attraction decreased. The fact that CSF $[HCO_3^-]$ fell only 2 mEq/l during hypoventilation at constant plasma $[HCO_3^-]$ implies to me that the plasma bicarbonate has an important role to play in the CSF bicarbonate maintenance. We saw no evidence of any specific active transport mechanism in that experiment.

SØRENSEN

You are inferring from measurements of lactate concentration about the role of lactic acid in reducing CSF bicarbonate concentration, but there is not in the steady state a one-to-one relation between the increase in lactate concentration and the decrease in bicarbonate concentration due to lactic acid formation. We studied the changes in CSF lactate and bicarbonate concentrations during six hours of hypoxia, while plasma bicarbonate concentration, plasma pH, and therefore CSF-blood potential were kept constant. The lactate concentration only increased one third as much as bicarbonate decreased (Mines & Sørensen). It emphasizes that the use of the lactate ion concentration is somewhat irrelevant in this connection.

SIESJÖ

We found a good agreement between the increase in lactate and the decrease

Mines, A. H. & Sørensen, S. C. Changes in the electrochemical potential difference for HCO_3^- between blood and cerebrospinal fluid and in cerebrospinal fluid lactate concentration during isocarbic hypoxia. *Acta physiol. scand.* In press.

in bicarbonate during the first 5 to 10 minutes of very severe hypoxia (Kaasik *et al.* 1970). Dr. Sørensen, you claim that there are two ways of explaining the $\triangle \mu$'s for hydrogen ions and bicarbonate between CSF and plasma. Could you explain the evidence that it is not an outflux of acids which creates the $\triangle \mu$'s?

SØRENSEN

Our working hypothesis was that $\triangle \mu$ was due to production of acids in the brain, but during hypoxia, to the extent we used, brain anaerobic glycolysis increased about 300 per cent, but this 300 per cent increase in lactic acid production only caused a 25–30 per cent increase in $\triangle \mu$.

SIESJÖ

If only part of that lactic acid being formed goes into the CSF, couldn't it still explain the increased $\triangle \mu$'s?

SØRENSEN

Not in the steady state.

COHEN

In addition to the 300 per cent increase in glycolysis, you really ought to consider the actual amounts of lactate that might be found in the area in which you are interested. This is why I was intrigued by Dr. Plum's figures, because at least if you can change the rate of return of pH towards normal by changing lactate production, you may have some idea of what fraction is produced by active transport, and what fraction might be accounted for by anaerobic glycolysis.

KRUHØFFER

I feel a little uneasy about the lactic acid story, because if we have a stream of CSF flowing and lactic acid is produced and added to that slowly, then we would expect that the drop in bicarbonate concentration would be the same as the rise in lactate concentration. The situation is of course more complex because you could have some of the hydrogen ions which are pro-

---

Kaasik, A. E., Nilsson, L. & Siesjö, B. K. (1970) The effect of asphyxia upon the lactate, pyruvate, and bicarbonate concentrations of brain tissue and cisternal CSF, and upon the tissue concentrations of phosphocreatine and adenine nucleotides in anesthetized rats. *Acta physiol. scand. 78*, 433–477.

duced together with the lactate ions, passing the blood-brain barrier separately and then the alterations of the concentrations would no more be equal. But then, are we not saying that there is something else to it, there is another factor. That might include a regulation, a speeding up of hydrogen ion passage into the blood or a slowing down of hydrogen ion passage in the other direction.

SEVERINGHAUS

I prefer to think of it as two different streams. The CSF stream is a very slow stream of a large volume, its rate of formation is less than 1 ml/min. The stream of lactic acid is coming from cells through the extracellular fluid going to blood, and certainly under anaerobic conditions it is a very fast stream, flowing crossways through the CSF. The interaction of these two is very complex.

SØRENSEN

In relation to the production rates of hydrogen ions from anaerobic glycolysis we can nearly disregard bulk CSF formation as a source of bicarbonate in the brain.

Considering that in man only ½ ml of CSF is produced per minute only about 12 μEq of bicarbonate is entering in this way each minute. In comparison, a human brain during hypoxia produces about 200 μEq of H^+ per minute (Cohen et al. 1967, Sørensen et al. 1969).

MINES

I wonder if we have to think about the lactic acid production by the cells coming cross-wise through the CSF, or if we haven't got cells which are feeding on one side the blood and on the other side the CSF. Isn't it possible that a great deal of the lactic acid which is produced in hypoxia may in some way get directly into the blood without dissociating and grabbing on to bicarbonate? So even though the lactic acid production may increase 300 per cent one might not expect a considerable change in the bicarbonate concentration and in the $\triangle \mu$ for bicarbonate and hydrogen ions.

Cohen, P. J., Alexander, S. C., Smith, T. C., Reivich, M. & Wollman, H. (1967) Effects of hypoxia and normocarbia on cerebral blood flow and metabolism in conscious man. *J. appl. Phkysiol. 23*, 183–189.

Sørensen, S. C., Milledge, J. S. & Severinghaus, J. W. (1969) Cerebral anaerobic metabolism and ventilatory acclimatization to chronic hypoxia. *Fed. Proc. 28*, 337.

Intracellular pH

William J. Waddell

The pH value of a solution is a measure of the relative chemical potential of the proton in that solution. pH is now defined as the potential, directly proportional by a factor to the difference in potential, between a standard solution and an unknown solution of an electrode system reversible to hydrogen ions when that electrode system is immersed in an unknown solution and in the standard solution.

The pH of a solution can, also, as you know, be related to the logarithm of the concentration ratio of the two species of an indicator compound such as a weak acid or base by an operational constant, the pK'.

Both of these, that is, glass electrodes and indicator compounds, have been used widely and with great precision on simple or at least well-defined solutions. Both also have been used in attempts to obtain information on the pH of water within living cells. The aqueous solution within living cells, however, is neither simple nor well defined. Consequently, interpretation of the results of these determinations on living tissue is not as clear as those on simpler solutions. Not only are the identity and concentration of solutes in this water difficult to establish, but even the volume of this water is a matter of controversy. The extent of the binding of solutes and water to the various organelles within cells is often difficult, if not impossible, to ascertain.

In spite of all of these uncertainties, there is rather remarkable agreement among the various measurements of the pH of the intracellular water. A variety of nervous tissue has been investigated. Small electrodes constructed of pH-sensitive glass have been inserted into the giant axons of squid by Caldwell (1958) and Spyropoulos (1960). The pH value in the interior of these axons was about 7.1 to 7.4 when the axons were immersed in solutions similar to those which bath them *in vivo*. The pH value of the axoplasm

Dental Research Center, University of North Carolina, Chapel Hill, North Carolina 27514 USA.

expressed from these fibers, measured with more conventional electrodes, was only a few tenths of a pH unit lower.

Microelectrodes, less than 1μ in diameter, also of pH-sensitive glass were inserted into ganglion nerve cells of snails by Sorokina (1965). The pH recorded was about 7.2 in spite of rather wide fluctuations in the pH of external fluid from summer to winter.

Two weak acids have been used for the calculation of intracellular pH in brain. These compounds are carbonic acid and 5,5-dimethyloxazolidine-dione (DMO). The assumptions, in applying these calculations, are:

(1) That the undissociated form of the acid diffuses through the cellular membrane and reaches the same concentration in the water on both sides of the membrane.
(2) Neither species of the indicator is bound to any cellular constituent.
(3) The apparent dissociation constant of the indicator is the same in the cell water as that in the extracellular water.

With these assumptions and knowledge of the concentration of total indicator in extracellular and cellular water, and the pH of the extracellular water, the intracellular pH can be calculated.

The overall intracellular pH value of brain tissue of dogs, cats, rats and the dogfish has been calculated from the distribution of one or the other of these two acids under a variety of conditions (see Waddell & Bates 1969). The pH values from the untreated mammals range from about 7.0 to 7.2. Respiratory acidosis usually produces the most profound change in the intracellular pH. Metabolic acidosis and alkalosis usually have less effect and the effect of respiratory alkalosis is unpredictable.

The values found for brain tissue, as well as the changes induced by alterations of the pH of the extracellular fluid, are in general those that have been found for other tissues.

All of the reports in recent years, except for one, indicate that the proton is not in electrochemical equilibrium across the cellular membrane. The factors regulating the intracellular pH are largely unknown. It is the purpose of this and the following session to consider some of the aspects of this regulation.

REGULATION OF THE pH OF INTRACELLULAR WATER*

Although the control of the pH of the intracellular water is a more complex matter than the regulation of the pH of a simple solution, a review of the factors which regulate the pH of a simple solution will help to outline the problem and provide insight into the mechanisms by which the cells may regulate their internal pH. Buffer capacity was originally defined by Van Slyke (1931) as the amount of *strong* acid or base required to produce in a solution a unit change of pH. In a biological fluid or compartment, it is frequently impossible to know how much of a strong acid or base has been in fact added to the solution. Carbonic acid, however, is always present and many calculations have been made relating pH to the partial pressure of carbon dioxide and to the bicarbonate concentration.

Consider a solution that contains carbonic acid plus another weak acid and a known concentration of fixed cations. A pH value will be established in this solution which will be related to the concentrations of the two species of carbonic acid and of the other acid. In Fig. 1, "C" represents the total concentration of the other weak acid and pK' represents the dissociation constant of that acid. The concentration of the two anions of the acids must be equal, for electrical neutrality, to the concentration of the fixed cations which are available. This concentration is represented by "B" in the figure. This is the buffer base as originally referred to by Singer & Hastings (1948) and it constitutes the excess of fixed cations over fixed anions in the solution. It may be represented by the difference between the sum of the sodium, potassium, and other cations and the positive charges on proteins, minus chloride and other fixed anions and the negative charges on proteins in the solution. These three equations may be combined to give the lower equation in Fig. 1. Arranged in this form, one can readily visualize how changes in the concentration of the other acid, "C", and changes in the concentration of net cations, "B+", affect the cation available for balancing the bicarbonate. If the concentration of the other acid is zero, then the equation simplifies to that describing the dissociation of carbonic acid and its relationship to available fixed cations. However, the equation also allows us to substitute various concentrations of the other acid at different pK' values and determine the effect on the pH of the solution. The effect of changes in the net con-

---

* The following part of Dr. Waddell's introduction was not given orally at the Symposium. It was therefore not followed by any discussion.

$$pH = pK' + \log \frac{[A^-]}{[HA]} = 6.12 + \log \frac{[HCO_3^-]}{0.03(PCO_2)}$$

$$[C] = [A^-] + [HA]$$

$$[B^+] = [A^-] + [HCO_3^-] = [Na^+] + [K^+] + [X^+] + [Pr^+] - [Cl^-] - [Y^-] - [Pr^-]$$

$$\log PCO_2 = \log \left\{ [B^+] - [C] \left(\frac{10^{pH-pK'}}{10^{pH-pK'} + 1} \right) \right\} + 7.62 - pH$$

Fig. 1. The pH of a solution that contains a weak acid, HA, plus carbonic acid plus a net concentration of fixed cations (B⁺) is solved as a single equation for log PCO₂.

centration of fixed cations, of course, can be also evaluated. If there were a third acid, the equation could be expanded further to subtract the contribution of this anion. However, this simplification to only one additional buffer acid will allow a visualization of the situation.

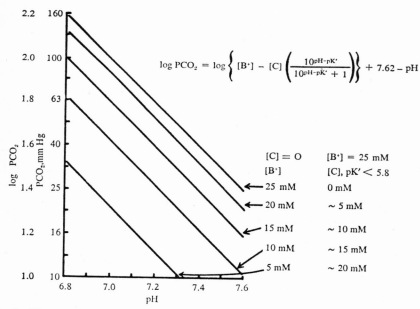

Fig. 2. The equation derived in Fig. 1 is solved for (C)=O and several values of (B⁺) and the resulting log PCO₂ plotted against the values of pH. The values are the same as those that would result from a fixed (B⁺) of 25 mM, and the listed values of (C) if the pK' of the other weak acid is less than 5.8.

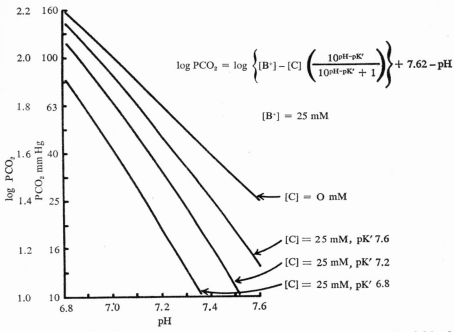

$$\log PCO_2 = \log \left\{ [B^+] - [C] \left(\frac{10^{pH-pK'}}{10^{pH-pK'} + 1} \right) \right\} + 7.62 - pH$$

$[B^+] = 25$ mM

[C] = O mM

[C] = 25 mM, pK' 7.6

[C] = 25 mM, pK' 7.2

[C] = 25 mM, pK' 6.8

Fig. 3. The equation derived in Fig. 1 is solved for (B⁺) of 25 mM and (C) of 25 mM for pK' values of the other weak acid of 6.8, 7.2, and 7.6.

In Fig. 2 the equation has been solved for various values of net fixed cations and a concentration of the other acid of zero. These isobicarbonate lines are, of course, the familiar buffer base lines, which have been thoroughly discussed by Astrup (1961), Siggaard Andersen (1960), and others. The lines shown in the figure range from 5 millimolar to 25 millimolar concentration of buffer base. However, the same lines describe approximately the values that would result if the net fixed cation concentration was 25 millimolar and the concentration of the other acid, with a pK' below 5.8, was changed between zero and 20 millimolar. This is at least one pH unit below the lowest value plotted on the graph. It can be seen in the equation that if the pK' value is one full unit below the pH value, at least 90 per cent of the total concentration of the other acid will exist in the ionized form, and this anion will neutralize an equivalent amount of the cations that are available. Lactic acid, with a pK' of about 3.8, as well as other carboxylic acids, would neutralize fixed base in this fashion. The appearance of lactic acid without a

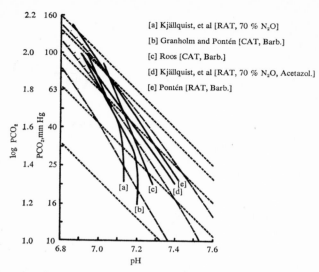

Fig. 4. Values for the pH of the intracellular water of brain is plotted against the log PCO₂ of brain from five reports in the literature. The lines from Figs. 2 and 3 are included as dashed lines.

change in concentration of fixed base would cause a shift of the pH of the solution from one isobicarbonate line to another corresponding to that concentration of lactic acid.

In Fig. 3 the same equation has been solved for a concentration of net fixed cations of 25 millimolar with the addition of 25 millimolar concentration of the other weak acid whose pK' value is either 6.8, 7.2, or 7.6. The line for zero concentration of the other fixed acid is drawn at the top for reference. It can be seen that the stronger the acid, the greater the displacement of the isobicarbonate line. Also displacement is greater at higher pH values, since at these values the amounts of the anion of the acid are greater. Using these calculations for assumed values of fixed cation and an additional buffer, let us consider the buffer capacity curves for brain tissue that have been described.

The lines shown in Fig. 4 are from the 5 systematic studies that have been done *in vivo* over a wide range of PCO₂ values to assess this effect on intracellular pH. In this figure the lines representing the calculations shown in Figs. 2 and 3 are shown also in order that the closeness of fit of the experimental values may be assessed with respect to the calculations that have been made. It can be seen that three of the experiments have linear slopes. Also, there are linear portions of the other two curves.

Precise values for the linear portions of each of the curves could be calculated from the formula presented in the previous figures for the concentration of fixed cations, pK' value, and concentration of the other buffer. Pontén (1966b) calculated these values for the curve shown as "e" in the figure. The concentration of buffer base was 36 millimolar and the concentration of the other buffer was 35 millimolar if it had a pK' value of 7.1. However, alterations in the slope or position of the curve could be accounted for by changes in either the concentration of fixed cations or the concentration of the other acid or both. Different values of pK' for the other buffer would also affect the slope.

The very interesting increase in the buffer capacity for curves "a" and "b" at low PCO_2 values were very nicely accounted for by the increase of lactic acid that occurred during this extreme hypocapnia. The appearance of about 5 millimolar lactic acid under these conditions almost quantitatively accounted for the shift of the experimental line from one isobicarbonate line to another. Even the slight decrease in pH with decreasing PCO_2, which was observed experimentally, is easy to understand.

The anesthetic agent, as well as pretreatment with acetazolamide, was suggested to be responsible for shifts in the slope of the experimental line. Barbiturate or acetazolamide could have inhibited the ability of the cell to remove protons and thus decrease the buffer capacity. However, the experiments by Roos (1965) with cats, which were anesthetized with pentobarbital, show the greatest linear buffer capacity. The experiments lasted for hours, however, without administration of additional barbiturate. The calculated slopes require either additional buffers or a systematic decrease in net fixed cations, in the experiments by Roos, to account for the very high buffer capacity.

The many factors which can influence pH within this compartment make it difficult to clarify the factor or factors responsible for the apparent buffer capacity of the intracellular water.

Fig. 5 is a diagrammatic representation of some of the factors which may influence intracellular pH. The circular shape represents a cell. The equation in the center of the cell is the same equation which was derived in Fig. 1. The net fixed cations are a function of the total cations and anions in the cell. The protein may change in amount or degree of ionization as the PCO_2 or

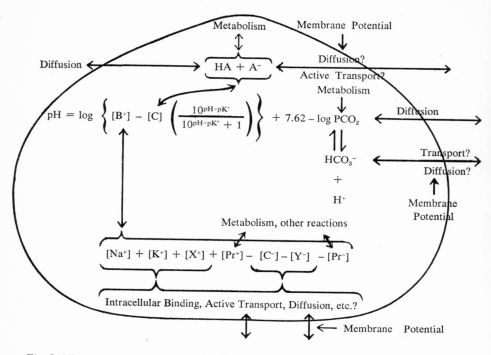

Fig. 5. The many variables that change in a living cell which will effect the pH of the intracellular water are schematized. Bicarbonate transfer across the cell membrane is only one of these variables. The transfer of the proton itself across the cell membrane is not indicated.

pH changes; conformational changes could influence the net charge on the protein. The other cations and anions are subject to active transport or free diffusion. Diffusion would, of course, be influenced by the membrane potential.

It seems clear now that at least some of the sodium and potassium in cells is bound. Intracellular sodium electrodes indicate that at least 25 per cent of the intracellular sodium is bound and unavailable to contribute to the cation concentration in the free cell water (Hinke 1961). Nuclear magnetic resonance spectroscopy of muscle tissue demonstrates also that a portion of the sodium within cells is bound (Cope 1967). Substitution experiments suggest that a large part of the intracellular potassium also is bound (Ling & Cope 1969). It seems likely that even some of the intracellular water is bonud and unavailable for solution of these solutes (Bratton *et. al.* 1965,

McLaughlin & Hinke 1966). The effect of these bindings and possible changes in binding on pH could be large.

It has been shown that potassium, sodium, and protons distribute between cell water and extracellular water in a linear and predictable manner (Waddell & Bates 1969). These calculations also suggest that most of cellular sodium is bound.

The introduction of another buffer into the cell through metabolism, such as lactic acid, or by active transport or diffusion, could also influence the intracellular pH. The dissociation of carbonic acid is shown in Fig. 5 because it is always present and is sometimes considered to be one of the more important of the intracellular buffers. However, calculations by Pontén (1966b), and the slopes seen in these figures, suggest that other buffers may be more important than carbonic acid in regulating intracellular pH.

Transport or diffusion of the proton itself is omitted in the figure. The multitude of other factors provide a plethora of possibilities for regulation of the intracellular pH without requiring a mechanism for the transport or diffusion of the proton itself.

In view of these many possibilities for the control of intracellular pH and the apparently small contribution of the carbonic acid buffer system, it might be better to consider the regulation of intracellular pH relative only to the pH of the extracellular fluid. One does not then have to compare the relative buffer capacity of the extracellular and intracellular fluids on the same chart, but merely compare the relative pH changes directly. The extracellular pH may effect the transfer of constituents that indirectly affect the intracellular pH.

Of the five systematic studies of the buffer capacity of the intracellular water of brain shown previously, three contain sufficient information to plot pH of intracellular water directly against the pH of the blood or extracellular water (Fig. 6). It can be seen that the change of intracellular pH with unit change of extracellular pH approaches 1 in the study of rat brain by Pontén (1966a) and is only about half a unit in the study on cat brain by Roos (1965). Extreme hypocapnia stimulated formation of lactic acid in Granholm & Pontén's study (1969) and consequently the intracellular pH changed very little. This is the same curve whose change in slope in the log PCO_2 versus pH graph was seen as crossing from one isobicarbonate line to another.

In summary, then, the regulation of intracellular pH in the brain as well

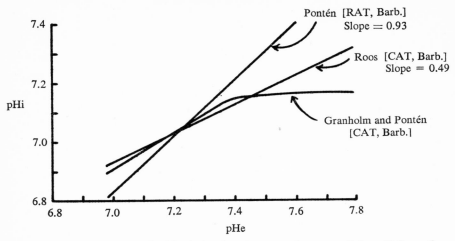

Fig. 6. The intracellular pH of brain is plotted against the extracellular pH from three reports from the literature.

as that in any tissue cannot be interpreted as that which would occur in a closed system. It is regulated by a multitude of factors, some of which may remain constant in a particular experiment, while others may change under the experimental conditions and consequently cause an appropriate change in the intracellular pH. The buffer capacity of the intracellular water must obviously be evaluated from *in vivo* experiments. Because of the meager, current knowledge of the many factors involved, it can best be assessed by considering the change in intracellular pH versus the change in extracellular pH, and by simply stating the other conditions which are known in the particular experiment.

REFERENCES

Astrup, P. (1961) Acid-base metabolism. *Clin. Chem. 7*, 1–15.

Bratton, C. B., *et. al.* (1965) Nuclear magnetic resonance studies of living muscle. *Science 147*, 738–739.

Cope, F. W. (1967) NMR evidence for complexing of Na^+ in muscle, kidney, and brain, and by actomyosin. The regulation of cellular complexing of Na^+ to water structure and to transport kinetics. *J. gen. Physiol. 50*, 1353–1375.

Granholm, L. & Pontén, U. (1969) The *in vivo* CO_2 buffer curve of the intracellular space of cat cerebral cortex. *Acta neurol. scand. 45*, 493–501.

Hinke, J. A. M. (1961) The measurement of sodium and potassium activities in the squid axon by means of cation-selective glass micro-electrodes. *J. Physiol. 156,* 314–335.

Kjällquist, Å., Nardini, M. & Siesjö, B. K. (1969) The regulation of extra- and intracellular acid-base parameters in the rat brain during hyper- and hypocapnia. *Acta physiol. scand. 76,* 485–494.

Kjällquist, Å., Messeter, K. & Siesjö, B. K. (1970) The *in vivo* CO_2 buffer capacity of rat brain tissue under carbonic anhydrase inhibition. *Acta physiol. scand. 78,* 94–102.

Ling, G. N. & Cope, F. W. (1969) Potassium ion: is the bulk of intracellular K^+ absorbed? *Science 163,* 1335–1336.

McLaughlin, S. G. A. & Hinke, J. A. M. (1966) Sodium and water binding in single striated muscle fibers of the giant barnacle. *Canad. J. Physiol. Pharmacol. 44,* 837–848.

Peter, J. P. & Van Slyke, D. D. (1931) *Quantitative Clinical Chemistry,* Vol. 1, p. 889. Williams and Wilkins Co., Baltimore.

Pontén, U. (1966a) Consecutive acid-base changes in blood, brain tissue and cerebrospinal fluid during respiratory acidosis and baseosis. *Acta neurol. scand. 42,* 455–471.

Pontén, U. (1966b) Acid-base changes in rat brain tissue during acute respiratory acidosis and baseosis. *Acta physiol. scand. 68,* 152–163.

Roos, A. (1965) Intracellular pH and intracellular buffering power of the brain. *Amer. J. Physiol. 209,* 1233–1246.

Siggaard Andersen, O. (1960) A graphic representation of changes of the acid-base status. *Scand. J. clin. Lab. Invest. 12,* 311.

Singer, R. B. & Hastings, G. B. (1948) An improved clinical method for the estimation of disturbances of the acid-base balance of human blood. *Medicine 27,* 223.

Sorokina, Z. A. (1965) Izmerenie aktivnosti ionov vodoroda vne i vnutri nervnykh kletok gangliev mollyuskov. *Zh. Evolyutsionnoi Biokhim. i. Fiziol. 1,* 343–350.

Spyropoulos, C. S. (1960) Cytoplasmic pH of nerve fibres. *J. Neurochem. 5,* 185–194.

Waddell, W. J. & Bates, R. G. (1969) Intracellular pH. *Physiol. Rev. 49,* 285–329.

Factors Determining Intracellular pH

B. K. Siesjö & K. Messeter

Little is known about the factors which regulate the intracellular pH (pH_i') of various tissues. This is partly due to the difficulty of measuring pH directly in minute and often very fragile cells, and to the difficulty of interpreting the results obtained with the indirect CO_2 and DMO methods in terms of defined anatomical compartments (Caldwell 1956, Waddell & Bates 1969).

The present communication aims at describing some of the mechanisms which affect intracellular pH'. It also represents a quantitative approach to the regulation of the intracellular pH' of the brain in respiratory acidosis. Before we start to discuss the factors which operate in a transient acid-base state, it may be appropriate to consider the relation between the intra- and extracellular pH under normal acid-base conditions.

THE INTRACELLULAR pH OF BRAIN CELLS

We may start considering the acid-base parameters of rat brain tissue, as these can be analysed with the CO_2 method. In this particular context, we will just remind you that the method is based on measurements of the mean tissue CO_2 tension (p_tCO_2), the tissue CO_2 content (TCO_2), the blood and CSF bicarbonate concentrations, and the tissue water content. Having information about the solubility coefficient for CO_2 in the tissue (S), and the pK' for carbonic acid (pK_1'), we can calculate both the mean intracellular bicarbonate concentration, $[HCO_3^-]_i$, and the intracellular pH (pH_i'), from the following equations (Siesjö 1962a, c, Pontén & Siesjö 1964, 1966).

$$[HCO_3^-]_t = TCO_2 - p_tCO_2 \cdot S \tag{1}$$

$$[HCO_3^-]_i = \frac{[HCO_3^-]_t - [HCO_3^-]_{bl} \cdot V_{bl} - [HCO_3^-]_{ECF} \cdot V_{ECF}}{V_i} \tag{2}$$

From the Brain Research Laboratory, E-Blocket, University Hospital, S-220 05 Lund, and from the Department of Surgery, University Hospital, Lund, Sweden.

CSF		**I.c. fluid**	

CSF		I.c. fluid	
pCO_2	$= 40$ mm Hg	pCO_2	$= 40$ mm Hg
(HCO_3^-)	$= 26$ mEq/kg	(HCO_3^-)	$= 12$ mEq/kg
pH	$= 7.44$	pH	$= 7.10$
ψ	$= 0$	ψ	$= -75$ mV (assumed)

Fig. 1. Acid-base relations in cisternal cerebrospinal fluid and in brain intracellular fluid in anaesthetized rats during control conditions. The intracellular acid-base parameters were calculated from CO_2 data on the assumption of a 12 per cent extracellular volume and a 3 per cent blood volume.

$$pH_i = pK_1' + \log \frac{[HCO_3]_i}{p_t CO_2 \cdot S_i} \qquad (3)$$

In order to perform these calculations, we must know the volume of blood (V_{bl}) and of extracellular fluid (V_{ECF}) in the tissue. In the following we have used blood and ECF volumes of 0.03 and 0.12, respectively, whence V_i becomes equal to 0.64 (Rall *et al.* 1962, Woodward *et al.* 1967, see also Kjällquist *et al.* 1969).

The extra- and intracellular acid-base relations derived for normal anaesthetized rats with a tissue CO_2 tension of 40 mm Hg are shown in Fig. 1. The electrochemical potential differences ($\triangle\mu$) were calculated assuming a mean transmembrane potential difference of 75 mV:

$$\triangle\mu_{H^+} = 61.5 \,(pH_{CSF} - pH_i) - 75 \qquad (4)$$

$$\triangle\mu_{HCO_3^-} = 61.5 \log \frac{(HCO_3^-)_i}{(HCO_3^-)_{CSF}} + 75 \qquad (5)$$

When we insert the measured values for pH and $[HCO_3^-]$ shown in Fig. 1 into the equations, the calculated electrochemical potential differences for H^+ and HCO_3^- are 50–60 mV, which suggests that the H^+ and HCO_3^- ions are far from being distributed at equilibrium across the cell membranes (see Caldwell 1956, Waddell & Bates 1969). We can also exemplify the degree of disequilibrium by calculating the expected pH_i', and the expected $[HCO_3^-]_i$, if equilibrium had prevailed. Thus, with the given extracellular parameters, and with the given transmembrane potential, equilibrium would require an intracellular pH′ of 6.22 and an intracellular HCO_3^- concentration of 1.6 mEq/kg. The difference between these expected values, and those actually found, is another example of the deviation from equilibrium conditions.

FACTORS REGULATING pH_i' IN ACID-BASE TRANSIENTS

The existence of an appreciable electrochemical potential difference for H^+ and HCO_3^- between the extra- and intracellular spaces of the brain suggests that one or both of the ions are being actively transported across the cell membranes. However, although an active transport of H^+ or HCO_3^- would explain the pH_i', nothing is known about the rôle of such an active transport in regulating pH_i' during acid-base changes. Furthermore, the calculated electrochemical potential differences for H^+ and HCO_3^- do not necessarily indicate a direct link between the electrochemical disequilibrium and the process which depends directly on metabolic energy. Thus, the disequilibrium could equally well be the result of a coupling to another energy-dependent process, and it may then vary in relation to the process to which it is coupled. If this is so, it is not certain that a change in pH_i' will lead to a change in the active transport of H^+ or HCO_3^- which is purposeful in the sense that the change in pH_i' is counteracted.

The factors which determine pH_i' may conveniently be studied during hyper- and hypocapnia, since these situations lead to a sudden increase or decrease in the concentration of H^+ ions. In such situations, the changes in pH_i' are determined by a minimum of three mechanisms.

1. Physicochemical buffering
2. Consumption or production of nonvolatile acids
3. Transmembrane fluxes of H^+ or HCO_3^-

If the CO_2 tension is suddenly increased, the initial pH change will be limited by the physicochemical buffer capacity of the intracellular fluids (1). If hypercapnia gives rise to a metabolic consumption of lactic acid or other acids, H^+ ions will be removed, and the pH change will be further limited (2). Finally, if H^+ or HCO_3^- ions move across the cell membranes, an additional modification of pH_i' will occur (3).

Because the first two of the enumerated mechanisms are confined to the cell, the cell will behave as a closed system for ionic exchanges, but open to carbon dioxide, as long as they predominate. If we can determine the quantitative rôle of these two mechanisms, we can quantitate the changes in transmembrane fluxes of H^+ and HCO_3^- during hypercapnia.

In the following, we will present a quantitative approach to the rôles played by the various pH-regulating factors in acute and chronic hypercapnia.

However, before we discuss the individual factors, we shall consider a theoretical model system which can be made to fit the acid-base behaviour of the intracellular space. There are several reasons why we need this model system. Firstly, the calculation of a buffer capacity from tissue homogenates requires a theoretical evaluation of dilution effects. Secondly, the model will allow a comparison between measured buffer capacity and required buffer concentration. Thirdly, the model system is needed in order to calculate the pH_i' changes which result from a given production or consumption of acid by the cells.

A THEORETICAL MODEL FOR THE INTRACELLULAR SPACE

The basic equations describing buffering in nonbicarbonate systems were worked out by v. Slyke (1922), while Edsall & Wyman (1958) described the buffering characteristics of a mixture of bicarbonate and nonbicarbonate buffers in the presence of CO_2 (see also Siesjö & Pontén 1966, Pontén 1966). The following analysis extends previous studies by describing buffering characteristics to both strong acids and to CO_2 by a system which contains both bicarbonate and nonbicarbonate buffers.

The model system should, in order to resemble the intracellular compartment in brain, have a pH of 7.1 at a CO_2 tension of 40 mm Hg. The buffer capacity of the system to CO_2 will depend on the concentrations of available buffer acids ($C_1, C_2 \ldots\ldots C_n$) and on their ionization constants ($K_1', K_2' \ldots K_n'$). If we start with a 0.16 M NaCl solution which we equilibrate with a CO_2 tension of 40 mm Hg, we can add one or several buffer acids (Ha) in various concentrations and then titrate the solution with 0.16 N NaOH until the pH is 7.1 at a pCO_2 of 40 mm Hg. For this system we can write the equation for electrical neutrality

$$[Na^+] + [H^+] = [Cl^-] + [HCO_3^-] + 2\,[CO_3^{--}] + [OH^-] + [a_1^-] + [a_2^-] + \ldots\ldots [a_n^-] \tag{6}$$

We can for all practical purposes neglect the difference between the H^+ and OH^- concentrations at a pH of around 7.1. By substituting and by rearranging (see Edsall & Wyman 1958, Siesjö & Pontén 1966), we get

$$[Na^+] - [Cl^-] = \frac{pCO_2 \cdot S \cdot K_{H_2CO_3}}{[H^+]} \left(1 + \frac{2 \cdot K_{HCO_3^-}}{[H^+]}\right) + \frac{K_1' \cdot C_1}{K_1' + [H^+]} + \ldots$$

$$\frac{K_n' \cdot C_n}{K_n' + [H^+]} \tag{7}$$

where C is the total buffer concentration (Ha + a^-). The term ($[Na^+] - [Cl^-]$) expresses the amount of base added to the system to obtain a pH of 7.1. It is also equal to the sum of the buffer anion concentrations ($[HCO_3^-]$ + 2 $[CO_3^-]$ + $[a^-]_1$ + ... $[a^-]_n$) and is thus conveniently called the buffer base concentration [BB].

We can use this basic equation for analyses of the effect of changing the C and K'_{Ha} values on the buffer capacity to CO_2. The simplest way to do this is to insert the given values for the CO_2 tension (40 mm Hg), for the H^+ concentration ($10^{-7.1}$), and for the first and second apparent ionization constants of H_2CO_3 ($10^{-7.1}$ and $10^{-9.8}$, respectively). For any given combination of C and K_{Ha} values we can then solve the equation for the BB concentration. When we know the BB concentration, we can calculate the changes in pH as a function of changes in pCO_2, which gives us the buffer capacity of the solution to CO_2, which can be expressed as

$$\beta\, CO_2 = \frac{d \log pCO_2}{d\, pH} \tag{8}$$

We have used a computer program to calculate the buffer capacity as a function of the concentrations of buffer acids, of the pK values, and of the pH. Fig. 2 shows how the buffer capacity of the system varies with K_{Ha} at three different buffer acid concentrations (C = 0.010, 0.050 and 0.090 moles/l, respectively). The buffer capacity is markedly dependent on both the buffer acid concentration (C) and the K_{Ha} value (cf. v. Slyke 1922). A β_{CO_2} value of 2.0 requires a total buffer concentration of 0.050 moles/l and an optimal pK_{Ha} (7.1). When the pK_{Ha} is 0.5 units higher or lower than 7.1, β_{CO_2} decreases to about 1.7 with the same concentration of buffer acid. If buffer acids with pK values lower than 5.5 (e. g. carboxyl groups of organic acids), or higher than 8.5 (e. g. amino groups of amino acids) are present, the buffer capacity will be nearly unaffected even if the buffer acid concentration is very high.

Due to the fact that we know so little about the buffer systems operative under *in vivo* conditions, we have chosen to consider a mixture of five acids ($C_1 - C_5$) present in equal concentration and with pK values evenly dispersed over the physiological pH range (pK = 6.5, 6.8, 7.1, 7.4 and 7.7). Although

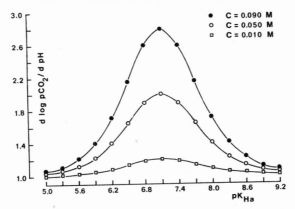

Fig. 2. The calculated CO_2 buffer capacity (d log pCO_2 / d pH) of a model system with a pH of 7.1 at a CO_2 tension of 40 mm Hg. The buffer capacity is depicted for three different concentrations of a nonbicarbonate buffer acid with acid pK′ values varying from 5.0 to 9.2.

this mixture by itself qualifies as a continuous ("universal") buffer in the v. Slyke sense (see v. Slyke 1922), the presence of bicarbonate and CO_2 in the system gives it a buffer capacity which increases towards the alkaline and decreases towards the acid range when strong base or acid is added (see Fig. 4 below). Of more interest in the present context is the buffer capacity of the mixture to CO_2. If we choose to study a mixture with a *total* buffer concentration of 0.050 moles/1, we find that the β_{CO_2} value at a CO_2 tension of 40 mm Hg is 1.8 (cf. the value of 2.0 for a system with a single buffer of the same concentration with an optimal pK_{Ha} of 7.1). If we plot the relation between pCO_2 and pH in a log pCO_2/pH diagram, the slope of the line gives us the buffer value β_{CO_2} = d log pCO_2/d pH. Such lines are usually considered to be essentially linear, but the CO_2 buffer capacity, so expressed, decreases at high and increases at low CO_2 tensions (Fig. 3). Therefore, if we want to compare the CO_2 buffer capacities of different systems, we should do so at the same CO_2 tensions.

Equation (7) also allows us to calculate the effect of titration with non-volatile acids or bases on the pH in the model system. Any increase or decrease in the concentration of a strong acid like lactic acid will give a mole to mole decrease or increase in the buffer base concentration. If we want to evaluate the influence of such acids on the pH of the system at any particular pCO_2, we may start by calculating the buffer base concentration

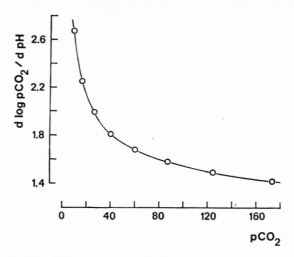

Fig. 3. The effect of the CO_2 tension (mm Hg) on the calculated CO_2 buffer capacity of a "continuous" buffer with a total buffer concentration of 0.050 moles/l. The buffer capacity varies with the CO_2 tension in spite of the fact that the pK_{Ha} values of the "continuous" buffer were evenly dispersed between 6.5 and 7.7.

at a pCO_2 of 40 mm Hg and a pH of 7.1 for any particular buffer acid concentration. The pCO_2 is then changed to the desired value at constant buffer base and the resulting pH calculated. Thereafter the pCO_2 is held constant and the pH is calculated as a function of the buffer base concentration. In Fig. 4 we have illustrated the variation of pH with the buffer base concentration at CO_2 tensions of 20, 40, 60 and 80 mm Hg, respectively, using a 0.05 moles/l "continuous" buffer.

THE PHYSICOCHEMICAL BUFFER CAPACITY OF BRAIN TISSUE

The derivation of a CO_2 buffer capacity for the intact tissue from diluted homogenates is hampered by the fact that neither the pH, nor the bicarbonate concentration, nor the calculated buffer capacity, are simple functions of the degree of dilution (Siesjö 1962 c).

The above theoretical analysis indicates that the calculated buffer capacity is linearily related to the total buffer concentration (C) if the system is studied at its original pH of 7.1. In other words, if we titrate a diluted buffer mixture, equilibrated with a CO_2 tension of 40 mm Hg, back to a pH of 7.1,

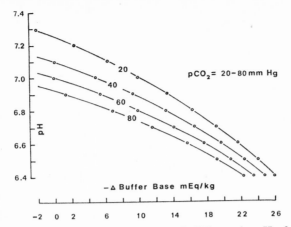

Fig. 4. The effect of addition of strong acid (— $\triangle$ BB) on the pH of a "continuous" CO_2 buffer with a total buffer concentration of 0.050 moles/l at four different CO_2 tensions (20, 40, 60 and 80 mm Hg, respectively). This "continuous" buffer was found to mimic the buffer capacity of brain intracellular fluid.

using e. g. a 0.16 N NaOH solution, the buffer capacity of the diluted system is a linear function of the degree of dilution. This is shown in Fig. 5 for a mixture of five buffer acids with total buffer concentrations of 0.01, 0.05 and 0.10 moles/l, respectively.

In order to analyse the physicochemical buffer capacity of brain tissue, we have titrated brain homogenates back to a pH of 7.1 at a CO_2 tension of 40 mm Hg before equilibrating the homogenates with various CO_2 tensions. The homogenates were prepared from brains of normocapnic rats, frozen *in situ* and homogenized in a 0.16 M NaCl-NaF solution (Siesjö 1962 b). The homogenates were equilibrated with a CO_2 tension of 40 mm Hg at 37° C and titrated with 0.16 N NaOH to a pH of 7.1. Aliquots of the homogenates were then equilibrated at 37° C with CO_2 tensions of 15–85 mm Hg, and the resulting pH values measured with a capillary glass electrode. Fig. 6 shows that the buffer capacity, calculated at a CO_2 tension of 40 mm Hg (β_{CO_2} = d log pCO_2/d pH), was a linear function of the degree of dilution when up to 50 per cent brain tissue was added to the homogenizing fluid. Extrapolation from the homogenates suggests that the buffer capacity of the intact tissue is close to 1.8. A comparison with our model system shows that this is the buffer capacity of our "continuous" five-acid buffer mixture if the total buffer concentration is around 0.050 moles/l. However, the conditions

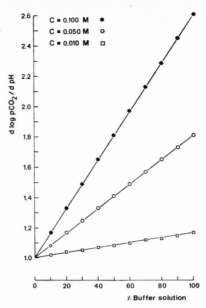

Fig. 5. The effect of diluting a "continuous" CO_2 buffer on the calculated CO_2 buffer capacity at three different (total) buffer concentrations. When the diluted system was titrated back to its original pH of 7.1 at a CO_2 tension of 40 mm Hg before it was titrated with CO_2, the calculated buffer capacity was a linear function of the degree of dilution.

of the experiments allow a complete hydrolysis of phosphocreatine and ATP, which will lead to a spuriously high buffer capacity. If we correct for these metabolic changes, we arrive at an approximate β_{CO_2} of about 1.6–1.7, corresponding to a total buffer concentration of about 0.040 moles/l.

REGULATING OF INTRACELLULAR pH BY METABOLIC PRODUCTION
OR CONSUMPTION OF ACIDS

When the intracellular concentration of lactate is increased in the brain during hypoxia, there is a corresponding decrease in pH_i' (Kaasik *et al.* 1970 a, b). Recent experiments have also shown that when the intracellular lactate concentration decreases during deep barbiturate anaesthesia, pH_i' increases in relation to the decrease in the lactate concentration (Nilsson & Siesjö 1970). These experiments, as well as theoretical considerations (see Siesjö *et al.* 1968), suggest that changes in the steady state lactate concentration in intra-

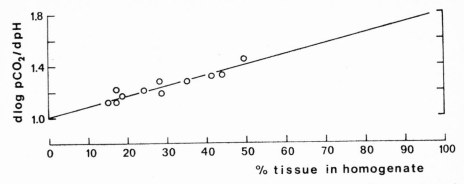

Fig. 6. The relation between the degree of dilution of brain tissue homogenates and the calculated CO_2 buffer capacity (d log pCO_2 / d pH). Before the CO_2 buffer capacities of the homogenates were determined they were titrated back to pH 7.1 at a CO_2 tension of 40 mm Hg.

cellular fluids will be accompanied by a stoichiometrical release or removal of H^+ ions. The stoichiometry can be expected to persist as long as no appreciable independent fluxes of H^+ ions or lactate anions have occurred. A corresponding acidifying or alkalinizing effect can be assumed to occur also when the tissue concentrations of other acids or bases are changed. It must be stressed that we are considering the acid-base effects of changes in the steady state concentrations of acids or bases, as these can be calculated from the differences in the concentrations of the anions, and that such differences may be poorly related to steady-state production or consumption rates.

In order to obtain information on the possible release or consumption of acids during acute hypo- and hypercapnia, we have measured in halothane-anaesthetized rats the lactate, pyruvate and α-ketoglutarate concentrations in the brain after a decrease in the arterial pCO_2 to 17–20 mm Hg, and after an increase in arterial pCO_2 induced by administering 10% CO_2, both conditions lasting for 15 min. The concentrations of phospocreatine and ATP were also measured since hydrolysis of these metabolites influences the intracellular pH' (see discussion by Hill 1955, Danforth 1968 and Siesjö *et al.* 1968). The results are shown in Table 1. The results confirm and extend previous results which have shown that hypo- and hypercapnia are accompanied by significant changes in the tissue lactate and pyruvate contents (Leusen *et al.* 1967, Granholm & Siesjö 1969, Kjällquist *et al.* 1969).

Table 1. The effects of a 15 min period of hypo- and hypercapnia upon the brain tissue concentrations of phosphocreatine, ATP, lactate, pyruvate and α-ketoglutarate in rats anaesthetized with 0.6 % halothane. The tissue CO_2 tension (p_tCO_2) was expressed in mm Hg and the metabolite concentrations in mMoles/kg of wet tissue. Means $\pm$ s. e.

Exp. group	p_tCO_2	PCr	ATP	La	Py	α–KG
Hypocapnia	25.5 $\pm$ 0.5	5.17 $\pm$ 0.08	2.82 $\pm$ 0.03	2.75 $\pm$ 0.02	0.16 $\pm$ 0.00	0.21 $\pm$ 0.01
Normocapnia	43.9 $\pm$ 1.4	5.13 $\pm$ 0.16	2.83 $\pm$ 0.04	1.28 $\pm$ 0.07	0.08 $\pm$ 0.03	0.12 $\pm$ 0.01
Hypercapnia	86.5 $\pm$ 1.5	4.29 $\pm$ 0.06	2.79 $\pm$ 0.01	0.75 $\pm$ 0.04	0.04 $\pm$ 0.00	0.05 $\pm$ 0.00

If we assume that the decreases in the tissue lactate, pyruvate and α-ketoglutarate contents have occurred by means of oxidation to CO_2 and water, and that a corresponding amount of H^+ ions have disappeared in the process, we may calculate the effect of the metabolic changes in alkalinizing the brain intracellular space during hypercapnia. In order to do this, we first had to convert the values of Table 1 to intracellular concentrations (mMoles/kg of intracellular water). We then assumed that a decrease in the (intracellular) phosphocreatine concentration of 1 mMoles/kg is equivalent to the disappearance of 0.5 mMoles/kg of strong acid. When adding up the change in the phosphocreatine concentration, and the changes in the lactate, pyruvate and α-ketoglutarate concentrations, it is found that they should be equivalent to the disappearance of 1.5–2.0 mEq/kg of strong acid. The decreases in the pyruvate and α-ketoglutarate concentrations suggest that also other glucolytic and Krebs cycle acids may be "consumed", but since most of these acids occur in rather small concentrations, the upper figure used probably represents a realistic estimate.

If we let our model system (see above) contain a total buffer acid concentration of 0.040 moles/l, an increase in the CO_2 tension from 40 to 85–90 mm Hg will shift the pH from 7.1 to 6.92. If, at this pCO_2, 2 mEq/kg of strong base is added, the pH is shifted back to about 6.95. This is equivalent to an increase in the buffer capacity (d log pCO_2/d pH) from about 1.6 to about 1.9. Thus, provided the titrations of the homogenates have given a realistic estimate of the true physicochemical buffer capacity of the brain intracellular fluids, and provided H^+ ions have been removed *in vivo* in an amount corresponding to the decreases in the intracellular lactate, pyruvate,

α-ketoglutarate and phosphocreatine concentrations, we may tentatively deduce an apparent CO_2 buffer capacity of about 2.0 in acute hypercapnia (mechanisms 1 and 2).

IN VIVO CONTROL OF INTRACELLULAR pH' IN THE BRAIN

We have chosen to study the regulation of intracellular pH' in the brain of rats which have been exposed to a gas mixture containing about 10% CO_2. This amount of CO_2 increases the tissue CO_2 tension from 40–45 to 85–90 mm Hg in unanaesthetized rats (Messeter & Siesjö 1970). In order to study the effect of the hypercapnia upon the intracellular acid-base parameters, groups of animals were exposed to the gas mixture for 15 and 45 min, and for 3, 24 and 48 hrs, respectively. In the last three groups, the animals were anaesthetized with 70% nitrous oxide or with 0.7% halothane during the last 45 min of the exposure periods. All animals were mechanically hyperventilated during the anaesthesia in order to bring the arterial CO_2 tension close to that observed in the unanaesthetized state. At the end of the exposure periods, CSF was drawn from the cisterna magna, and the brain was frozen *in situ* for subsequent bicarbonate analyses (see Messeter & Siesjö 1970).

Fig. 7 shows the gradual increase in the intracellular bicarbonate concentration during the hypercapnia, and the gradual return of the calculated intracellular pH' to the control value after 48 hrs (cf. Nicholls 1958, and Weyne *et al.* 1968, who reported a gradual increase in the total tissue bicarbonate in sustained hypercapnia). The calculated CO_2 buffer capacity at 15 min ($\beta = 1.9$) is close to that predicted from the inherent CO_2 buffer capacity (of the intracellular space), suggesting that the cells approach the behaviour of a "closed" acid-base system during such short hypercapnic periods (cf. also Granholm & Pontén 1969). At 3 and 24 hrs the calculated "buffer capacity" amounts to 3.2 and 6.8, respectively, indicating transmembrane fluxes of H^+ or HCO_3^-. The suggested return of the intracellular pH' to the control value at 48 hrs would make the "buffer capacity" infinitely large. It is evidently difficult to distinguish between a complete normalization and a near-normalization of pH_i'. However, even if we assume that the pH_i' is 0.01 units lower at 48 hrs than in the normocapnic control situation, the calculated "buffer capacity" would still be around 30.

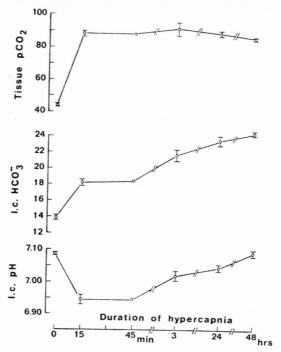

Fig. 7. The tissue CO_2 tension (mm Hg), the intracellular bicarbonate concentration (mEq/kg of H_2O), and the intracellular pH' of rat brain tissue during acute and chronic hypercapnia. The "chronic" animals (3, 24 and 48 hrs) were exposed to CO_2 while awake, and were anaesthetized with halothane during the last 45 min of the exposure periods. Note gradual increase in the intracellular bicarbonate concentration, and return of pH_i to the normal value at 48 hrs.

THE NATURE OF THE TRANSMEMBRANE H^+ AND HCO_3^- FLUXES

The experiments mentioned seem to establish that there are appreciable transmembrane fluxes of H^+ or HCO_3^- in sustained hypercapnia. The parallel increases in the CSF and in the intracellular bicarbonate concentrations during hypercapnia could suggest that these fluxes are passive, but we cannot distinguish between the roles played by active and by passive mechanisms without resorting to an analysis of transmembrane fluxes of H^+ and HCO_3^-. In order to do this we must introduce a number of assumptions, the validity of which remains unclear.

Before we can conclude anything about the changes in the ion fluxes during hypercapnia, we have to establish what must be considered a passive flux in a two-compartment system which apparently has the ability to transport H^+ or HCO_3^- actively. We can define the metabolic energy spent on HCO_3^- transport as a transport power, given by the equation

$$\dot{W}_{HCO_3^-} = - [\triangle\mu_{HCO_3^-}] \cdot [M^{in}_{HCO_3^-}] \tag{9}$$

(Ussing 1960, Woodbury 1961), where $W_{HCO_3^-}$ is the transport power and $M^{in}_{HCO_3^-}$ the net inward flux of HCO_3^-, which at steady state should equal the net passive outflux. If the changes in $[HCO_3^-]_i$ during sustained hypercapnia are a "passive" consequence of the changes in the extracellular HCO_3^- concentration, the following equation should be satisfied

$$\dot{W}_{HCO_3^-} = - [\triangle\mu_{HCO_3^-}]' \cdot [M^{in}_{HCO_3^-}]' = - [\triangle\mu_{HCO_3^-}]'' \cdot [M^{in}_{HCO_3^-}]'' \tag{10}$$

since then the two states would be associated with an unchanged energy expenditure. (In this and in the following equations the symbols ['] and [''] denote the normocapnic and hypercapnic states, respectively.)

We have already calculated $\triangle\mu_{HCO_3^-}$ on the assumption of transmembrane potential (Ψ) of $- 75$ mV. If we assume the same Ψ value in hypercapnia, the calculated $\triangle\mu_{HCO_3^-}$ is 3–4 mV higher than in normocapnia. However, $\triangle\mu_{HCO_3^-}$ would remain constant if the mean transmembrane potential decreased 3–4 mV during hypercapnia. The transmembrane potentials may decrease to this extent, since Cameron (this symposium) has found that acute hypercapnia is accompanied by a rise in the CSF potassium concentration. At any rate, the calculated differences are so small that we may, as a first approximation, assume that the $\triangle\mu_{HCC_3^-}$ remains constant between the normocapnic and the hypercapnic situations. This renders the analysis easier, since the net HCO_3^- flux in the steady state should then be an indicator of the energy spent on the transport of the ion.

In order to get an expression for the net passive flux of an ion moving in an electrical field, we must use the basic diffusion equation in an integrated form (Hodgkin & Katz 1949, Conway 1957, Ussing 1950, 1960). These authors all based their derivations on the "constant field" assumption of Goldman (1943). (For a different approach, see Teorell 1953). The flux equation may be written

$$M_{HCO_3^-} = \frac{u \cdot F \cdot \Psi \cdot \beta'}{a} \cdot \frac{(HCO_3^-)_i - (HCO_3^-)_{CSF} \cdot e^{-\Psi F/RT}}{1 - e^{-\Psi F/RT}} \tag{11}$$

where u is the mobility of the ion in the membrane, β' is a partition coeffi-

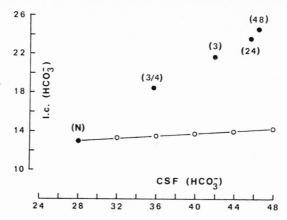

Fig. 8. The relation between the CSF and the brain intracellular bicarbonate concentrations (mEq/kg of H_2O) in control animals (N) and during continuous hypercapnia (¾, 3, 24 and 48 hrs, respectively). The measured intracellular concentrations (filled circles) were markedly higher than those predicted on the basis of a "passive" exchange of HCO_3^- between the extra- and intracellular spaces (unfilled symbols, see text).

cient expressing the difference in concentration between the membrane and the fluid phases, and a is the thickness of the membrane. We may express these parameters as a permeability coefficient P, where $P = u \cdot \beta'/a$.

If the transport power and the $\triangle \mu_{HCO_3^-}$ remain constant in the normocapnic and hypercapnic situations, then

$$\frac{\dot{W}''_{HCO_3^-}}{\dot{W}'_{HCO_3^-}} = \frac{M''_{HCO_3^-}}{M'_{HCO_3^-}} = 1 \tag{12}$$

Further, if one assumes that P is unchanged from the normocapnic to the hypercapnic situations, the following relation would be expected to hold

$$\frac{[HCO_3^-]''_i - [HCO_3^-]''_{CSF} \cdot e^{-\Psi F/RT}}{[HCO_3^-]'_i - [HCO_3^-]'_{CSF} \cdot e^{-\Psi F/RT}} = 1 \tag{13}$$

By inserting the values measured in the normocapnic situation, we can calculate the $[HCO_3^-]_i$ which would be expected for any given increase in $[HCO_3^-]_{CSF}$. This would then be the $[HCO_3^-]_i$ which one would expect if the transport work remained constant ("passive increase"). By using the values which we measured we get

$$\triangle [HCO_3^-]_i = 0.06 \cdot \triangle [HCO_3^-]_{CSF} \tag{14}$$

Therefore, we would expect that an increase of 1 mMole/l in $[HCO_3^-]_{CSF}$ should increase $[HCO_3]_i$ 0.06 mMoles/l, provided the transport work remained constant. The values calculated in this way are shown as open circles in Fig. 8. The measured increases in $[HCO_3^-]_i$ (solid circles) greatly exceed those expected.

The difference between the values predicted in this way, assuming "passive" distribution, and those found, suggests that the rate of active transport increases during hypercapnia. However, we must keep in mind that the calculation assumes that the permeability facor for HCO_3^- remains constant. Thus, changes in the permeability factor P could equally well explain the findings. There is presently no way of distinguishing between these alternatives, but it appears reasonable to suggest that hypercapnia, and hereby intracellular acidosis, accelerates an active extrusion of H^+ from the cells.

SUMMARY

A discussion is given of the factors which determine intracellular pH in tissues like the brain, both at steady state and after an induced hyper- or hypocapnia. When the CO_2 tension, and hereby intracellular pH, is suddenly changed, at least three mechanisms will affect the change in intracellular pH: (1) physicochemical buffering, (2) production or consumption of nonvolatile acids, and (3) transmembrane fluxes of H^+ or HCO_3^-.

In the *acute* state, the first two of these mechanisms may predominate because the cell behaves as a "closed" system for ionic exchanges. In the *chronic* state, the pH_i is mainly determined by the balance between passive influx and active extrusion of H^+ across the cell membranes.

A quantitative treatment of intracellular acid-base changes was facilitated by a computer analysis on a model system which contained both bicarbonate and nonbicarbonate buffers. A "true" physicochemical buffer capacity of brain tissue could in this system be obtained from CO_2 titration curves on brain homogenates. This analysis gave a buffer capacity for brain intracellular fluid, defined as d log pCO_2/d pH, of about 1.6 at a CO_2 tension of 40 mm Hg. When changes in tissue concentrations of lactate, pyruvate, α-ketoglutarate and phosphocreatine in rats exposed to about 10% CO_2 were analysed in relation to the model system, the intracellular buffer capacity, including both mechanisms 1 and 2, were found to approximate 2.0.

17*

In rats exposed to 10% CO_2 for 15 min, the calculated buffer capacity showed very good agreement with that derived above (about 1.9). However, at 45 min and thereafter, the "buffer capacity" was progressively increased above the value predicted from the first two mechanisms.

The results suggest that the cell in the chronic state of acid-base changes does not behave as a "closed" system, but that H^+ and/or HCO_3^- move across the cell membranes. In order to evaluate if the transmembrane fluxes are "passive" or "active", the relation between the transport work in the normo- and hypercapnic situations were analysed. The analyses indicate that most of the gradual increase in the intracellular HCO_3^- concentration during hypercapnia is due to a change in rate of active transport.

ACKNOWLEDGEMENTS

Supported by the Swedish Medical Research Council (Projects No. B70-14X-263-06 and No. B70-40X-2179-02), by the Swedish Bank Tercentary Fund, by Carl-Bertel Nathhorst's Vetenskapliga Stiftelse, and by PHS Research Grant No. R01 NB07838-01 from NIH.

REFERENCES

Caldwell, P. C. (1956) Intracellular pH. In *International Review of Cytology*, ed. Bourne, G. H. & Danielli, J. F., Vol. V, pp. 229–277. Academic Press, New York.

Conway, E. J. (1957) Membrane equilibrium in skeletal muscle and the active transport of sodium. In *Metabolic Aspects of Transport across Cell Membranes*, ed. Murphy, Q. R., pp. 73–114. The University of Wisconsin Press, Madison.

Danforth, W. H. (1968) Activation of glucolytic pathway in muscle. In *Control of Energy Metabolism*, ed. Chance, B., Estabrook, R. W. & Williamson, J. R., pp. 287–297. Academic Press, New York.

Edsall, J. T. & Wyman, J. (1958) *Biophysical Chemistry*, Vol. I, pp. 699–753. Academic Press, New York.

Goldman, D. E. (1943) Potential, impedance, and rectification in membranes. *J. gen. Physiol. 1*, 37–60.

Granholm, L. & Pontén, U. (1969) The *in vivo* CO_2 buffer curve of the intracellular space of cat cerebral cortex. *Acta neurol. scand. 45*, 493–501.

Granholm, L. & Siesjö, B. K. (1969) The effects of hypercapnia and hypocapnia upon the cerebrospinal fluid lactate and pyruvate concentrations and upon the lactate, pyruvate, ATP, ADP, phosphocreatine and creatine concentrations of cat brain tissue. *Acta physiol. scand. 75*, 257–266.

Hill, A. V. (1955) The influence of the external medium on the internal pH of muscle. *Proc. roy. Soc. B. 144*, 1–22.

Hodgkin, A. L. & Katz, B. (1949) The effect of sodium ions on the electrical activity of the giant axon of the squid. *J. Physiol. 108*, 37–77.

Kaasik, A. E., Nilsson, L. & Siesjö, B. K. (1970a) The effect of asphyxia upon the lactate, pyruvate and bicarbonate concentrations of brain tissue and cisternal CSF, and upon the tissue concentrations of phosphocreatine and adenine nucleotides in anesthetized rats. *Acta physiol. scand. 78*, 433–447.

Kaasik, A. E., Nilsson, L. & Siesjö, B. K. (1970b) The effect of arterial hypotension upon the lactate, pyruvate and bicarbonate concentrations of brain tissue and cisternal CSF, and upon the tissue concentrations of phosphocreatine and adenine nucleotides in anesthetized rats. *Acta physiol. scand. 78*, 448–458.

Kjällquist, Å., Nardini, M. & Siesjö, B. K. (1969) The regulation of extra- and intracellular acid-base parameters in the rat brain during hyper- and hypocapnia. *Acta physiol. scand. 79*, 485–494.

Leusen, I., Lacroix, E. & Demeester, G. (1967) Lactate and pyruvate in the brain of rats during changes in acid-base balance. *Arch. int. Physiol. Biochim. 75*, 310–324.

Messeter, K. & Siesjö, B. K. (1970) Regulation of intracellular pH in the rat brain in chronic hypercapnia. *Acta physiol. scand.* In press.

Nicholls, G. (1958) Serial changes in tissue carbon dioxide content during acute respiratory acidosis. *J. clin. Invest. 37*, 1111–1122.

Nilsson, L. & Siesjö, B. K. (1970) The effect of anaesthetics upon labile phosphates and upon extra- and intracellular lactate, pyruvate and bicarbonate concentrations in the rat brain. *Acta physiol. scand.* In press.

Pontén, U. (1966) Acid-base changes in rat brain tissue during acute respiratory acidosis and baseosis. *Acta physiol. scand. 68*, 152–163.

Pontén, U. & Siesjö, B. K. (1964) A method for the determination of the total carbon dioxide content of frozen tissues. *Acta physiol. scand. 60*, 297–308.

Pontén, U. & Siesjö, B. K. (1966) Gradients of CO_2 tension in the brain. *Acta physiol. scand. 68*, 152–163.

Rall, D. P., Oppelt, W. W. & Patlak, C. S. (1962) Extracellular space of brain as determined by diffusion of inulin from the ventricular system. *Life Sci. 2*, 43–48.

Siesjö, B. K. (1962a) The solubility of carbon dioxide in cerebral cortical tissue from the cat at 37.5° C. With a note on the solubility of carbon dioxide in water, 0.16 M NaCl and in cerebrospinal fluid. *Acta physiol. scand. 55*, 325–341.

Siesjö, B. K. (1962b) The bicarbonate/carbonic acid buffer system of the cerebral cortex of the cat, as studied on tissue homogenates. I. The amount of carbon dioxide bound at different carbon dioxide tensions. *Acta neurol. scand. 38*, 98–120.

Siesjö, B. K. (1962c) The bicarbonate/carbonic acid buffer system of the cerebral cortex of cats, as studied in tissue homogenates. II. The pK_1' of carbonic acid at 37.5° C, and the relation between carbon dioxide tension and pH. *Acta neurol. scand. 38*, 121–141.

Siesjö, B. K. & Pontén, U. (1966) The buffer capacity of brain tissue and of equivalent systems. *N. Y. Acad. Sci. 133*, 180–194.

Siesjö, B. K., Kaasik, A. E., Nilsson, L. & Pontén, U. (1968) Biochemical basis of tissue acidosis. In *CBF & CSF*, ed. Ingvar, D. H., Lassen, N. A., Siesjö, B. K. & Skinhøj, E. *Scand. J. clin. Lab. Invest.*, Suppl. 102, III:A

v. Slyke, D. D. (1922) On the measurement of buffer values and on the relationship of buffer value to the dissociation constant of the buffer and the concentration and reaction of the buffer solution. *J. biol. Chem. 52,* 525–570.

Teorell, T. (1953) Transport processes and electrical phenomena in ionic membranes. *Progr. Biophys. 3,* 305–369.

Ussing, H. H. (1950) The distinction by means of tracers between active transport and diffusion. The transfer of iodide across the isolated frog skin. *Acta physiol. scand. 19,* 43–56.

Ussing, H. H. (1960) The alkali metal ions in isolated systems and tissues. In *Handbuch der Experimentellen Pharmakologie,* ed. Eichler, O. & Farah, A., pp. 1–95. Springer Verlag, Berlin.

Waddell, W. J. & Bates, R. G. (1969) Intracellular pH. *Physiol. Rev. 49,* 285–329.

Weyne, J., Demeester, G. & Leusen, I. (1968) Bicarbonate and chloride shifts in rat brain during acute and prolonged respiratory acid-base changes. *Arch. int. Physiol. Biochim. 76,* 415–433.

Woodbury, J. W. (1965) The biophysics of cell membranes. *In Physiology and Biophysics,* 19th ed., ed. Ruch, T. C. & Patton, H. D., Chapter 1. W. B. Saunders, Philadelphia & London.

Woodward, D. L., Reed, D. J. & Woodbury, D. M. (1967) Extracellular space of rat cerebral cortex. *Amer. J. Physiol. 212,* 367–370.

DISCUSSION

LOESCHCKE

What you say about the transport of bicarbonate, could that not be expressed as a transport of chloride? The reason is that bicarbonate always fills the gap of the anions.

SIESJÖ

I cannot agree with that. In hyper-and hypocapnia, there are also changes in the organic anions in the cells, like lactate, pyruvate, α-ketogluterate and glutamate. However, I cannot give you the balance since we haven't measured the chloride in these situations. I should also add that when we conclude as a working hypothesis that there is an active transport of hydrogen ions, this of course does not necessarily mean that the hydrogen or bicarbonate ions are being actively transported themselves, since their movements could be coupled to transport of other ions.

WADDELL

Did you determine the physico-chemical buffer capacity only on homogenates of normal brain, or did you also determine it on brain from chronic hyper-capnia experiments?

SIESJÖ

We only determined it on normal brains.

WADDELL

If you had a net change in the difference between the sum of fixed cations and anions, could you detect this after your readjustment in chronic hyper-capnia?

SIESJÖ

It is possible, but we did not study "fixed" cations or anions.

ASTRUP

I have a question concerning the phospho-creatine values after equilibration *in vitro*. How long time did you equilibrate the tissue?

Siesjö

15, 30, and 45 minutes. At these times there is no phospho-creatine left. That is why we have to correct the original buffer value of 1.8 to approximately 1.6.

Astrup

What was the change in the organic phosporic compounds?

Siesjö

In acute hypercapnia *in vivo* there are no changes in ATP, ADP or AMP, but a decrease in phospho-creatine from 5.1 to about 4.3 mMoles/kg of wet tissue. In chronic hypercapnia, when the intracellular pH's seem to be completely normalized, the phospo-creatine has returned towards, but not to, normal values. The results make us wonder if not part of the metabolic effect of hypercapnia is due to CO_2 as such. This is also suggested by the fact that chronic hypercapnia is accompanied by lactate, pyruvate, and α-ketoglutarate values which are still significantly decreased in comparison to the control values in normocapnic animals.

Severinghaus

Have you also calculated the intracellular pH using the values for extracellular fluid space, which Dr. Rall reported at this symposium?

Siesjö

With 20 per cent extracellular space we calculated a value of 7.0 instead of 7.1 at a Pco_2 of 40 mm Hg (Kjällquist *et al.* 1969), but this is less important in the present context. The important thing is if you change the extracellular space during the procedure. According to what Dr. Cameron said yesterday, there is no indication that hypercapnia will change the size of the extracellular space.

Weyne

For the calculation of intracellular bicarbonate concentration you used the

Kjällquist, Å., Nardini, M. & Siesjö, B. K. (1969) The regulation of extra- and intracellular acid-base parameters in the rat brain during hyper- and hypocapnia. *Acta physiol. scand. 76*, 485–494.

values which you measured in the CSF for the concentrations in the extra-cellular fluid. In the steady state such a statement is to all knowledge correct, but I wonder if it is true during only five minutes of hypercapnic exposure which probably represents a transient state.

SIESJÖ

It is definitely not a steady state at that time. However, even if we use different values, assuming for instance that we are seeing only half of the changes in the ECF, we will arrive at rather similar buffer values. Besides, we only want an approximate value for acute hypercapnia to compare with sustained hypercapnia, and it does not matter if the 15 min group gives a buffer capacity of 1.8, 1.9, or 2.0 when it is compared to values of 5, or perhaps even 30.

MAREN

I would like to show the results from a preliminary experiment in rats. It shows the intracellular pH in muscle water after carbonic anhydrase inhibition. The bicarbonate concentration in plasma decreased from 24 to 13

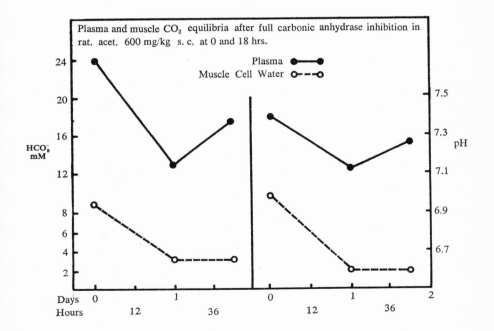

Plasma and muscle CO_2 equilibria after full carbonic anhydrase inhibition in rat. acet. 600 mg/kg s. c. at 0 and 18 hrs.

mEq/l due to the bicarbonate loss into the urine. The pH of plasma went down from about 7.4 to 7.1. Under these circumstances the total CO_2 and the calculated bicarbonate in the muscle goes down from about 9 to 4 mEq/l. The calculated muscle cell water pH based on the CO_2 equilibrium then declines from 7.0 to 6.6. This is perhaps the lowest intracellular pH that has been reported by the CO_2 or DMO methods and I don't think it is an error, because this amount of bicarbonate depletion corresponds with what one expects, knowing the bicarbonate that is lost in the urine. Since making this slide, we have obtained similar results on muscle cell water using DMO to measure the pH.

SIESJÖ

What was the plasma P_{CO_2}?

MAREN

It was about 40 mm Hg; it doesn't change much under these conditions, in which there is no anesthesia.

SIESJÖ

We injected carbonic anhydrase inhibitor for up to 10 hours, and we didn't find any decrease in the intracellular bicarbonate concentration in the brain (Kjällquist et al. 1969 and unpublished observations).

However, the brain is a very clever organ, since it surrounds itself by cerebrospinal fluid which has its own bicarbonate regulation, as we have discussed earlier.

MAREN

It is probably necessary to go a bit more than ten hours to get intracellular [HCO_3^-] depletion. In that time urinary [HCO_3^-] loss is actually reflected by decrease in plasma [HCO_3^-], representing extracellular fluid. By 24 hours, the continued urinary loss is reflected in cell water.

SIESJÖ

What dose did you give?

Kjällquist, Å., Nardini, M. & Siesjö, B. K. (1969) The effect of acetazolamide upon tissue concentrations of bicarbonate, lactate and pyruvate in the rat brain. *Acta physiol. scand.* 77, 241–251.

MAREN

It was an enormous dose (600 mg/kg) in order to cover the animal around the clock. We have also done it by giving a smaller dose at more frequent intervals. It doesn't make any difference, but you must keep it up for about 24 hours, so the kidney can do its business of sustained HCO_3^- excretion.

AMES

Since the bicarbonate is not in electrochemical equilibrium across the cell membrane, why does one need to invoke a change in active transport rather than a change in permeability of the cell membrane to account for the concentration changes observed in the chronic experiments?

SIESJÖ

If the permeability to bicarbonate increased, the effect of the electrochemical gradient would be to decrease intracellular bicarbonate and not to increase it. If the permeability decreases in hypercapnia, this would tend to give bicarbonate accumulation in the cell, but then we still need a mechanism for extruding hydrogen ions.

WADDELL

Dr. Ussing, suppose that the acidification of the cell is due to diffusion of H_2CO_3 into the cell as one increases the P_{CO_2}, and that sodium is being pumped out of the cell. When the carbonic acid enters into the cell and dissociates, it forms more bicarbonate with relatively less sodium. What would be the expected response of the sodium pump to this increased tendency for sodium to enter the cell. Would you expect a slow diffusion of the sodium into the cell which would make up for the increase in bicarbonate and relative decrease in sodium under those conditions?

USSING

If the sodium pump exchanges Na^+ against H^+, Na-pumping should give acidification; if it pumps Na^+ as well as H^+ it should give alcalization. If we assume that the sodium pump is a sodium-potassium exchange pump it should not change the number of positively charged ions in the cell. Unfortunately we do not know enough to make a choice between these possibilities. Both the red cell people and the axon people have found that the rate of transport of the sodium pump depends on the cellular sodium concentration.

When the sodium concentration increases the pumping increases. So that is the kind of self regulation that the sodium pump can be responsible for. But only if it handles at least one more ionic species can it be responsible for the pH effects. I agree with Dr. Siesjö that there must be some kind of additional active transport responsible for his observations.

WADDELL

Couldn't it just as well be sodium?

USSING

If we are dealing with a sodium-potassium exchange pump it couldn't be of much help, but if the sodium transport was coupled to the transport of hydrogen or some anion it might be different. If we assume a system similar to that described by Diamond (1962) for gall bladder; that is a sodium-chloride coupled pump, the pumping might lead to a transitory alcalinization of the cell. But so far this is highly hypothetical.

J. W. WOODBURY

Your data indicated that the intracellular pH returns completely to normal. I wonder if you could saturate the pump by going to high enough Pco_2's. The reason I ask is that in the whole body, there is complete compensation of chronic hypercapnia up to Pco_2's of 60 to 65 mm. At higher pressures the kidneys regulate along a titration curve of slope ~ 40 slykes (Woodbury 1965).

SIESJÖ

We don't know. We used 6 % and 10 % CO_2 with mechanical hyperventilation. The highest Pco_2 values were thus around 90 mm Hg.

SØRENSEN

Dr. Ussing, are you horrified by the use of the flux equations on these very complex systems?

Diamond, J. M. (1962) The mechanism of solute transport by the gall bladder. *J. Physiol. (Lond.)*. *161*. 474–502.
Woodbury, J. W. (1965) Regulation of pH. In: *Physiology and Biophysics,* ed. Ruch, T. C. & Patton, H. D., Chapter 46. W. B. Saunders, Philadelphia.

USSING

Not particularly.

WEYNE

You showed a picture relating buffer capacity (β) to pK for three different concentrations of buffer. In each instance the value of β is higher with higher buffer concentration. I wonder also if the buffer capacity defined as $\triangle$ HCO$_3^-$/$\triangle$ pH varies as β does. I ask that question because Dr. Brown (this symposium) describes a change of buffer capacity from 30 to 12 slykes, representing a fall of 60 per cent, whereas the fall seems much less, when expressing the data in β units, going from 1.53 to 1.22 which is only a 20 per cent decrease. Is the relationship between the buffer concentration and the buffer capacity a linear one?

SIESJÖ

There is a direct linear relation between the buffer capacity and the buffer acid concentration, if you study the system at a given pH value. About the two buffer capacity expressions: The difference in results, using either $\triangle$ log PCO$_2$/$\triangle$ pH or $\triangle$ [HCO$_3^-$]/$\triangle$ pH, is only apparent and due to the fact that an "unbuffered" bicarbonate solution has a $\triangle$ log PCO$_2$/$\triangle$ pH value of 1.0 and a $\triangle$ [HCO$_3^-$]/$\triangle$ pH value of close to zero. In your example, the results are rather similar if you take these basic differences into account.

Fluxes of H^+ and HCO_3^- Across Frog Skeletal Muscle Cell Membranes

*J. W. Woodbury**

In order to estimate the steady-state rates of active transport of H^+ and/or HCO_3^- through cell membranes, the passive fluxes of these ions must be either measured directly or calculated from permeabilities and electrochemical gradients. Such measurements are particularly difficult for H^+/HCO_3^- because tracer methods for measuring fluxes are not usable for these two labile ionic species. Hence, it is necessary to seek other, less direct methods for measuring the abilities of these ions to penetrate cell membranes. One such method is to measure the changes in transmembrane voltage and resistance produced by a change in the H^+ and/or HCO_3^- concentrations of the medium bathing an excised muscle. This is the basic maneuver used in the experiments described here.

METHODS

Two microelectrodes are inserted into a single cell of an excised frog sartorius muscle; current is applied through one electrode and transmembrane potential measured with the other. The interelectrode distance, 100 to 200 μm, is kept much less than the space constant, $\sim$ 2 mm. The steady transmembrane potential, V_m, and the deviations from it, $\triangle V_m$, produced by a current, I, are measured and recorded. The characteristic resistance, R_c, of the muscle fiber is defined as $R_c = \triangle V_m/I$. Since intracellular electrodes will seldom pass depolarizing currents for long periods, the applied current was a sine wave (0.2 Hz) superimposed on a steady bias current such that the current was zero at the peak of the sine wave, i.e., $I = {}^-I_0$

Department of Physiology and Biophysics, University of Washington School of Medicine, Seattle, Washington 98105, USA.
* This investigation was supported by PHS research grant no. NSO1752 from NINDS.

+ I_o sin $0.4\pi t$ with $I_o = 5$ na. Thus, in all figures the true value of V_m is given by the peaks of the sine waves.

The specific membrane resistance, R_m, (ohm-cm²) is related to characteristic resistance by a square relation:

$$R_m = 8\pi^2 a^3 R_c^2 / \rho_i$$

where a is fiber radius and ρ_i is specific resistivity of the myoplasm. More precisely, this technique gives an estimate of slope resistance at zero current in the hyperpolarizing direction.

The procedure is to impale a cell with the two electrodes, apply the current, obtain a baseline for V_m and R_c and then rapidly change the medium bathing the excised muscle. If conditions are propitious, the resulting changes in V_m and R_c can be interpreted in terms of ion permeabilities.

The available data indicate that the fluxes through membranes of H^+ and HCO_3^- are small compared to those of K^+ and Cl^- under normal conditions. In particular the membrane is highly permeable to chloride and its concentration in a normal bathing medium is high (120 mM), hence the presence of Cl^- in the medium swamps out the changes in V_m and R_c expected from changing [HCO_3^-]. It is thus desirable to replace Cl^- by an "impermeant" anion in order to increase the size of effects resulting from changes in [HCO_3^-] or [H^+].

Sulfate has been frequently used as an impermeant anion but has substantial drawbacks: (1) $CaSO_4$ is not very soluble and excess amounts must be added to maintain [Ca^{++}]. (2) The association constants of $SO_4^=$ to form KSO_4^- and $NaSO_4^-$ complexes are appreciable and reduce Na^+ and K^+ activities by amounts that are difficult to determine.

RESULTS

Anion Permeability Sequence

Many other impermeant anions have been found to be relatively impermeable (cf. Hutter & Warner 1967). Nevertheless, I tried several different anions in an attempt to find a convenient one (an easily available, chemically pure compound). The results of one experiment in which Cl^- was replaced by benzoate, glutamate, isethionate, or proprionate are shown in Fig. 1. These results are shown because they clearly illustrate how electrical measurements can be interpreted in terms of relative ion permeabilities. The

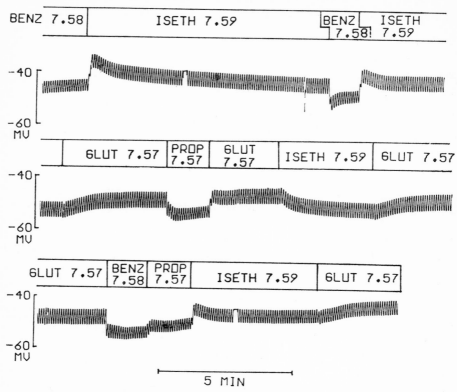

Fig. 1. Transmembrane potential of a frog skeletal muscle fiber as a function of time. A 10 na peak to peak sinusoidal current was applied via a second intracellular electrode. A steady current was also applied such that peaks of sine waves are at the resting potential. Anion in the solution bathing muscle is indicated by symbols above the recordings. Solutions were changed at vertical lines. BENZ = benzoate; ISETH = isethionate; GLUT = glutamate; PROP = proprionate. Numbers give the pH of the solution. Solution composition: [Na anion] = 115 mM, [K proprionate] = 2.5 mM, [Ca proprionate] = 2.0 mM and [Tris proprionate] = 5.0 mM. Time and voltage scales are given. See text for interpretation of records.

perfusing solution was changed at the vertical bars, the only difference being the predominant anion as shown by the abbreviations above the recording.

At the start of the record (upper left Fig. 1) the solution bathing the muscle contained benzoate (BENZ) as the principle anion. At the vertical bar, the anion was changed to isethionate (ISETH). There was an immediate depolarization of about 15 mv followed by a gradual return to near the original level; simultaneously there was an increase in $\triangle V_m$ (proportional to R_c) the amplitude of the sinusoidal voltage excursions. The immediate depolarization, slow repolarization and the gradual increase in $\triangle V_m$ are strong indications that benzoate ions are substantially more permeant than isethionate ions: Replacing external benzoate with a less permeant anion left an unbalanced efflux of negative (benzoate ions that had previously entered) which depolarized the membrane. This depolarizing action died out as the internal benzoate leaked out. This is confirmed by the gradual increase in resistance (from 0.45 to 0.56 megohm) along approximately the same time course as the voltage change. The reverse change occurs when isethionate is replaced by benzoate (upper right).

The change from isethionate to glutamate (GLUT) at the start of the middle record shows a similar train of events but much slower, indicating that isethionate is slightly more permeant than glutamate. Study of the remaining records leads to the following anion permeability sequence for frog skeletal muscle: benzoate $\simeq$ proprionate $>$ isethionate $>$ glutamate. Other experiments with lactate and trichloroacetate indicate that the latter is in the same group as benzoate and proprionate and that lactate is slightly more permeable than isethionate. The reproducibility and reversibility of these voltage and resistance changes strongly support this interpretation of the results. Hutter & Warner (1967) used this technique to establish the pH sensitivity of the Cl$^-$ permeability.

Results of this type led to the adoption of glutamate as the "impermeant" anion. It was later discovered that the glutamate chelates calcium; 115 mM glutamate reduces ionized [Ca^{++}] to approximately 0.5 mM, whereas it was about 2 mM in the other solutions. This is unlikely to have had much affect on membrane properties (Curtis 1963).

STABLE VOLTAGE STATES IN CL$^-$ FREE SOLUTIONS

Fig. 2 illustrates one of the peculiar properties of skeletal muscle (which complicates interpretation of results) when Cl$^-$ is replaced by a much less permeant anion. The upper two rows of the figure show spontaneous "action potentials" having durations of nearly 3 minutes. The cause of this spontaneous activity is not known, but see Adrian & Freygang (1962a). There are also thresholds for both depolarization and repolarization as shown by the transition in voltage from one steady level to another (lower trace, bottom

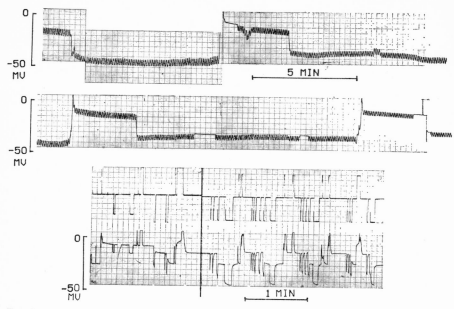

Fig. 2. Spontaneous action potentials and induced voltage transitions. Upper two strips, spontaneous, 3 minute duration "action potentials" of a muscle fiber soaked in gluta-mate solution. Lower strip, induced transitions: lower trace, transmembrane voltage, upper trace, current applied via second intracellular electrode. Currents cause transi-tions between three stable voltages at left and middle of record and two at right side. Vertical line divides change in time scale. Solution composition: [Na glutamate] = 115 mM, [K glutamate] = 2.5 mM, [Ca glutamate] = 2.0 mM, [Tris glutamate] = 5.0 mM. See text.

record) produced by applying depolarizing and hyperpolarizing currents (upper trace). This behavior is due in part to the anomalous rectification properties of the K$^+$ channel of muscle (Adrian & Freygang 1962b). Anom-alous rectification means that the resistance of the membrane to outward flow of K$^+$ is much higher than to inward flow, the reverse of the rectification expected from simple theories of ion penetration through membranes. Anomalous rectification gives rise to a negative slope resistance region on the K$^+$ current-voltage curve and this, in combination with a small, inward Na$^+$ current, creates an N-shaped I–V curve with two stable voltages and an intervening threshold voltage.

Unfortunately the situation in this cell was not this simple; the middle portion of the lower record shows that there were three, not two stable voltages for a short period of time. The most depolarized stable voltage had disappeared by the end of the record.

The records in Fig. 2 were obtained after the muscle had been bathed in glutamate solution overnight in the refrigerator. Unfortunately, such spontaneous voltage changes tend to cause contractions and hence loss of the electrode impalement. This behavior, which makes experiments of this type nearly impossible, disappears on further soaking. Eventually, the membrane potential goes to $\sim$ -30 mv and is quite stable; the contractile machinery is inactivated and the membrane resistance is high. Hence, measurements can frequently be made on the same cell for periods of hours.

NON-ZERO BICARBONATE ION PERMEABILITY

Fig. 3 shows the effects of sudden changes in P_{CO_2} and HCO$_3^-$ concentration on the V_m and R_c of a fiber previously soaked in glutamate solution for several hours. The upper line shows V_m at moderate gain. The lower trace is a capacity coupled, high gain version of the upper trace and thus shows R_c more clearly. At the start of the record in Fig. 3, the potential was -48 mv. The muscle had been perfused with a solution of composition [NaHCO$_3$] $= 115$ mM, [K$^+$ glutamate] $= 2.5$ mM, [Ca^{++} glutamate] $= 2.0$ mM for several minutes prior to the start of the record. The solution was equilibrated with 10% CO$_2$, and pH was 7.64 as indicated by the numbers below HCO$_3^-$ in the figure. Some (or most) of the calcium was precipitated as CaCO$_3$ at this pH.

At the first vertical line, the perfusate was changed to a solution of the same composition but equilibrated with 25% CO$_2$ (pH $= 7.24$). This change in solution caused a small but distinct depolarization and a fall in membrane resistance. The sudden jump up and down in V_m shortly after the solution change is attributed to transitions, induced by the sinusoidal current, between two steady states of the type shown in the bottom line of Fig. 2. The depolarization caused by the solution change cannot be attributed to changes in perfusate [H$^+$] or [HCO$_3^-$] because these changes were negligibly small. Hence, the depolarization must be attributed to some effect of the 2.5 fold increase in P_{CO_2}. The obvious and very likely correct explanation is that the depolarization is due to the exit of HCO$_3^-$ produced by the titration of intracellular buffers with CO$_2$.

Succeeding portions of the record show that the changes are reversible

18*

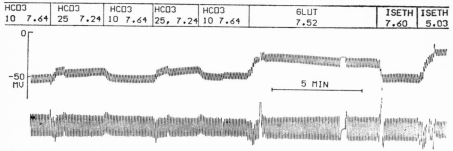

Fig. 3. Effects of changes in P_{CO_2} and pH on transmembrane potentials and characteristic resistance of a muscle fiber. Upper trace, transmembrane potential, lower trace, amplified a. c. coupled version of upper trace to accentuate R_c changes. HCO_3 10 7.64 means that $[HCO_3^-] = 115$ mM in bathing solution, was equilibrated with 10% CO_2 and had a pH of 7.64. HCO_3^- 25 7.24 is the same composition but equilibrated with 25% CO_2. Other abbreviations have same meaning as in Fig. 1. All solutions also contained [K glutamate] $= 2.5$ mM, [Ca glutamate] $= 2.0$ mM. The isethionate and glutamate solutions also had [Tris glutamate] $= 5.0$ mM. See text.

and reproducible except that the voltage and resistance are slowly declining probably because of a slow increase in internal $[HCO_3^-]$. Mainwood (1966) found that CO_2 depolarizes muscles bathed in solutions in which most of the ions are replaced by sucrose. He interprets his results in the same way: an efflux of HCO_3^-. However, he found no hyperpolarization in response to an increase in $[HCO_3^-]$ of the perfusate (see below). He did not measure membrane resistance.

The right-hand section of the record shows that changing the bathing solution to glutamate produces the transient depolarization and rise in R_c characteristic of changing from a more to a less permeable anion. Thus, this record clearly establishes that frog muscle cell membrane is permeable to HCO_3^- in the ionized form. This conclusion is difficult to establish by any other experimental procedure.

Unfortunately, it is difficult to calculate P_{HCO_3}, the membrane's permeability to HCO_3^- because $[HCO_3^-]$ inside cells is unknown and because of the presence of transitions in most of the records.

HIGH HYDROGEN ION PERMEABILITY

Woodbury (1965) and Woodbury *et al.* (1968) estimated that H^+ are about 100 times more permeant than K^+. This extremely high permeability of the membrane to H^+ is confirmed by the results of the two right-hand solution changes shown in Fig. 3. Isethionate is used as an anion because about 10 per cent of glutamate is un-ionized at pH = 5.03 ($pK_2 \simeq 4.00$ for glutamate). It can be seen that a decrease in pH from 7.60 to 5.03 produces a large depolarization and a fall in membrane resistance. Even taking account of the probable presence of a transition between two steady-states, the depolarization produced by a decrease of pH from 7.60 to 5.03 (increase of $[H^+]$ from 0.025 to 10 μM) is about 10 mv. Unfortunately, this data is insufficient by itself to estimate the permeability of the membrane to H^+, both because of transitions and lack of knowledge of the driving forces and permeabilities of the other ions carrying current through the membrane (primarily K^+ and Na^+) in these circumstances. It is clear, however, that P_H, the H^+ permeability of the membrane, is high since 10 μM H^+ is roughly equivalent to an increase in internal $[HCO_3^-]$ of several millimoles/liter, indicating that P_H/P_{HCO_3} is of the order of several hundred to a thousand.

This series of experiments established the need of comparing the action of H^+ and HCO_3^- on V_m and R_c with the same effects of Cl^- to allow estimation of the permeability ratios P_H/P_{Cl} and P_{HCO_3}/P_{Cl}.

ESTIMATES OF P_H AND P_{HCO_3}

Fig. 4 shows the results of initial attempts to estimate P_H/P_{Cl} and P_{HCO_3}/P_{Cl}. The lower trace in each strip shows the direct voltage changes and the upper trace the amplified, a.c. coupled version of the lower trace to emphasize the R_c changes. The upper strip shows results from one cell and the lower two strips another cell from the same muscle.

When the bathing solution was changed from glutamate, pH = 7.38 to glutamate, pH = 5.79 (first change, upper strip), there was a distinct depolarization and fall in R_c attributable to the increased $[H^+]$. This depolarization was completely reversed when the pH was returned to 7.38.

The next change from 115 mM glutamate, pH = 7.38 to a solution containing 114 mM glutamate and 1 mM HCO_3^- equilibrated with 10% CO_2, pH = 6.75 (labelled BI 1 10) produced a slight depolarization attributable both to the fall in external pH and the increase in internal $[HCO_3^-]$. However, a further increase in the CO_2 from 10 to 100 per cent, keeping $[HCO_3^-]$ = 1, reduced the pH to 5.80 and produced a much larger depolarization. The contribution of internal $[HCO_3^-]$ can be estimated from the difference in

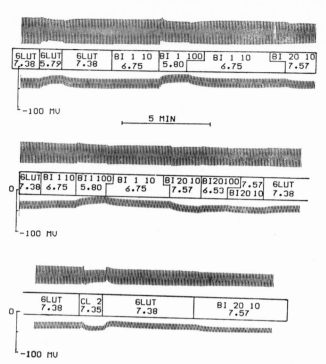

Fig. 4. Effects of changes in external pH and [HCO₃] on V_m and R_c of skeletal muscle cells. Upper strip is from one cell, lower two strips from another cell in the same muscle. Lower trace recording in each strip, transmembrane potential, upper recording, a. c. coupled, amplified version of lower recording. BI 1 10 6.75 means [HCO₃] = 1 mM, [glutamate] = 114 mM, equilibrated with 10% CO_2, pH = 6.75. BI 1 100 5.80, same solution equilibrated with 100 % CO_2, pH = 5.80 BI 20 10 7.57 means [HCO₃] = 20 mM, [glutamate] = 95 mM, pH = 7.57 equilibrated with 10% CO_2. BI 20 100 6.53, same solution but equilibrated with 100% CO_2, pH = 6.53. All solutions also contained [K glutamate] = 2.5 mM; [Ca glutamate] = 2.0 mM. The glutamate and glutamate-chloride solutions also had [Tris glutamate] = 5.0 mM. See text.

depolarizations produced by the high P_{CO_2} and zero P_{CO_2} solutions at pH = 5.79. The glutamate solution produced an 8 mv depolarization and the high P_{CO_2} solution a 12 mv depolarization. Still, P_{HCO_3} is difficult to estimate since [HCO₃]ᵢ is unknown.

The hyperpolarizing effect of raising external [HCO₃], keeping internal [HCO₃] constant (constant P_{CO_2}), is shown by the last change top strip,

Fig. 4, where the [HCO$_3^-$] was increased from 1 to 20 mM and pH from 6.75 to 7.57 with CO$_2$ kept constant at 10 per cent (BI 20 10 7.57). There is a hyperpolarization of 6 mv and a slight fall in R$_c$. Nearly all this change is attributed to the increase in external HCO$_3^-$ because pH $=$ 6.75 does not appreciably depolarize compared with pH $=$ 7.57 and P$_{CO_2}$ was kept constant.

Unfortunately this cell deteriorated before the effects of a low [Cl$^-$] could be measured.

The lower two strips in Fig. 4 show much the same type of results as in the upper strip. However, in this cell a "calibration" was obtained by exposing the muscle to 2 mM Cl$^-$ (first change in solution, bottom strip). The resulting hyperpolarization, fall in resistance, and rapid rate of equilibration are all indicative of the high Cl$^-$ permeability of the membrane. Unfortunately the simplest, accurate way to estimate P$_H$/P$_{Cl}$ and P$_{HCO_3}$/P$_{Cl}$ from this type of procedure is to wait for the internal concentrations to come into equilibrium with the new external concentrations. This would permit an accurate comparison of estimates of permeability ratios from changes in V$_m$ with estimates from the changes in R$_c$. The relationship between ion permeabilities (estimated from V$_m$) and conductances (from R$_c$) depends on concentrations, voltages and the assumptions made in the underlying theory. All these things could probably be estimated from careful analysis of transients of the type shown in Fig. 4. However, the same amount of time invested in experiments of better design would likely lead to results of higher accuracy and more definite interpretation.

Nevertheless, fair estimates of P$_H$/P$_{Cl}$ and P$_{HCO_3}$/P$_{Cl}$ can be made from Fig. 4. Thus, an increase of [HCO$_3^-$] from 1 to 20 mM produces about the same size hyperpolarization as an increase of Cl$^-$ from 0 to 2 mM. V$_m$ is about the same in the two cases; hence, the relation P$_{HCO_3} \triangle$[HCO$_3^-$]$_o \simeq$ P$_{Cl}\triangle$[Cl$^-$]$_o$ holds approximately. Thus P$_{HCO_3}$/P$_{Cl} \simeq \triangle$[Cl$^-$]$_o/\triangle$[HCO$_3^-$]$_o =$ 2/19 $\simeq$ 0.1.

The same type of argument can be used to estimate P$_H$/P$_{Cl}$ but in this case the effects of transmembrane potential do not cancel out. The size of the depolarization produced by reducing pH to 5.8 is about equal to the size of the hyperpolarization produced by 2 mM Cl$^-$. In this case, the appropriate approximation is P$_H\triangle$[H$^+$]$_o$e$^{-FV_m/RT} \simeq$ P$_{Cl}\triangle$[Cl$^-$]. This gives P$_H$/P$_{Cl} \simeq \triangle$[Cl$^-$]$_o/\triangle$[H$^+$]$_o$e$^{-FV_m/RT} \simeq$ 500.

DISCUSSION

H^+ Permeation

The value of P_H/P_{Cl} obtained here is several times larger than the value $P_H/P_K \simeq 100$ reported by Woodbury et al. (1968) and that calculated from the data of Gilbert & Lowenberg (1964) by Woodbury (1965). However, the ratio P_K/P_{Cl} must be known in order to make a comparison. K^+ permeability depends markedly on the direction of current flow (Hodgkin & Horowicz 1959b). $P_K \geq P_{Cl}$ for inward currents and $P_K < P_{Cl}$ for outward currents. In the experiments of Woodbury et al. (1968), V_m was near V_K so $P_{Cl} \simeq P_K$. Hence, the present result for P_H/P_{Cl} is about five times greater than the previous ones. The uncertainties are so large that the two results cannot be regarded as contradictory. However, the higher value obtained here for P_H/P_{Cl} may be a result of the greater sensitivity of the method and consequently smaller value of $[H^+]$ necessary to produce a detectable change.

The extremely high relative permeability of H^+ poses the question of what ion channels the H^+ use in crossing the membrane. No insight is presently available on this question. The current-voltage relations and other properties of H^+ penetration through membranes must be measured to shed light on this problem. Woodbury et al. (1968) infer that the H^+ do not use the anomalous K^+ channel but this is not proven.

HCO_3^- Permeation

Although Mainwood's (1966) data are a strong indication that HCO_3^- can penetrate the membrane, to the best of my knowledge, this paper presents the first clear, unequivocal evidence that P_{HCO_3} is appreciable and the first estimate of P_{HCO_3}/P_{Cl}. The main lines of evidence are that (1) an increase in P_{CO_2} with $[HCO_3^-]$ fixed causes the depolarization and fall in R_c expected from an increase in internal $[HCO_3^-]$ and (2) an increase in $[HCO_3^-]_o$ hyperpolarizes the membrane and decreases R_c.

An important question is whether or not HCO_3^- ions traverse Cl^- channels. An experiment was designed to test this hypothesis using the important findings of Hutter & Warner (1966) that P_{Cl} depends sensitively on external pH. A pH of 5 reduces P_{Cl} to near zero. However, the experiment was a failure partly because of the unavoidable difficulty that low pH's are incompatible with high HCO_3^- concentrations unless hyperbaric chambers are available and partly because the P_{Cl} of the one cell successfully impaled in this experiment showed little sensitivity to pH in the range 6.2 to 7.4. However, *a priori* the most likely possibility is that bicarbonate ions do use chloride ion channels.

Active Transport of H$^+$/HCO$_3^-$

The finding that $P_{HCO_3} \simeq 0.1\ P_{Cl}$ firmly establishes the need for an active transport process for H$^+$ and/or HCO$_3^-$ ions in muscle cells, since it is also well-established that H$^+$ and HCO$_3^-$ are not equilibrated with the trans-membrane voltage.

The metabolic cost of the H$^+$/HCO$_3^-$ transport system can be roughly esti-mated from the data given here for P_H and P_{HCO_3} and data in the literature for [H$^+$]$_i$ and [HCO$_3^-$]$_i$. Despite the high P_H, normal internal and external H$^+$ concentrations are so low that the H$^+$ flux is negligible ($\simeq 0.1 \times 10^{-12}$ moles/cm^2-sec). However, the metabolic cost of HCO$_3^-$ transport is appreciable. The net passive efflux of HCO$_3^-$ calculated from the Goldman equation, $P_{HCO_3} = 0.1\ P_{Cl}$ and $P_{Cl} = 4 \times 10^{-6}$ cm/sec (Hodgkin & Horowicz 1959b) is $M_{HCO} = 10 \times 10^{-12}$ moles/cm^2-sec. This is 5 times the passive Na$^+$ influx of 2×10^{-12} moles/cm^2-sec (Hodgkin & Horowicz 1959a). The electrochemical gradient on Na$^+$ is $V_m - V_{Na} = -160$ mv while that on HCO$_3^-$ is only $V_m - V_{HCO_3} = -90-(-30) = -60$ mv. Hence the energy cost of transporting out 5 times as much HCO$_3^-$ as Na per unit time is nearly twice that of the Na$^+$ transport cost. This value is so large that it casts doubt on the applicability of the estimated P_{HCO_3} value to the normal muscle cell.

The existence of a H$^+$/HCO$_3^-$ pump has long been assumed but it has hitherto been difficult to specify its rate even to an order-of-magnitude. The numbers given here do permit an order-of-magnitude calculation–if the measurements are applicable to normal muscle. There is no evidence on the nature of the pump but to me the most attractive possibility is that H$^+$ use the outward limb of the Na$^+$–K$^+$ exchange pump (Woodbury 1965). If HCO$_3^-$ flux is as large as calculated, this would require that out of six ions using the outward limb of the Na$^+$ pump five would be H$^+$ and one would be a Na$^+$. The affinities of H$^+$ (A_H) and Na$^+$ (A_{Na}) for the Na$^+$-carrier are given approxi-mately by the relation $A_H[H^+]_i = 5A_{Na}[Na^+]_i$ whence $A_H/A_{Na} = 5[Na^+]_i/[H^+]_i = 5 \times 0.120$ M/10^{-7} M $= 6 \times 10^6$. If this is true the Na$^+$-carrier should be called a H$^+$-carrier. Such an affinity ratio is reasonable, the carrier would simply be a weak acid with some affinity for Na^+ and much less for K^+. Keynes (1963) has data showing that a decrease in pH_i (produced by increasing P_{CO_2}) changes the kinetics of Na transport from third order to second order. This suggests that H^+ do compete with Na^+ for carrier sites but only to the extent of 1 H^+ per 2 Na^+ at normal pH_i's. Hence, it would be interesting to know the pH sensitivity of the transport ATP-ase system, particularly the effects of pH on the K_m of activation of ATP-ase by Na^+. All in all, the estimate of $P_{HCO_3} \simeq 0.1\ P_{Cl}$ seems too high; a more reasonable value is $P_{HCO_3} \simeq 0.02\ P_{Cl}$ or smaller. The resolution of this question must await further experimentation.

SUMMARY

(1) The transmembrane voltage, V_m, and membrane characteristic resistance, R_c, of frog skeletal muscle cells were measured by means of two intracellular electrodes. Cl^- was replaced by relatively impermeant glutamate ions.

(2) The effects on V_m and R_c of changes in pH, P_{CO_2} and $[HCO_3^-]$ in the solution bathing the muscle were measured.

(3) These measurements strongly indicate that HCO_3^- ions can penetrate the membrane and that H^+ ions are highly permeant. It is estimated that $P_{HCO_3} \simeq 0.1\ P_{Cl}$ and $P_H/P_{Cl} \simeq 500$.

(4) These estimates together with data from the literature permit the calculation that net H^+ influx is about 0.2×10^{-12} moles/cm²-sec and net passive HCO_3^- efflux is about 10×10^{-12} moles/cm²-sec, 5 times the passive Na^+ influx. The minimum energy cost of an equal and opposite active transport of HCO_3^- is about twice the minimum cost of active Na^+ transport. Hence this estimate of P_{HCO_3} is regarded as unreasonably high for normal cells.

(5) The permeable hydrogen ion
Is always in there a tryin'
   To enter the cell
   And thus make it swell:
If you don't pump it out, you're a dyin'.

REFERENCES

Adrian, R. H. & Freygang, W. H. (1962a) The potassium and chloride conductance of frog muscle membrane. *J. Physiol (Lond.) 163*, 61–103.

Adrian, R. H. & Freygang, W. H. (1962b) Potassium conductance of frog muscle membrane under controlled voltage. *J. Physiol (Lond.) 163*, 104–114.

Curtis, B. A. (1963) Some effects of Ca-free choline-Ringer solution on frog skeletal muscle. *J. Physiol (Lond.) 166*, 75–86.

Gilbert, D. L. & Lowenberg, W. E. (1964) Effect of pH on the resting membrane potential of frog sartorius muscle. *J. cell. comp. Physiol. 63*, 359–364.

Hodgkin, A. L. & Horowicz, P. (1959a) Movements of Na and K in single muscle fibres. *J. Physiol (Lond.) 145*, 405–432.

Hodgkin, A. L. & Horowicz, P. (1959b) The influence of potassium and chloride ions on the membrane potential of single muscle fibres. *J. Physiol (Lond.) 148*, 127–160.

Hutter, O. F. & Warner, A. E. (1967) The pH sensitivity of the chloride conductance of frog skeletal muscle. *J. Physiol (Lond.) 189*, 403–425.

Keynes, R. D. (1963) Dependence of the sodium efflux from frog muscle on internal sodium concentration and internal pH. *J. Physiol (Lond.) 166*, 16P–17P.

Mainwood, G. W. (1966) Some electrical characteristics of sucrose-washed frog sartorius muscle. *Canad. J. Physiol. Pharmacol. 44*, 663–674.

Woodbury, J. W. (1965) Regulation of pH. In *Physiology and Biophysics*, ed. Ruch, T. C. & Patton, H. D., Chapter 46. W. B. Saunders Co., Philadelphia.

Woodbury, J. W., White, S. H. & Weakly, J. N. (1968) High membrane H$^+$ permeability of frog skeletal muscle. *Abstracts, XXIV International Congress of Physiological Sciences*, p. 472.

DISCUSSION

J. W. WOODBURY

I would like to start the discussion by postulating a crude model of CSF secretion. The driving force for secretion is a standard Na^+–for–K^+ exchange pump in the membranes of choroid plexus cells facing the CSF but not in the membranes facing the blood. I believe that by properly choosing the passive permeability characteristics of the two membranes a fluid of the right composition would be produced by operation of the Na^+ pump. In particular, the possible affinity of H^+ for the Na^+ pump mentioned in my paper probably plays an important role in regulation (see discussion on last day for figure and a detailed explanation of this model).

ORKAND

What level of pump activity is required to maintain the hydrogen ion out of electrochemical equilibrium?

J. W. WOODBURY

The hydrogen ion concentration in the cell is so low (10^{-7} Mol/liter) that the leakage flux of hydrogen ions is negligibly small in normal conditions. Therefore the metabolic cost of pumping H^+ is small. However, the metabolic cost of pumping bicarbonate is higher because its concentration is proportionately higher than the permeability is lower.

SIESJÖ

Many of us working with intracellular pH have been deceived for a number of years, looking at the cell as a rather closed box to exchanges of hydrogen and bicarbonate ions. I think this is partly due to the papers published by Caldwell (1958) and Conway (1957) where they tried to calculate the time necessary to get a certain change in the intracellular pH after a step change in the extracellular fluid. They didn't know the membrane permeability to H^+ and used the value for K^+. This gave equilibration times which were exceedingly long. I am delighted to hear that there is such an appreciable

Caldwell, P. (1958) Studies on the internal pH of large muscle and nerve fibres. J. Physiol. (Lond.) 142, 22–62.
Conway, E. J. (1957) Nature and significance of concentration relations of potassium and sodium ions in skeletal muscle. Physiol. Rev. 37, 84–132.

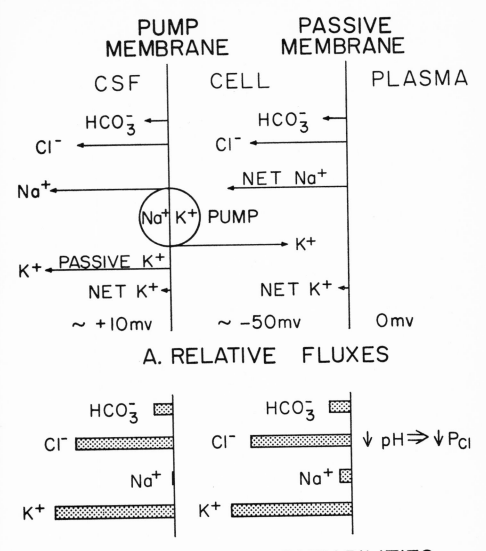

Fig. 1. Model of CSF secretion. *A.* Lengths of arrows indicate relative sizes of ion fluxes through membranes. Water flux is too large to show. Net K⁺ flux arrow is exaggerated in length. *B.* Relative ion permeabilities. Na⁺ permeability of pump membrane is near zero. Water permeability is too large to show.

permeability to hydrogen and bicarbonate ions, and that we really need a pump to get the H$^+$ ions out.

J. W. WOODBURY

I agree. Your comment reminds me that people have been using frog sartorius muscles for a hundred years as a standard preparation. Ever since Sidney Ringer they have been using phosphate buffered Ringer with no bicarbonate in it, and no one seems to have wondered why the muscle is functional since there should be a dreadful respiratory alkalosis in cells bathed in a solution with zero Pco$_2$ and if HCO$_3^-$ is impermeable. I think the muscle is functional because much of the bicarbonate leaks out and keeps the muscle in pretty good shape.

DAVSON

I suppose you have a permeability to hydroxyl ions which is undistinguishable from that to hydrogen ions. Jacobs studied the permeability of the red cell to hydrogen ions or hydroxyl ions. He concluded that it was really an exchange of hydroxyl ions rather than hydrogen ions.

J. W. WOODBURY

I used quite acid pH's so the hydroxyl ion concentration was low. I seriously doubt if hydroxyl fluxes are important in these circumstances.

DAVSON

It is not a matter of concentration. I can't see that you can distinguish between hydrogen ions going one way or hydroxyl ions going the other way.

J. W. WOODBURY

I believe that the enormously high permeability has to be to hydrogen ions. I don't think anything as large as hydroxyl ions could do that. Besides at pH = 5, pOH = 9 and so the permeability to OH$^-$ would have to be at least $500 \times 10^4 \, P_{Cl} = 5 \times 10^6 \, P_{Cl}$. For a 70 Å membrane this would give a diffusion constant greater than in water.

DAVSON

In the red cell it is definitely hydroxyl ions. So it has nothing to do with size at all.

SEVERINGHAUS

Which are bigger, hydrogen ions or hydroxyl ions?

J. W. WOODBURY

I don't know. The mobility of H^+ in water is greater than of OH^- indicating that H^+ is smaller.

SEVERINGHAUS

Isn't it H_3O^+ which is moving?

J. W. WOODBURY

I don't know. Nobody knows. The standard picture is for H_3O^+. The high permeability to hydrogen ion raises the question just where the H^+ go through the membrane. The P_H is so large that it is unlikely that H^+ just go through regular ion channels. Perhaps the H^+ go through the lipid parts of the membrane also. P_H, however, is not as high as water permeability, so H^+ may go through with water.

ORKAND

It seems to me that the fluxes of hydrogen and bicarbonate ions will be swamped under normal conditions by changes in chloride and potassium permeability.

J. W. WOODBURY

They will produce little or no effect on the voltage but that doesn't mean that the fluxes of hydrogen and bicarbonate ions aren't there.

ORKAND

Are the changes in chloride and potassium permeability produced by changes in hydrogen ion concentration greater than the changes in the hydrogen ion permeability itself?

J. W. WOODBURY

No. The changes observed can't be explained by such changes anyway. However, if a low pH increases P_{Na} then a depolarization would also be produced. In one not very satisfactory control experiment, the depolarization due to lowering pH was still observed with all Na^+ replaced by Tris. I also did one experiment designed to see if HCO_3^- uses Cl^- channels but it was a failure.

SØRENSEN

After you have obtained these data on hydrogen ion permeability, would you then be willing to accept the suggestion that the CSF-blood potential could be a hydrogen ion diffusion potential. In order to explain it this way we would have to assume an exceedingly high permeability to hydrogen ions of the particular membrane involved. Do you think it is possible?

J. W. WOODBURY

That is implied by the model I drew. It assumes a pump on the CSF side and a passively permeable membrane on the blood side, which carries roughly equal fluxes of hydrogen ions and potassium ions. This means that the membranes would have to be fantastically permeable to hydrogen ions. The reason is because of the 30 mV change per decade for H^+ and the 15 mV per decade change for K^+.

SIESJÖ

You mentioned that the permeability to lactate was relatively low. Would you dare to explain how lactate is coming out from the cell?

J. W. WOODBURY

I don't know. When I found a high bicarbonate permeability I expected an equally high lactate permeability. The experiment in which I tried to measure lactate permeability wasn't very good. But it was clear that lactate is quite a bit less permeable than bicarbonate.

USSING

I would propose that it is going as the free acid because carbonic acid is going much faster than bicarbonate.

J. W. WOODBURY

If the internal pH is somewhere around 7, then the fraction of lactic acid in form of lactic acid is 1/2000 of the lactate concentration.

WADDELL

That is not as important as the difference in solubilities of the membrane to the two species.

SEVERINGHAUS

R. Mitchell in our laboratory recently had a microelectrode in several respiratory neurones while changing P_{CO_2}. He found no depolarization.

J. W. WOODBURY

That indicates to me that the cell is probably not very permeable to bicarbonate. The changes I found were small, and I designed the experiment to maximize them; under ordinary circumstances you would never see them. So, if the neuron, like muscle, has a reasonably high chloride permeability there would probably be no detectable change in potential even if the membrane is somewhat permeable to HCO_3^-.

ORKAND

How did he identify a respiratory neuron?

SEVERINGHAUS

It was depolarizing in synchrony with inspiration, but it was not a chemoreceptor cell.

SIESJÖ

If the sodium pump is pumping hydrogen ions in a hypercapnic situation, wouldn't that affect the sodium and potassium concentrations in the cell?

J. W. WOODBURY

Yes. The size of the effect will depend on the relative sizes of active Na^+ and H^+ fluxes. If the $P_{HCO_3^-}$ is actually as large as $0.1 \times P_{Cl}$ in normal cells, which I seriously doubt, then there must be separate H^+ and Na^+ pumps. The cell must closely regulate both its H^+ and Na^+ concentrations. The two can be combined only if the maximum required transport of one ion is quite a bit less than the ordinary transport of the other.

The Effect of Acetazolamide on HCO_3^- and Cl^- Uptake into Cerebrospinal Fluid of Cat and Dogfish

Thomas H. Maren

The role of carbonic anhydrase in cerebrospinal fluid (CSF) secretion has not been worked out in satisfactory physiological or chemical detail, as for example in kidney or pancreas. The effects of acetazolamide and the presence of carbonic anhydrase in choroid plexus and glia strongly suggest an important role for the enzyme.

The facts known to date have been reviewed in some detail (Maren 1967) and may be summarized as follows:

(1) There is carbonic anhydrase in choroid plexus and glia, but probably not in neurones. From these and other observations it is maintained that this enzyme has solely a secretory role in brain.

(2) Acetazolamide, which specifically inhibits this enzyme (see also data given below), reduces CSF formation rate.

(3) Acetozolamide reduces the transfer of sodium from plasma to CSF.

(4) Acetazolamide reduces or abolishes the chloride excess in CSF, which is perhaps the most constant and typical chemical characteristic of CSF in vertebrates.

Secretory systems through the body dependent upon carbonic anhydrase can be described in a general way as cellular or enzymic mechanisms which separate water to H^+ and HO^- ions, which are polarized at opposite sides of the cell. In some cases, the secretory component is H^+ (kidney, stomach); in others (pancreas, aqueous humor) it is OH^-, which is buffered by CO_2 to form HCO_3^-. The opposite ion passes into the blood and is buffered. Fig. 1

Department of Pharmacology and Therapeutics, University of Florida College of Medicine, Gainesville, Florida 32601, USA.

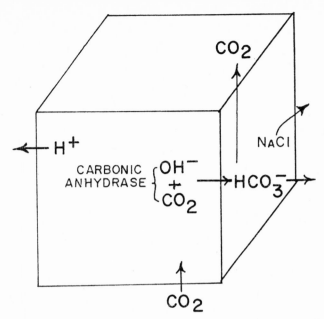

Fig. 1. Dissociation of water in secretory cells, with OH^- buffering by CO_2.

shows this general concept. The role of carbonic anhydrase is simply the acceleration of rate of buffering of OH^- by CO_2. Fig. 1 shows also that Cl^- ion, in certain situations, is involved in carbonic anhydrase activity, associated either with H^+ secretion (stomach) or HCO_3^- formation (aqueous humor).

The data and conclusions of items 1–4 above, however, do not answer the question implicit in Fig. 1, with respect to CSF: How is the choroid plexus (and presumably glia) oriented in respect to its secretion? Is the primary fluid derived from OH^- or from H^+ secretion? Since the CSF is in most (but not all) species slightly acid, it appeared reasonable to suggest that the choroid plexus, like stomach and kidney, produces H^+ on its luminal side (Maren 1967). The present experiments were designed to test this question; in addition we returned to the question of chloride transport.

METHODS

Cats and dogfish (*S. acanthias*) were given intravenous injections of $NaHC^{14}O_3$ or $NaCl^{36}$, and the passage of isotope into the CSF was studied.

The partition of isotope between CO_2 gas and HCO_3^- was done by application of the pH to the total counts, in the usual Henderson-Hasselbalch relation.

Details of the experiments in cats are given in the paper by Maren & Broder (1970), from which these data are taken. These may be summarized as follows: Cats were anesthetized with pentobarbital and artificially ventilated so that normal acid-base balance was maintained. Ventriculo-cisternal perfusion was done at the rate of 123 μl/min. Isotope was injected at 0 time, and the concentration of total label in plasma 1½ minutes later was set at 100. All counts in plasma and CSF are recorded relative to this.

In *S. acanthias,* two different protocols were used for the $NaHC^{14}O_3$ study (Maren *et al.* 1970). (1) Fish were placed in a "divided box" and arranged so that gills were continuously perfused with sea water (Maren *et al.* 1968) while CSF was sampled at intervals through a small opening in the skull. Plasma was obtained from a catheter in the dorsal aorta. (2) Fish were allowed to swim freely in 25 gallons of fresh sea water. Indwelling catheters permitted blood sampling at intervals. CSF was sampled 6 minutes after injection of 20–80 μcuries of isotope. Plasma concentration of total label in the untreated (control) animals 3 minutes after isotope injection was set as 100, in both protocols.

Chloride transport into CSF of *S. acanthias* was so slow that neither of the above protocols was satisfactory. In this case 20 μcuries of label was injected and fish were allowed to swim in live cars in the sea. The plasma concentration of label at 12 minutes in controls are assigned the value of 100.

Carbonic anhydrase was inhibited by intravenous injection of 30 mg/kg (fish) or 50 mg/kg (cat) of acetazolamide, as its sodium salt. The injection was made 30 minutes before zero time, when the isotope was given. The half-life of this drug in *S. acanthias* is 1–2 days (Maren 1962) and in the cat about 2 hours (Maren 1967). The doses given provide complete inhibition of enzyme throughout the body for the duration of the experiment.

RESULTS

1. *Effect of acetazolamide on CSF production*

(a) Cat. In the system used, acetazolamide reduced CSF formation rate from 25 μl/min to 14 μl/min (Maren & Broder 1970). Similar data as given by Oppelt *et al.* (1964).

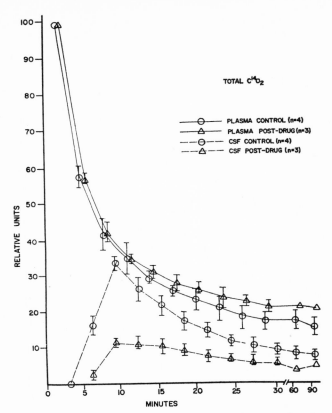

Fig. 2. Plasma and CSF perfusate levels of total $C^{14}O_2$ in normal and acetazolamide (50 mg/kg i.v.) treated cats. Drug injected at –30 minutes; isotope at zero time. Each point in the figure gives the relative count in the fluid ($\pm$S.E.M.) collected at that time. In the case of perfusate, the entire fluid was collected for the period preceeding the point noted, and the counts give the relative concentration in that total volume.

(b) Fish. Earlier work by Oppelt *et al.* (1966) showed that acetazolamide decreased CSF production in *S. acanthias* by about 30 per cent.

2. *Effect of acetazolamide on CO_2 uptake into CSF*

(a) Cat. Fig. 2 shows that acetazolamide reduces the uptake of total $C^{14}O_2$ from plasma to CSF. It will be noted that in control animals, the label in CSF reached equilibrium with that in plasma in 9 minutes, agreeing precisely with data of Coxon & Swanson (1965) who did a similar experiment but analyzed CSF rather than perfusate. The initial (first 10 minutes) decay of label from plasma represents distribution; from 10 to 25 minutes the two-fold decay agrees approximately with the relation between oxidative metabolism and CO_2 store in body fluids (excluding bone) in which this store is turned over every ½ hour. The slower rate thereafter may represent incorporation of label into various metabolites; data from this period are not used.

The rates of uptake in the 3 periods between 9–18 minutes average 9 units per minute for control cats; in the same interval the inhibited series yielded a rate of 3.6 units per minute. It is important to note that 9 minutes is adequate time for injected $HC^{14}O_3$ to equilibrate fully with $C^{14}O_2$ in blood in the absence of carbonic anhydrase (Roughton 1935), and that acid-base equilibria and plasma levels of label were the same in treated and untreated cats.

The significant question is the nature of the change in CSF elicited by acetazolamide. Among the possibilities are: change in CSF-blood potential, change in HCO_3^- transport, and change in formation of HCO_3^- from CO_2. It will be shown that the data support the last of these.

No change in CSF potential from the normal value of $+5mV$ for this blood pH (Held et al. 1964) would be expected, since blood pH did not change following acetazolamide. Acetazolamide has never been reported to change potentials; a specific example will be given below for the fish (Hogben et al. 1960). It is also evident that HCO_3^- ion is not in electrochemical equilibrium between CSF/blood, since in this case the distribution ratio would be 1.21.

Transport of HCO_3^- from plasma to CSF as a factor in these experiments appeared unlikely, since it is known from a long series of experiments (see Davson 1967) that passage of HCO_3^- in this direction is a slow process. Thus hours or days are required before a metabolic alkalosis in plasma is manifest in CSF. However, a more rigorous proof is available, since it may be shown that the passage and hydration of CO_2 gas from plasma to CSF is entirely adequate to account for the data, and there is in fact no room for any additional process. This treatment of the data follows.

From the concentration of total $C^{14}O_2$ in plasma (in relative units) and the pH, the partition between HCO_3^-/CO_2 is readily estimated. Using the mean value between 11–18 minutes for total $C^{14}O_2$ of 30 and the pH of 7.4, the concentration of gaseous CO_2 is 1.5. This applies to both control and treated cats. Using this value of CO_2, we may test the idea if the reaction $CO_2 + OH^- \rightarrow HCO_3$ can account for the appearance of CO_2 label in the

CSF. In this scheme the gaseous CO_2 in the concentration noted is assumed equilibrated through all of body fluids, for it will be shown that the amount reaching the choroid plexus from blood is not enough to account for the concentration of HCO_3^- in CSF; the hydration must also take place in brain cells lining the CSF.

The hypothesis just suggested is most readily tested in terms of the uncatalyzed or inhibited reaction, for the rate constant of $CO_2 \rightarrow HCO_3^-$ (k_1) is known. The maximum rate of the uncatalyzed reaction *in vivo*, assuming perfect mixing and diffusion, is then

$$V_{unc} = k_1 (S)$$

where S is 1.5 units as explained above. k_1 for 37° from our own data is 2.7 min^{-1}, whence $V_{unc} = 4$ concentration units per min.[1] We may compare this to the observed rate of accumulation of HCO_3^- (95 per cent of total CO_2) in CSF, as shown in the bottom line of Fig. 2. This averages 3.4 units per min for the 11–18 minute interval considered. Since this transport rate is less than the lowest estimate of formation of HCO_3^- from CO_2, it would seem that the latter process is adequate to explain HCO_3^- accumulation in CSF, and HCO_3^- transfer as such need not be invoked.

Fig. 2 may be considered also in terms of the difference in rates between the uncatalyzed or fully inhibited (3.4 per min) and catalyzed or control (8.6 per min) accumulation of HCO_3^-. This suggests, quite independently of the foregoing argument comparing theoretical and actual uncatalyzed rates, that we are dealing with the formation of CSF HCO_3^- from plasma on tissue water CO_2. The closest parallel to this chemical situation is found in the pancreas (Rawls *et al.* 1963).

(b) Fish. Table 1 shows experiments in the free-swimming fish, indicating that at 6 minutes the CSF counts in controls were 58 per cent that in plasma, while in acetazolamide treated fish this value was 31 per cent. However, these results must also be considered in the light of the acid-base balance of the two groups; unlike in the cat (which was artificially ventilated) the two groups were not alike. Normal values for this species are pH = 7.6–

---

[1] Our k_1 is the lowest of the three literature values for this temperature. Pinsent *et al.* (1956) give 3.5 min^{-1}, and a recent value by Magid & Turbeck (1968) is inexplicably high at almost 9 min^{-1}. However the argument does not suffer if the theoretical V_{unc} exceeds the observed inhibited rate. In fact, we should expect this, if there are limitations imposed by mixing and diffusion and sampling at a distance from the source of secretion.

THOMAS H. MAREN

Table 1. Uptake of $C^{14}O_2$ from Plasma to CSF in *S. acanthias* Following
Injection of $NaH^{14}CO_3$ at 0 Time
Free Swimming Fish

| | Counts relative to control plasma at 3 min = 100 Concentration units | | CO₂ partition | | | Counts of gaseous CO_2 at 3 min |
	3 min	6 min	pH	CO₂ mM	pCO₂ mm Hg	
			Controls			
Plasma	100	64	7.30	5.3	6	6.7
CSF	–	37	–	7.5	–	–
			Acetazolamide at −30 min			
Plasma	297	168	7.15	6.9	13	27
CSF	–	52	–	11.3	–	–

n = 5 for each group.
Plasma chemistry (CO_2 partition) are means of 3 and 6 minute values. CSF based on 6 min value.

7.7, total CO_2 6–8 mM, pCO₂ 3–4 mm Hg. Controls showed a slight respiratory and metabolic acidosis, a common finding following capture, removal from the sea, and manipulation. Acetazolamide treated fish showed a large increase in the component of respiratory acidosis, as shown by retention of label and elevation of pCO₂. Thus the last column of Table 1, giving the counts of gaseous CO_2 in plasma at the mid-point of the experiment – the substrate for the proposed reaction as described above – shows a much higher value for inhibited than control animals. Despite this, the uptake of label in CSF relative to plasma in inhibited fish was about ½ that of controls. This point will be further quantified at the end of the section.

Table 2 shows a more complete series of experiments in the fish, now in the divided box so that sequential sampling of CSF is possible. It will be observed that the data are nearly identical to those of Table 1, an important point in showing that for this period of time the box does not compromise the experiments. It is evident from Table 2 that labelled CO_2 in plasma reaches equilibrium in CSF in 12 min, whether normal or inhibited. However, the 6 minute figures show (as in Table 1) a delay in uptake into CSF in the inhibited fish, the counts in control being 45 per cent, and in treated 32 per cent of plasma.

Table 3 shows an analysis of the experiments of Tables 1 and 2, based

Table 2. Uptake of $C^{14}O_2$ from Plasma to CSF in *S. acanthias* Following
Injection of $NaH^{14}CO_3$ at 0 Time
Box Experiments

	Counts relative to control plasma at 3 min = 100 Concentration units			pH	CO_2 partition CO_2 mM	pCO_2 mm Hg	Counts of gaseous CO_2 at 3 min
	3 min	6 min	12 min				
				Controls			
Plasma	100	60	41	7.27	5.2	7	6.8
CSF	12	27	38	–	9.2	–	–
				Acetazolamide at –30 min			
Plasma	255	136	94	7.12	6.4	12	24.3
CSF	20	44	89	–	10.4	–	–

n = 8 for each group
Plasma chemistry (CO_2 partition) are means of 3 and 6 minute values. CSF based on 6 min value.

on the main premise previously discussed, that plasma CO_2 is the source of CSF HCO_3^-. The rates are those for the first 6 minutes (columns 1 and 2 of Tables 1 and 2) and the substrate is the figure in the last column of these

Table 3. Rate Constant for Plasma $CO_2 \rightarrow$ CSF HCO_3^-, min^{-1}

$$k_{in} = \frac{\text{Rate of appearance of } HC^{14}O_3^- \text{ in CSF}}{\text{Conc. gaseous } C^{14}O_2 \text{ in plasma}}$$

	k_{in} min^{-1} Control	Inhibited	k_1 min^{-1}
S. acanthias free swim	$\frac{5.0}{6.7} = .74$	$\frac{4.2}{27} = .16$	
S. acanthias box	$\frac{3.5}{6.8} = .51$	$\frac{3.3}{24.3} = .14$	0.68 (14° C)
Cat	$\frac{8.6}{1.5} = 5.7$	$\frac{3.4}{1.5} = 2.3$	2.7 (37° C)

Gaseous CO_2 concentration is subtracted from total CO_2 counts in CSF to yield HCO_3^-. Note that fish and cat experiments cannot be directly compared in terms of rates and concentrations since all units used are relative, and the design of experiments are somewhat different. However, it would appear valid to compare the k_{in} data for the two species.
k_1 is the chemical hydration rate constant (Maren 1963).

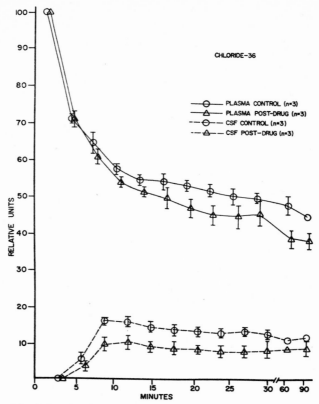

Fig. 3. As for Fig. 2, but for Cl^{36}.

tables. This yields a rate constant k_{in}, which may be compared with the chemical constant for the hydration reaction.[2] Data for cat, from Fig. 1, are included for comparison.

This treatment shows again that the accumulation of HCO_3^- in CSF can be satisfactorily accounted for by hydration of CO_2, in that the chemical $k_1 >$ inhibited or uncatalyzed k_{in}, and carbonic anhydrase causes a marked increase in the rate.

3. *Effect of acetazolamide on Cl uptake in CSF*

    (a) Cat. Fig. 3 shows that the appearance of labelled Cl^{36} in CSF perfusate

---

    [2] We use our figure for 14° C, of 0.68 min⁻¹. Pinsent's data (1956) yield 0.54 min⁻¹ and Magid's (1968) 0.90 min⁻¹, by extrapolation from surrounding temperatures.

Table 4. Uptake of $^{36}Cl^-$ From Plasma to CSF. Plasma Counts at 12 Minutes in Controls Set at 100.

| | Concentration units | | | | | | Cl⁻ conc. (mM) | |
	12 min	30 min	1 hr	2 hr	3 hr	6 hr*	0 time	3–6 hrs†
Controls								
Plasma (n = 6)	100	81	68	58	52	41	239	246
CSF (n)	4	10	–	14	20	39	–	263
	(2)	(1)		(2)	(1)	(6)		
Azetazolamide at –30 min								
Plasma (n = 6)	120	102	85	68	60	48	240	244
CSF (n)	6	12	–	23	34	31	–	253
	(2)	(1)		(1)	(1)	(6)	(n = 9)	

* The difference in plasma/CSF counts between control and treated fish at 6 hours is significant at the level of P between 0.05 and 0.1.

† The difference in CSF Cl⁻ concentration between control and treated fish is significant at $P < 0.05$.

is delayed about 2-fold by acetazolamide. These data do not yield the true time of Cl⁻ equilibration from plasma to CSF, since the rate of perfusion (123 μl/min) exceeds the rate of formation of fluid (25 μl/min) which in turn has about the same turnover time as sodium (Davson 1967) and presumably of chloride. Taking the volume of cat CSF as 5 ml, the rate constant for fluid formation is $\frac{25 \ \mu l/min}{5 \ ml} = 0.005$ min⁻¹, which may be compared to Davson's net value for sodium influx of 0.006 in dog and rabbit. The unidirectional flow of chloride may be roughly calculated from Fig. 3. At a plasma concentration of about 55 units, the uptake into CSF perfusate is about 6 units/min in the control, yielding a rate constant of about 0.1 min⁻¹. Inhibition reduces this to about 0.06 min⁻¹. These rates are about 2 per cent of the corresponding ones for HCO_3^- formation (Table 3). It is of interest that the influx or formation of Na^+, (from Davson 1967), Cl⁻, and fluid are all reduced to the same degree, 30–45 per cent, by acetazolamide. It is reasonable to postulate from these data that the effect of acetazolamide on fluid formation is secondary to the effect on the major ions, Na^+ and Cl⁻.

(b) Fish. Table 4 shows preliminary experiments in which $NaCl^{36}$ was injected into *S. acanthias,* and uptake of label into CSF was studied. It is evident that Cl^{36} decay in plasma is slow, and similar in treated and untreated

Table 5. Showing Carbonic Anhydrase in Choroid Plexus as Receptor for Sulfonamides

Choroid Plexus Enzyme Concentration μM	Choroid Plexus Drug Concentration, μM		
	Acetazolamide 5 mg/kg		Benzolamide 1 mg/kg
	48 hrs	144 hrs	4 hrs
6.6 ± 1.0	6.9	2.7	5.9 ± 1.1*

Maren 1967; *Broder & Oppelt 1969. Dog; Cat. Plasma levels of free drug $< 0.1 \mu$M.

fish. There appears to be a modest initial retention of isotope (20 per cent) in treated fish. Plasma decay of chloride in this species is dependent upon three routes of excretion: kidney, rectal gland and gill, very roughly in equal proportions (Burger 1962). There may be some dependency upon carbonic anhydrase in the latter two. The data on uptake into CSF is suggestive of an effect of acetazolamide at the 6 hour time. Similarly, the actual concentration of unlabelled Cl⁻ in CSF is decreased at this time, confirming our earlier experiments (Maren 1962). Access of Cl⁻ from plasma to CSF appears to have a half-time of about 3 hours in this species, not very different from Davson's data for sodium in the mammal. Half-time for turnover of CSF in *S.acanthias* is about 5 hours, based on formation of 5 μl/min (Oppelt et al. 1966) and volume of 2–3 ml. Work is in progress to quantify relations between Na⁺, Cl⁻, and fluid turnover in this species.

4. Carbonic anhydrase as the receptor for acetazolamide in choroid plexus

Table 5 shows experiments in which the molar concentration of carbonic anhydrase in choroid plexus is compared with the concentration of acetazolamide bound in the tissue. Details are given in the original publications; the principle is that after drug disappears from plasma and tissue water generally, the residue in tissues is specifically bound to enzyme. The appropriate time for such a measurement for actazolamide begins at about 12 hours. Table 5 also shows binding by another inhibitor, benzolamide, whose half-life from plasma is about 30 minutes, so that at 4 hours essentially all the drug left in the body must be that specifically bound. As for acetazolamide, the concentration of benzolamide in choroid plexus agreed well with that of enzyme.

A final point shown by Table 5 is the concentration of acetazolamide in choroid plexus at 144 hours after injection. This datum is taken from a decay curve of acetazolamide in choroid plexus, which runs parallel to those from red cells and kidney, and whose slope may be related to the dissociation constant of the complex between sulfonamide and carbonic anhydrase (Maren 1967).

These data indicate that within the limits of error of these measurements, carbonic anhydrase is the sole receptor for acetazolamide (and benzolamide) in choroid plexus. This will have relevance in consideration of the chloride effect of acetazolamide on CSF, since such an effect is not fully understood, on a cellular or molecular basis, or seen in all tissues, notably kidney.

DISCUSSION

There are two essential findings in this work: that CSF HCO_3^- is formed from plasma or tissue CO_2 at choroid plexus or glia under the influence of carbonic anhydrase, and that the same enzyme is involved in the transfer of Cl^- (and Na^+) from plasma to CSF. These findings have raised numerous questions, particularly at this Symposium, and some attempt will be made to answer these and to relate our findings to those of others.

1. *Effect of respiratory acidosis on CSF chemistry and formation*

An early experiment by Swanson & Rosengren (1962) is typical in showing that elevation of plasma pCO_2 drives CSF HCO_3^- above that of plasma. It is clear that chemically, CSF has little buffering capacity for CO_2, and thus the observed effect can only be due to $OH^- + CO_2$ *in vivo*. This is precisely the mechanism proposed here (Fig. 1). Secretory cells separate H^+ and OH^- from water; OH^- at the lumenal or CSF side reacts with CO_2 to yield CSF HCO_3^-, while H^+ passes into blood and is buffered. It is of interest that Ames (1965) had found that 10 % CO_2 increases CSF production rate. At this symposium Fencl has reviewed the literature showing the sensitivity of CSF HCO_3^- to plasma pCO_2, and the same effects were noted in the papers of Brown and Messeter.

Perhaps the most striking example of the effect of respiratory acidosis on CSF HCO_3^- comes from our own early experiments on *S. acanthias* which were not understood at the time. Carbonic anhydrase inhibition causes a very large respiratory acidosis in this species, with pCO_2 3x normal. This caused a 2x elevation in plasma HCO_3^-, but a 3x elevation in CSF HCO_3^-, so that CSF HCO_3^- was about 8mM higher than that of plasma (Maren

1962). Thus, even though enzyme was inhibited at choroid plexus, the excess substrate (CO_2) drove the uncatalyzed reaction to the abnormal HCO_3^- value in CSF. See also note added in proof in Conclusion, p. 309.

2. Homology to other systems for HCO_3^- accumulation

The present experiments are entirely analogous to those of Kinsey & Reddy on aqueous humor secretion (1959) which have now been analyzed in terms of uncatalyzed and catalyzed rates (Maren 1967). That case is particularly instructive, because the HCO_3^- accumulation and its inhibition by acetazolamide are more significant in the posterior chamber (close to the primary secretion) than in the anterior chamber, and show how the fluid in the latter chamber is relatively acid to the primary secretion, doubtless the effect of metabolites from lens and retina. It is felt that the same may be true of CSF. Ames (1964) did not directly measure HCO_3^- of primarily secreted fluid, but when he compared the anion deficit of cisternal with choroid plexus fluid, there was an excess of 7mM (presumed to be HCO_3^-) and 0.15 pH in the latter.

The pancreas is the most obvious example of an organ that makes HCO_3^- from plasma CO_2 and glandular OH^- secretion. Because of its relative ease to study, it has been used as a model of this type of chemical system (Maren 1967). Such systems are very widespread in both vertebrate and invertebrate physiology, and are generally found to be dependent upon carbonic anhydrase.

3. Chemical characteristics of CSF

All vertebrates thus far examined have Cl^- excess in CSF, which is reduced or abolished by acetazolamide. As will be noted below, this excess is not necessarily in electrochemical equilibrium with plasma. We shall return to the probable reason(s) for the acetazolamide effect on Cl^-; we now must discuss the acid-base characteristics of CSF. It is generally held that CSF is acid to arterial plasma, and mean values for most species usually show a gradient in this direction of about 0.05–0.1 unit, with a corresponding HCO_3^- gradient of 1–2mM (Davson 1967). In some vertebrates (goat) this gradient is greater; in others (cat) less or even reversed (Erulkar & Maren, 1961, Coxon & Swanson 1965); in most, such as man or dog, plasma and CSF are close enough so that only mean data can show the gradient, which is usually not statistically significant (Wistrand et al. 1961, Posner et al. 1965). In the dogfish, S. acanthias, where sampling is very close to the secretory source, the fluid is slightly alkaline as follows: plasma pH 7.56 $\pm$ 0.03 (n = 13); CSF pH 7.66 $\pm$ 0.01 (n = 10). Plasma total CO_2 7.96 $\pm$ 0.18mM (n = 47); CSF total CO_2 8.57 $\pm$ 0.21mM (n = 19) (Maren 1962). Oppelt et al. (1966 and personal communication) have reported that the bonnet, black tip and lemon shark have CSF total CO_2 up to 3x that of plasma. This may be due to great susceptibility of CSF CO_2, particularly in elasmobranch, to respiratory acidosis (see first section of discussion) but deserve further documentation.

In any case, it would seem unwise to consider primary CSF as an acidic secretion. It is likely that acidic brain metabolites, to varying degrees, alter the compostition of this poorly buffered fluid, to produce the acidity, in those cases where it is observed. That is strongly suggested by Ames' (1964) finding that 7mM of an anion (presumably HCO_3^-) is dissinated between the choroid plexus and cisterna magna. His calculated HCO_3^- value for primary CSF secretion is 25.6 mM, considerably higher than usual plasma HCO_3^- in the cat (Wallace & Hastings 1942; Erulkar & Maren 1961, Swanson & Rosengren 1962, Coxon & Swanson 1965) which is about 20mM.[3] If acid secretion were a primary event, our experiments would produce the opposite result to that seen; in such a case, as for kidney, inhibition of carbonic anhydrase would produce more, not less HCO_3^-.

4. Relation to observed potentials

In the mammal, the $+5mV$ potential in the ventricle implies a passive ratio for anions of 1.21. This is not obeyed for either HCO_3^- or Cl^- (Davson 1967). At this Symposium, Siesjö supported the idea that "transmembrane flux" of HCO_3^- is active. We would only substitute the term "formation of HCO_3^-". The greatly increased HCO_3^- concentration of CSF in hypercapnia described above cannot be ascribed to a change in potential, for in most experiments

---

[3] Unfortunately, Ames (1964) did not give his plasma HCO_3^-. Davson (1967) and his earlier work cited gives higher plasma HCO_3^- for cat than the four references given here. In the experiments of Fig. 2, the plasma HCO_3^- was about 18–20mM, in agreement with the references cited above.

(V. Fencl, this Symposium, Swanson & Rosengren 1962, Maren 1962) there is enough compensation to minimize pH change in plasma.

Finally, the dogfish, which has CSF chemistry very close to that of the mammal, has a *negative* potential of some 15mV which is unaffected by acetazolamide (Hogben *et al.* 1960, Patlak *et al.* 1966), and which does not appear to change with pH (Rall, comment on this paper).

These data support those of the present paper in showing that passage of Cl^- and HCO_3^- into CSF are active processes and processes independently of the potentials.

5. *Role of carbonic anhydrase in Cl^- transport*

Since carbonic anhydrase did not affect Cl^- excretion in kidney, attention was not focused on this aspect of its action until Durbin & Heinz (1958) showed that acetazolamide reduced the chloride potential of the stomach. Then it was shown that acetazolamide abolished nasal salt secretion in seabirds (Nechay *et al.* 1960) without any alteration in the pH of the secreted fluid. It has also been shown recently that acetazolamide reduces both Cl^- and HCO_3^- secretion into the aqueous humor of cats (Garg & Oppelt 1970).

The data are compatible with at least two mechanisms, which further experiments might clarify. The first is that rapid buffering of the cell by CO_2 has a permissive or activating role in the systems which transport Cl^-. This idea seemed to be supported by the changes that acid-base balance itself made on nasal gland secretion. Similar experiments by Oppelt *et al.* on CSF were not as conclusive, but suffer from the fact that only CSF production and not the chemistry was studied (1963). The second possibility is that carbonic anhydrase might be considered a transport protein for Cl^-. Chloride in physiologic concentrations has definite affinity to carbonic anhydrase (Roughton & Booth 1946) with a dissociation constant of about 45mM. Chloride interaction with carbonic anhydrase is further indicated by widening of its nuclear magnetic resonance band (Ward 1969). Finally, the 2 Angstrom resolution model of carbonic anhydrase based on X-ray crystallography (B. Strandberg & A. Gilays, personal communication) shows that there could be halide interaction at the active site.

It would seem possible to decide between these two alternatives by study of Cl^- transport into CSF under conditions of varied acid-base balance. If there are pronounced effects, it would seem to favor the first mechanism,

Table 6. Chloride and HCO_3^- Transfer by Carbonic Anhydrase.

Isotope Expts.	Cl^-	HCO_3^-
CSF		
Cat (Maren & Broder 1970)	+	+
Fish (Maren et al. 1970)	+	+
Aqueous		
Cat (Garg & Oppelt 1970)	+	
Rabbit (Kinsey & Reddy 1959)		+
Conc. & Flow Expts.		
Salt Gland – Bird (Nechay et al. 1960)	+	+
Pancreas (Rawls et al. 1963)	+	+
Kidney*	0	+†
Alkaline Gland (Maren et al. 1963)	0	+
Stomach*	+	0
Liver*	+†	0

+ means acetazolamide reduces output of the ion. 0 means no effect. See footnote†.

* Data reviewed in Maren (1967).

† In these cases, the drug effect is to increase output of the ion.

while it would seem less likely that such relatively small changes would affect an active site for Cl^- on the enzyme molecule.

Table 6 shows how Cl^- and HCO_3^- are affected by acetazolamide in the various organ systems. Although the salt gland appears largely involved with Cl^- (or Na^+) and the pancreas with HCO_3^-, analyses of the data (Nechay et al. 1960, Rawls et al. 1963) show that with the decrease in flow, the output of both anions is decreased. It is clear from the other entries in this table that this is not always the case, nor does it appear likely that the primary effect of acetazolamide could be on flow, with the anionsfollowing. The proportions of Cl^- and HCO_3^- in the aqueous and CSF make it almost certain that the effect reducing flow is secondary to that of reducing chloride. This is particularly obvious in the dogfish where CSF Cl^- is 260mM and HCO_3^- is 8mM. In the secreting pancreas, on the other hand, the pilot ion appears to be HCO_3^- (Rawls et al. 1963).

6. Limiting factors in HCO_3^- and Cl^- accumulation in CSF: site of entry

Table 3 shows that in the cat the (control) k_{in} for HCO_3^- (according to the equation given and assumptions made) is 5.7 min^{-1}. This is exceedingly rapid, being equivalent to a half time of about 7 seconds.[4] This approaches the time for the equivalent (but reverse) reaction in the lung, the latter being faster (about 1 second) since blood flow relative to organ size is greater for lung than for brain.

We may inquire what sets this rate constant of 5.7 min^{-1}, and find that this agrees quite precisely with the maximum figure set by delivery of blood to the brain divided by volume of CSF. This quotient is for cat, $\dfrac{30 \text{ ml/min}}{5 \text{ ml}}$ = 6 min^{-1}, and the same number is obtained for man. If we add to the denominator the volume of extra-cellular fluid, this rate constant is about half as large, but does not seriously distort the argument. The limitation clearly is not the catalytic rate, which is hundreds of times more rapid than 6 min^{-1}; Table 3 gives the uncatalyzed rate constant at 2.7 min^{-1}, and enzyme in tissues augments this some 100–10,000 fold, to nearly the rate of ionic reactions (Maren 1967).

The choroid plexus has about 0.1 per cent of the blood flow of the brain (Welch 1963) so that delivery of CO_2 from blood to CSF would be far less than required for the observed data. It thus appears that CO_2 must be hydrated to HCO_3^- and transferred to CSF in the tissues of the brain. The catalytic hydration almost certainly takes place in the glia (and choroid plexus) which contain high concentrations of carbonic anhydrase (Giacobini 1962). Diffusion does not appear to be limiting, probably because the perfusion system provides good mixing, but more significantly because the CSF volume is small compared to the surrounding brain.

In the dogfish, considerations are similar: precise calculations are limited by ignorance of brain blood flow. Cardiac output is 60 ml/min in this species (Robin et al. 1966), of which, from the weights of tissue (brain is only 0.25 per cent of body weight) and gill vasculature, we might guess that 1/20 goes to the brain. If the CSF volume is taken as 3 ml, the maximum rate constant for CSF passage would be about 1 min^{-1}, in reasonable agreement with Table 3.

---

[4] Note that this is the half-time for the overall hydration and transfer, not the half-time to equilibrium from total CO_2 in plasma to CSF. The latter figure requires that the denominator of the equation in Table 3 is total CO_2, a number 20x greater than gaseous CO_2. k then is 0.3 min^{-1} and the half-time about 2.3 min, corresponding to the way the data of Fig. 2 are plotted.

It is of much interest that this transfer constant 0.3 min^{-1}, agrees very closely with that for ethyl alcohol (Davson 1967), the most rapidly penetrating substance recorded.

It therefore appears that CO_2 is hydrated to HCO_3^- throughout the brain. It should be clear from previous sections that this demands a source of OH^-, and this appears to be a secretory role of choroid plexus and glia. The observed rates and effect of acetazolamide show that carbonic anhydrase must be involved. In the presence of the enzyme, blood flow to brain is the rate limiting step; but when enzyme is inhibited the hydration step itself is rate-limiting.

Chloride entry is very much slower than HCO_3^- (some 60 fold, as noted in section 3 above) but still could not be accounted for by choroid plexus activity, because of insufficient blood flow through this very small organ. Extrapolating from Welch's (1963) figure of 11 μl/min for choroid plexus blood flow in rabbit to 20 μl/min in the cat, we obtain $\dfrac{20 \ \mu l/min}{5 \ ml} = 0.004$ min^{-1} as the maximum rate constant of transfer, if only choroid plexus and CSF are involved.[5]

Our value for chloride was about 0.1 min^{-1} (section 3 above). It is likely that brain is involved in both the secretion and distribution of label, so that the true maximal figure is brain blood flow/CSF + ECF volume. This would yield a value of about 2 min^{-1}, much greater than the Cl^- transfer. It therefore seems likely that some Cl is secreted at non-choroidal sites, but that there is a distinct limitation on its passage, as with other charged substances.

7. Suggested roles for carbonic anhydrase in choroid plexus and glia

The data show that carbonic anhydrase in secretory elements of brain plays a role in both Cl^- and HCO_3^- accumulation in CSF, and possibly in brain extra-cellular water. Different functions are visualized for the two anions, as follows:

Chloride appears involved in the secretion of fluid, linked of course to sodium. The effect of acetazolamide in reducing CSF formation is almost certainly linked to these major ions. Carbonic anhydrase might be considered a receptor for Cl^-; or NaCl transport is affected by subtle intracellular shifts in CO_2 equilibria, mediated by the enzyme.

---

[5] However, note that this is about the same as the rate constant for Na^+ (Davson 1967). Our Cl^- value is thus 25-fold higher than the literature value for Na^+; whether this is accountable to a real difference or is because of different methodology remains to be clarified.

20*

The role of rapid HCO_3^- formation in CSF (and probably brain water) can only be guessed from these experiments, but a reasonable possibility is in the control of respiration. If CSF pH is indeed a controlling element in respiration (Brooks 1965), the CO_2-carbonic anhydrase system provides an exquisite regulation for it. We have seen repeated examples, through this Symposium, of how finely CO_2 is "buffered" by CSF – not simple chemical buffering as we now see, but *in vivo* adjustment fy OH^- secretion and HCO_3^- formation. This system, which provides pH regulation so widely and admirably throughout nature, is ideally designed for respiratory control. It appears reasonable and stimulating to think about new experiments to test these ideas; this is the ultimate virtue of the Symposium.

8. Cl^- and HCO_3^- transfer in the same direction

The present idea of Cl^- and HCO_3^- moving in the same net direction is somewhat at odds with traditional schemes, which usually postulate exchange of the two ions. Actually, for CSF, Welch (1963) showed that exchange could not be the case, since Cl^- secretion from blood to CSF would then demand a large efflux of HCO_3^- at the choroid plexus. This was not found.

In reviewing our general experience with the carbonic anhydrase system (Table 6) it appears that there are systems other than CSF in which Cl^- and HCO_3^- do move in the same direction. These, to date, are aqueous humor, avian salt gland, and pancreas. Table 6 also shows examples of HCO_3^- and Cl^- moving independently.

It is conceivable that in these different situations the tissue carbonic anhydrase has different characteristics, but there is no evidence on this point. In terms of turnover number and susceptibility to inhibition, tissue enzymes (unpurified) appear remakably stable through the animal kingdom, and are analogous to human red cell fraction C (reviewed in Maren 1967).

A more reasonable hypothesis is that in the general case the enzyme is concerned with both anions (see section 5 above), but that in certain physiological situations (i.e. kidney, liver) secondary adjustments, perhaps distal to the prime secretory or enzymic site, modify the secretion to give the composition and rate observed. This view fits the finding that CSF and aqueous humor, which have only the prime secretory cell system, are the fluids that show transport of both anions.

CONCLUSION

Both Cl^- and HCO_3^- are transported into CSF from plasma; the former by an active process, the latter by formation from CO_2. Both appear to be dependent, for normal rates, upon carbonic anhydrase. Other work in this laboratory shows that the same situation applies to aqueous humor. It appears that this is a general vertebrate pattern for both CSF and aqueous formation, obscured in some cases by seemingly anomalous concentrations of ions which may be secondary alterations imposed on the primary secretion.

In the summer of 1970 (following the Symposium) the effects of hypercapnia in the dogfish were directly studied. Gills were perfused with sea water containing 3–5 % CO_2, raising the pCO_2 of plasma from about 4 to 16 mm. Hg. Over a three hour period plasma HCO_3^- rose from 6 to 10 mM. CSF HCO_3^-, however, rose from about 7 to 24 mM. The rate of HCO_3^- increase in CSF was halved by carbonic anhydrase inhibition. These data strongly support the thesis of the above paper, that CSF HCO_3^- is formed by hydroxylation of CO_2, and that pH of CSF is finely regulated by this mechanism.

ACKNOWLEDGMENT

This work was supported by National Institute of Health Grant GM 16934.

REFERENCES

Ames, A. III, Higashi, K. & Nesbett, F. B. (1965) Effect of P_{co_2}, acetazolamide and ouabain on volume and composition of choroid plexus fluid. *J. Physiol (Lond.)* *181*, 516–524.

Ames, A. III, Sakanoue, M. & Endo, S. (1964) Na, K, Ca, Mg and Cl concentrations in choroid plexus fluid and cisternal fluid compared with ultrafiltrate. *J. Neurophysiol. 27*, 672–681.

Broder, L. E. & Oppelt, W. W. (1969) Effect of benzolamide on cerebrospinal fluid formation. *J. Pharmacol. exp. Ther. 169*, 271–276.

Brooks, C. McC., Kao, F. F. & Lloyd, B. B. (1965) *Cerebrospinal Fluid and the Regulation of Ventilation*. F. A. Davis Company, Philadelphia.

Burger, J. W. (1962) Further studies on the function of the rectal gland in the spiny dogfish. *Physiol. Zool. 35*, 205–217.

Coxon, R. V. & Swanson, A. G. (1965) Movement of [14C] bicarbonate from blood to cerebrospinal fluid and brain. *J. Physiol (Lond.) 181*, 712–727.

Davson, H. (1967) *Physiology of the Cerebrospinal Fluid*. J. & A. Churchill, London.

Durbin, R. P. & Heinz, E. (1958) Electromotive chloride transport and gastric acid secretion in the frog. *J. gen. Physiol. 41*, 1035–1047.

Erulkar, S. D. & Maren, T. H. (1961) Carbonic anhydrase and the inner ear. *Nature (Lond.) 189*, 459–460.

Garg, L. C. & Oppelt, W. W. (1970) The effect of ouabain and acetazolamide on transport of sodium and chloride from plasma to aqueous humor. *J. Pharmacol. exp. Ther.* In press.

Giacobini, E. (1962) A cytochemical study of the localization of carbonic anhydrase in the nervous system. *J. Neurochem. 9*, 169–177.

Held, D., Fencl, V. & Pappenheimer, J. R. (1964) Electrical potential of cerebrospinal fluid. *J. Neurophysiol. 27*, 942–949.

Hogben, C. A. M., Wistrand, P. J. & Maren, T. H. (1960) Role of active transport of chloride in formation of dogfish cerebrospinal fluid. *Amer J. Physiol. 199*, 124–126.

Kinsey, V. E. and Reddy, D. V. N. (1959) Turnover of carbon dioxide in the aqueous humor and the effect thereon of acetazolamide. *Arch. Ophthal. 62*, 78–83.

Magid, E. & Turbeck, B. O. (1968) The rates of the spontaneous hydration of CO_2 and the reciprocal reaction in neutral aqueous solutions between $0°$ and $38°$. *Biochim. biophys. Acta 165*, 515–524.

Maren, T. H. (1962) Ionic composition of cerebrospinal fluid and aqueous humor of the dogfish, *Squalus acanthias* – II. Carbonic anhydrase activity and inhibition. *Comp. Biochem. Physiol. 5*, 201–215.

Maren, T. H. (1963) Carbonic anhydrase kinetics and inhibition at 37°C: An approach to reaction rates *in vivo*. *J. Pharmacol. exp. Ther. 139*, 129–139.

Maren, T. H. (1967) Carbonic anhydrase: chemistry, physiology and inhibition. *Physiol. Rev. 47*, 595–781.

Maren, T. H. & Broder, L. E. (1970) The role of carbonic anhydrase in anion secretion into cerebrospinal fluid. *J. Pharmacol. exp. Ther. 172*, 197–202.

Maren, T. H., Ellison, A. C., Fellner, S. K. & Graham, W. B. (1966) A study of hepatic carbonic anhydrase. *Molec. Pharmacol. 2*, 144–167.

Maren, T. H., Rawls, J. A., Burger, J. W. & Myers, A. C. (1963) The alkaline gland of the skate. *Comp. Biochem. Physiol. 10*, 1–16.

Maren, T. H., Welliver, R. C. & Woodworth, R. M. (1970) Transfer rates of CO_2 and Cl^- from plasma to cerebrospinal fluid (CSF) in *Squalus acanthias:* Effect of carbonic anhydrase inhibition. *Bull. Mt. Desert Island Bio. Lab. 9*, 33–36.

Nechay, B. R., Larimer, J. L. & Maren, T. H. (1960) Effects of drugs and physiologic alterations on nasal salt excretion in sea gulls. *J. Pharmacol. exp. Ther. 130*, 401–410.

Oppelt, W. W., Adamson, R. H., Zubrod, C. G. & Rall, D. P. (1966) Further observations on the physiology and pharmacology of elasmobranch ventricular fluid. *Comp. Biochem. Physiol. 17*, 857–866.

Oppelt, W. W., Maren, T. H., Owens E. S. & Rall, D. P. (1963) Effects of acid-base alterations on cerebrospinal fluid production. *Proc. Soc. exp. Biol. (N. Y.) 114*, 86–89.

Oppelt, W. W., Patlak, C. S. & Rall, D. P. (1964) Effect of certain drugs on cerebrospinal fluid production in the dog. *Amer. J. Physiol. 206*, 247–250.

Patlak, C. S., Adamson, R. H., Oppelt, W. W. & Rall, D. P. (1966) Potential difference of the ventricular fluid *in vivo* and *in vitro* in the dogfish. *Life Sci. 5*, 2011–2015.

Pinsent, B. R. W., Pearson, L. & Roughton, F. J. W. (1956) The kinetics of combination of carbon dioxide with hydroxide ions. *Trans. Fareday Soc. 52*, 1512–1520.

Posner, J. B., Swanson, A. G. & Plum, F. (1965) Acid-base balance in cerebrospinal fluid. *Arch. Neurol. 12*, 479–496.

Rawls, J. A., Wistrand, P. J. & Maren, T. H. (1963) Effects of acid-base changes and carbonic anhydrase inhibition on pancreatic secretion. *Amer. J. Physiol. 205,* 651–657.

Robin, E. D., Murdaugh, H. V., Jr. & Millen, J. E. (1966) Acid-base, fluid and electrolyte metabolism in the elasmobranch – III. Oxygen, CO_2, bicarbonate and lactate exchange across the gill. *J. cell. comp. Physiol. 67,* 93–100.

Roughton, F. J. W. (1935) Recent work on carbon dioxide transport by the blood. *Physiol. Rev. 15,* 241–296.

Roughton, F. J. W. & Booth, V. H. (1946) The effect of substrate concentration, pH and other factors upon the activity of carbonic anhydrase. *Biochem. J. 40,* 319–330.

Swanson, A. G. & Rosengren, H. (1962) Cerebrospinal fluid buffering during acute experimental respiratory acidosis. *J. appl. Physiol. 17,* 812–814.

Wallace, W. M. & Hastings, A. B. (1942) The distribution of bicarbonate ion in mammalian muscle. *J. Biol. Chem. 146,* 637–649.

Ward, R. L. (1969) [36]Cl nuclear magnetic resonance studies of a zinc metalloenzyme carbonic anhydrase. *Biochemistry 8,* 1879–1883.

Welch, K. (1963) Secretion of cerebrospinal fluid by choroid plexus of the rabbit. *Amer. J. Physiol. 205,* 617–624.

Wistrand, P. J., Nechay, B. R. & Maren, T. H. (1961) Effects of carbonic anhydrase inhibition on cerebrospinal and intra-ocular fluids in the dog. *Acta pharmacol. 17,* 315–336.

DISCUSSION

SIESJÖ

It is difficult to understand how you can put such significance to the $^{14}CO_2$ concentration in the CSF, since radioactive CO_2 must exchange quickly with CO_2 and with bicarbonate. A few minutes after you give radioactive CO_2 you must have a steady state concentration of $^{14}CO_2$ in plasma, in choroid plexus, and in CSF, and to my understanding the difference in $^{14}CO_2$ content between CSF and plasma must then be due to the difference in the concentration of cold bicarbonate.

MAREN

When we inject radioactive $NaHCO_3$, there is, within a few minutes, equilibration in plasma between HCO_3^- and gaseous CO_2. If only the gaseous CO_2 as such diffused into CSF, the number of counts there would be very low, about 1/20 that of plasma. But in nine minutes we obtain a carbon count in CSF about equal to that in plasma (Fig. 2). This can only represent the hydration of CO_2 to HCO_3^-, which occurs in choroid plexus and secretory tissue of the brain.

SEVERINGHAUS

Do you think that the radioactive CO_2 is getting into the CSF as bicarbonate or as CO_2?

MAREN

The gaseous CO_2 is only 1/20 of the total CO_2 count, in either plasma or CSF. The gaseous CO_2 diffuses, reacts, and forms bicarbonate, and then the bicarbonate from plasma accumulates in the CSF.

SEVERINGHAUS

Does that indicate any bicarbonate movement across the blood-brain barrier?

MAREN

That is an important point. The fact that our chemical calculated uncatalyzed rate (CO_2 to HCO_3^-) agrees so well with the actual *in vivo* inhibited rate suggests that over this period of time bicarbonate movement as such is negligible, and certainly ionic movement, if fairly represented by Cl$^-$, is much slower than what is shown in Fig. 2.

SEVERINGHAUS

I am not quite sure what the experiment is done to show.

MAREN

It was done to show whether on the CSF side there was accumulation of bicarbonate – because if you did this experiment on the stomach or on the kidney you would not get accumulation of bicarbonate on the luminal side. I am trying to find out primarily whether the carbonic anhydrase system in choroid plexus and brain works to accumulate acid in the direction of CSF or bicarbonate in the direction of CSF.

SEVERINGHAUS

Do you think it showed either of them?

MAREN

Yes, I think it clearly showed bicarbonate accumulation.

BRADBURY

You say that labelled CO_2 is going into the cells of the choroid plexus, and there being converted to bicarbonate, which goes into the CSF. Then you find a reduction in the presence of Diamox. Could the explanation for this in fact be that less labelled CO_2 is getting in in the presence of Diamox, because you are blocking the hydration reaction?

MAREN ..

That is precisely what I am saying. But if you mean hydration or dehydration in red cells, the answer is that the fully inhibited or uncatalyzed equilibria $CO_2 \rightleftarrows HCO_3^-$ virtually go to completion in about 4 minutes (Roughton 1935). As you have seen here, our critical measurements were made from 9 to 18 minutes after $NaH^{14}CO_3$ injection, at which time labelled CO_2 and HCO_3^- are certainly in equilibrium in blood.

LASSEN

The point raised here is whether the CO_2 goes in as the gas and labels the bicarbonate already in the CSF. But I think that when you infuse an artificial

Rougthon, F. J. W. (1935) Recent work on carbon dioxide transport by the blood. *Physiol. Rev. 15*, 241–296.

CSF at a known high rate and see an effect of Diamox, then this does suggest that you are dealing with a specific phenomenon at the site of secretion.

KRUHØFFER

As I understand Dr. Bradbury's comment, he suggests that Diamox could slow down the entrance of labelled CO_2 into CSF by blocking the enzymic conversion of labelled bicarbonate into CO_2 within the erythrocytes. I would like to ask you about the carbonic anhydrase of the glial cells. You could have a diffusion of CO_2 into the glial cells and depending upon whether you have enzyme blockade or not you could have labelled bicarbonate coming out of them at different rates.

MAREN

I am very pleased that you raised that point because I think that glia have been neglected in this context. Our concept has been all along that the glial cells were a secretory system analogous to the choroid plexus. And that the same thing as I drew here (Fig. 1) occurs in the glial cells. And that might be the explanation also for the type of experiment that Dr. Siesjö showed us. We haven't done the inhibition experiment in the extracellular fluid of the brain, but they obviously should be done.

KRUHØFFER

It all depends on how fast the bicarbonate gets out of the glial cells and gets into the CSF.

SIESJÖ

Is it your opinion that the accumulation of bicarbonate ions in the CSF, when you increase the CO_2 tension, is due to choroid plexus secreting bicarbonate into the CSF?

MAREN

Not precisely HCO_3^- secretion in the typical sense. It is due to the hydration of CO_2 and the *formation* of bicarbonate within those cells, and that reaction occurs by this mechanism of OH^- secretion on the luminal side. It occurs faster when there is carbonic anhydrase present. And in your experiments, for example, when you increase P_{CO_2}, you are increasing substrate, and you naturally drive the reaction. All the data that we saw this morning show very clearly that the controlling factor in CSF or brain total HCO_3^- is the Pco_2 of the plasma.

SIESJÖ

I would disagree with that, because the fluxes seem to be in the other direction. The bicarbonate must be going into the cells during hypercapnia, so that cannot explain the increase in the CSF bicarbonate concentration. What I think is disturbing is that we don't consider the potential changes and their possible influence on the bicarbonate fluxes. Do you get decreases in the plasma pH during your experiments?

MAREN

In the cat experiments there were no pH changes whatsoever, because ventilation was controlled. In the fish there are changes in pH about 0.15 units, shown in Table 2. This is due to hypercapnia.

SIESJÖ

I was referring to your hypercapnic experiments and your reference to Swanson & Rosengren.

MAREN

It is exactly like your experiments. In the initial period there is a decrease in plasma pH and at a later time the pH is normal, as there becomes compensation for the respiratory acidosis.

BRADBURY

I believe that Dr. Hogben some time ago determined a very negative potential in dogfish ventricular fluid. This would seem to be ample confirmatory evidence for active chloride transport at least into dogfish CSF. Do you have any further evidence on the potential in the dogfish?

MAREN

I did these experiments with Dr. Hogben (1960), and the results have been confirmed by Rall's group (1966). The ventricular fluid is about 15 mV negative to plasma in several species of shark, and those fish have the typical chloride excess in CSF. Held *et al.* (1964) thought that this negative potential in the dogfish agreed fairly well with the high pH (7.6–7.7) of their plasma.

RALL

But we also showed that the negative potential in the dogfish persisted when the pH of plasma is lowered to 7.0–7.3 by infusion of HCl (Patlak *et al.* 1966).

Hogben, C. A. M., Wistrand, P. J. & Maren, T. H. (1960) Role of active transport of chloride in formation of dogfish cerebrospinal fluid. *Amer. J. Physiol. 199.* 124–126.

Patlak, C. S., Adamson, R. H., Oppelt, W. W. & Rall, D. P. (1966) Potential difference of the ventricular fluid in vivo and in vitro in the dogfish. *Life Sci. 5,* 2011–2015.

Held, D., Fencl, V. & Pappenheimer, J. R. (1964) Electrial potential of cerebrospinal fluid. *J. Neurophysiol. 27.* 942–949.

Whole Body Buffer Capacity*

E. B. Brown, Jr.

Buffer capacity of a tissue or of the whole body may be obtained by making an homogenate of the body or tissue and titrating with an acid or base. The slope of the titration curve, dB/dpH, is the buffer value as defined by Van Slyke (1922). If the titration is carried out with H_2CO_3 by equilibrating the tissue with different CO_2 tensions, the noncarbonic buffers are titrated. If a strong noncarbonic acid is used, the bicarbonate pair itself becomes an important part of the buffering. In either case buffer concentration of the tissue is the important factor determining buffer value. Such *in vitro* buffer capacity determinations have been made on a number of tissues (Brodie 1930, Brown 1950, Fenn 1928, Freeman & Fenn 1953, Furusawa & Kerridge 1927, Kazemi *et al.* 1967, Wallace & Hastings 1942).

It has become increasingly apparent during the past few years that information gained from these *in vitro* determinations is not applicable to the living intact animal because factors in addition to original buffer content play an important role. Among these factors are the following:

(1) The capacity of the tissue or fluid compartment to exchange electrolytes with other tissues or compartments, and the relative volumes and compositions of such exchanging compartments.
(2) The rate at which exchanges take place between tissues or compartments and the time lapse after acid or base invasion before buffer capacity is measured.

Department of Physiology, University of Kansas Medical Center, Kansas City, Kansas 66103, U. S. A.

* Some of this material was presented in the Symposium on Dynamics of CO₂ Exchange, XXIV International Congress, International Union of Physiological Sciences, Washington, D. C., 1968.
* Supported by U. S. A. F. Contract AF 41(609)-3005 and by a grant HE 12231 from the National Institutes of Health.

(3) The metabolic production or destruction of acids, bases, or buffers in a
     body compartment and the rate at which these processes take place.

In the remainder of this paper I will review the manner in which these
factors influence the *in vivo* buffering of certain tissues.

IN VITRO AND IN VIVO CO_2 BUFFERING OF BLOOD — EXCHANGES BETWEEN
BLOOD AND INTERSTITIAL FLUID

The CO_2 buffer characteristics of blood as an isolated system have been
studied extensively over the past 75 years. Four years ago Lloyd & Michel
(1966) derived an equation on theoretical grounds to describe the buffer
curve obtained by titrating blood with CO_2, plotting pH against HCO_3^-. If
we ignore the small difference in slope between reduced and oxygenated
hemoglobin, the equation reduces to

$$\frac{dpH}{d(HCO_3^-)p} = \frac{1.04\ bj}{0.786\ Hb_Bj + Y_Bb} \tag{1}$$

in which $(HCO_3^-)p$ is in mM/l plasma water.

Hb_B is hemoglobin in mM/l of blood water.
b   is the slope of the titration curve of oxygenated hemoglobin.
Y_B is buffer anions other than hemoglobin (primarily plasma proteins -
       Pr_B) in mM/l of blood water.
j   is the slope of the titration curve of Y.

Inverting this expression to conform to our previous definition of buffer
value we have

$$\frac{d(HCO_3^-)}{dpH} = -\left(\frac{0.755\ Hb_B}{b} + \frac{0.961\ Y_B}{j}\right) \tag{2}$$

and substituting values for b and j

$$\frac{d(HCO_3^-)p}{dpH} = -(2.54\ Hb_B + 10\ Pr_B) \tag{3}$$

With normal values of hemoglobin and plasma proteins, and converting
bicarbonate concentrations to mM/l of plasma, this expression gives a slope
of approximately 29.5 mM $(1 \times pH)^{-1}$. Woodbury (1965) has given this
awkward dimension the name "slyke" in honor of Dr. Donald D. Van Slyke,

and that term will be used in this paper. Other investigators have derived expressions for this buffer value and have calculated values ranging from 26.9 to 31 for blood of normal hemoglobin and plasma protein concentration. (Roos & Thomas 1967, Peters & Van Slyke 1931, Woodbury 1965).

It has been re-discovered within the past few years, and well-established by a number of investigators, that blood has a much lower buffer capacity in the whole body (i.e., *in vivo*) than it does *in vitro*. (Brown & Clancy 1965, Cohen *et al.* 1964, Michel *et al.* 1966). This difference is due primarily to the fact that the bicarbonate generated by buffering of CO_2 *in vivo* is distributed through the total extracellular fluid rather than just through blood water. The expression, similar to the previous equation, for CO_2 buffering of total extracellular fluid, or that volume in ready diffusion equilibrium with blood would be

$$\frac{d(HCO_3^-)_P}{dpH} = -\left[\frac{V_B}{V_e}(2.54\, Hb_B + 10\, Pr_B) + (1 - \frac{V_B}{V_e})\,(10\, Pr_I)\right] \qquad (4)$$

in which V_B and V_e are volume of blood water and extracellular water respectively, and $(Pr)_I$ is concentration of proteins in interstitial fluid water. (Because of the assumptions which have gone into the derivations, these equations represent reasonable approximations at best.) With normal values for adult humans a slope of approximately 11.5 sl is obtained. If blood bicarbonate distributes freely through interstitial fluid and does not exchange with intracellular fluid, this equation expresses the CO_2 buffer value of true plasma *in vivo*. The ratio of *in vitro* to *in vivo* buffer slopes then would be 2.6. Shaw & Messer reported this discrepancy between *in vivo* and *in vitro* CO_2 buffering in 1932.

Values obtained for *in vivo* CO_2 buffering of blood in humans are listed in Table 1. It should be pointed out here that all of these values have been taken from slopes obtained by increasing the CO_2 tension above normal. The difficulty with meaningful buffer slopes derived from low CO_2 tensions will be discussed later. With one exception it is apparent that the *in vivo* values obtained by these authors using arterial blood or arterialized venous blood are higher than predicted by the equation. Roos & Thomas (1967), and Michel (1968) have pointed out that CO_2 buffer slopes obtained from arterial blood may give false values. If, for example, cardiac output increases with an increase in P_{CO_2}, the buffer value from arterial blood will be falsely high.

Solberg, Lindholm & Brown 1960

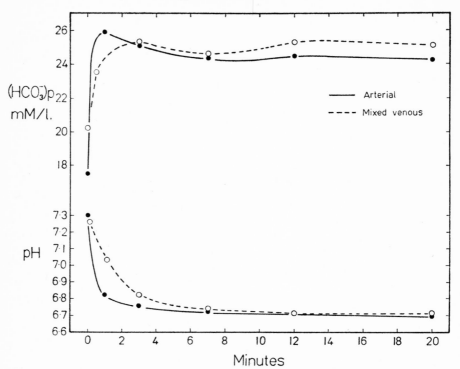

Fig. 1. Mean values from 8 dogs during the first 20 minutes after starting to breathe 30% CO_2, and 70% O_2. Venous samples were drawn from the pulmonary artery.

Table 1. Human Blood
In Vivo CO_2 Buffer Values of True Plasma

	No.	In Vitro	In Vivo	
Brown (1966)	10	30.0 ± 1.4	18	arterialized
Michel et al. (1966)	12	*29.3	18.8	–
Brackett (1965)	9	32	11.6	arterial
Prys-Roberts et al. (1966)	9	33	22.4	–
Prys-Roberts (1968)	25	*29.9	19.6	–
Ichiyanagi et al. (1969)	32	33	15	–

* Calculated

Solberg, Lindholm, & Brown. 1960

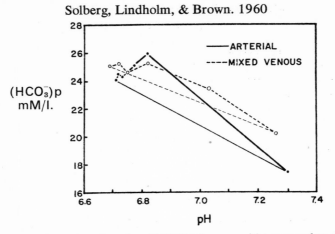

Fig. 2. Data from Fig. 1 plotted on the pH-HCO$_3^-$ diagram without regard to time.

Precise evaluation of the *in vivo* CO$_2$ buffer slope then requires analyses on mixed venous blood and such data are understandably scarce. In one study made ten years ago in my laboratory (Solberg *et al.* 1960), arterial and mixed venous blood samples were drawn at intervals for 20 min after dogs began to breathe 30% CO$_2$ in O$_2$. Fig. 1 shows the mean values for pH and (HCO$_3^-$)p on six dogs. The transient increase in arterial (HCO$_3^-$)p above the early steady-state value appears in blood samples drawn from the arterial side before the blood has reached systemic capillaries and exchanged bicarbonate with interstitial fluid. Fig. 2 shows these values plotted on the pH-bicarbonate diagram without respect to time. It is apparent that the slope obtained on the first arterial sample approximates the *in vitro* slope, and those obtained later give the lower slope that results from exchange with interstitial fluid. In these experiments the values after 12 min of CO$_2$ breathing gave a buffer slope for arterial blood of 12.2 sl, and for mixed venous blood of 9.3 sl. The values at 20 min were essentially unchanged; i. e., there was a relative "steady-state" after 12 minutes. *In vitro* buffer curves were not determined in these experiments. Recently we have obtained mixed venous and arterial blood samples with dogs breathing 10 and 15% CO$_2$ and measured cardic output at the time the blood samples were obtained. The usual increase in cardiac output was observed in most experiments, but in two experiments cardiac output decreased, and as would be expected,

Table 2. Dogs Breathing 20% CO_2 for 15 Minutes

	A	B	C
In vitro slope (slykes)	31	25	14.7
In vivo slope-venous	12.4	3.2	5.7
In vivo slope-arterial	8.8	8.1	8.5
△ Cardiac output	+20	−14 %	−12 %

arterial blood buffer slope was less than venous buffer slope in these experiments. These data are presented in Table 2.

EXCHANGE BETWEEN EXTRACELLULAR AND INTRACELLULAR FLUIDS

It has been recognized for some time that an exchange of intracellular sodium and potassium for extracellular hydrogen ions takes place when CO_2 tension is increased, or when acid is infused into the extracellular fluid. The precise time at which this intracellular contribution becomes effective in increasing the slope of the mixed venous blood CO_2 buffer curve, however, has not been well delineated. More than 50 years ago Van Slyke & Cullen (1917) infused 75 mEq of H_2SO_4 into a 14 kg dog and found that only 1/6 of the hydrogen ions could be accounted for by ECF buffering, making it apparent that some intracellular source of buffer had become available. More recently Giebisch, Berger & Pitts (1955) reported that 51 per cent of the hydrogen ions added to ECF when dogs breathed 20% CO_2 for 6 hours were buffered by exchange of ECF H^+ for intracellular fluid Na^+ and K^+ ions. In one experiment in which they reported values at hourly intervals, one-half of the increase in ECF Na^+ and K^+ had taken place within the first hour.

The importance of considering the way a tissue buffers in the whole body as compared with its capacity to buffer in an isolated *in vitro* system is illustrated by comparing the values Fenn and his associates obtained (Fenn 1928, Fenn 1961, Broby 1930) on blood, skeletal muscle, and cardiac muscle *in vitro,* with the results we (Clancy & Brown 1966) have obtained on these same tissues *in vivo* (Table 3). Fenn and his group worked primarily with frog tissues; our results were obtained on dogs. The absolute values for buffer slopes are of less significance than the relative values. The order of buffering *in vitro* was: Blood > Muscle > Heart; *in vivo* the order was reversed. The *in vivo* values were obtained after 1½ hours of breathing 15 % or 30 % CO_2 in O_2. The extraordinarily high buffer values we have

Table 3. Tissue CO_2 Buffer Values

	Fenn (1928, 1961) *In Vitro*	Clancy & Brown (1966) *In Vivo*
Blood	18 sl	10 sl
Skeletal Muscle	5 sl	20 sl
Heart Ventricle	$\simeq$ 2* sl	70 sl

* Brody (1930)

obtained on cardiac tissue after 1½ hours of breathing high CO_2 again strongly suggest that exchange between tissues is an important part of buffering *in vivo,* even over intervals of 1½ hours. This is also illustrated by the fact that CSF has a very low buffer capacity for CO_2 *in vitro,* but has a remarkably high capacity for CO_2 buffering over relatively short intervals of time *in vivo.* Table 4 lists data from the literature indicating that in the dog the *in vitro* buffer value of dog CSF is only 4 sl. After ½ hour *in vivo* it has doubled and in 1 hour tripled. After 2 to 3 hours it has increased to 30 sl, a value equivalent to the *in vitro* value of blood with 15 gm% hemoglobin.

METABOLIC PROCESSES

In addition to the exchanges of extracellular H^+ for intracellular Na^+ and K^+, changes in extracellular lactate must be kept in mind when CO_2 buffer curves are being evaluated. CO_2 acidosis results in a decrease in extracellular lactate; hyperventilation alkalosis is accompanied by the reverse change. The increase in extracellular lactate is of such a magnitude and takes place at such a rate that it is difficult, if not impossible, to evaluate the initial CO_2 buffer slope in extracellular fluid during hypocapnia. Almost any buffer slope can be

Table 4. CSF Buffer Capacity (slykes)

Source	Animal	In Vitro	½	1	2	3	6	8	24
Lee *et al.* (1969)	dog	4			29				
Kazemi *et al.* (1967)	dog			11			56		
Kjällquist *et al.* (1969)	rat			43					
Bleich *et al.* (1964)	dog		9			31		66	83

21*

obtained, depending on the time at which the blood sample is drawn and the degree of elevation of lactate that has taken place (Brown 1966, Ichiyanagi et al. 1969, Engel et al. 1969). We have indicated a break in the slope at pH 7.4 and P_{CO_2} 40, whereas Ichiyanagi (1969) has drawn the buffer slope as continuously changing over the range studied. It seems likely that his data would also fit straight lines of different slope intersecting at pH 7.4. Recently Engel, Kildeberg & Winters (1969) have attempted to define the in vivo CO_2 buffer curve of dog blood during 1.5 hours of hyperventilation. They conclude, "Thus, there is no single time independent slope for the in vivo CO_2 equilibration curve in the hypocapnic range, but rather a continuously changing slope as a function of time after the onset of hyperventilation".

EFFECT OF TIME ON IN VIVO BUFFER VALUE

In experiments which are still in progress (Martin et al.) we have exposed rats to 5, 10 or 15% CO_2 in a chamber in which CO_2 tension, oxygen tension, temperature and humidity can be maintained constant. After time intervals ranging from 20 min to 18 days, animals are lightly anesthetized, all of the blood that can be obtained is drawn from the inferior vena cava, and tissue samples are taken. These procedures are carried out without removing the animal from the chamber. Mean mixed venous blood values for the first 24 hours after elevation of the inspired CO_2 tension are shown in Fig. 3. Each point is an average of determinations on 6–9 different animals. Notice that the early plateaus, i. e., the 10–30 min plateaus, are lost in the continuing changes that are taking place over 24 hours. The initial dip in pH followed by an increase between one-half and 4 hours is characteristic of all three CO_2 tensions. Part of this early recovery in pH may be the result of an increase in respiratory ventilation, as evidenced by the transient decrease in Pv_{CO_2}, and part appears to be the result of an increase in $(HCO_3^-)_P$ in the face of a constant Pv_{CO_2}. This increase in (HCO_3^-) is probably related to the exchange of intracellular sodium and potassium for extracellular hydrogen ion referred to earlier. If skeletal muscle is one of the sources of these cations, it would be expected that muscle intracellular (HCO_3^-) would decrease during this interval in which extracellular (HCO_3^-) is increasing. Fig. 4 indicates that this is the case. Intracellular (HCO_3^-) in these experiments was calculated from mixed venous blood P_{CO_2} and intracellular pH determined by the DMO technique.

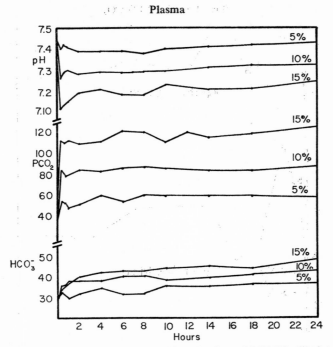

Fig. 3. Venous plasma values on rats breathing 5, 10, or 15% CO_2 for intervals up to 24 hours. Each point is a mean value for at least 6 animals.

Fig. 5 illustrates changes in CO_2 buffer slope of skeletal muscle with time in these experiments. The slope was steeper at 1 hour than 5 to 10 hours. Similar results were obtained in Nichols' (1958) experiments in which he measured total CO_2 directly in muscle in rats breathing 24% CO_2. It appears then that in the early hours following a step increase in CO_2 tension, intracellular buffer stores of skeletal muscle are being depleted in order to support buffering of the extracellular fluid. Our data suggest that both skeletal and cardiac muscle participate in this exchange.

In both dogs and rats the ratio of concentrations of extracellular to intracellular bicarbonate decreases initially in skeletal and cardiac muscle following a step increase in CO_2 tension. We have not followed this change in the dog long enough to determine the point at which restoration of the normal bicarbonate concentration ratio occurs. In the rat it would appear that within 4 to 10 hours this ratio has been restored to its original value. Both an

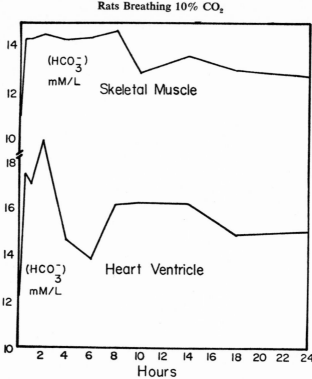

Fig. 4. Bicarbonate concentrations in skeletal and cardiac muscle in rats breathing 10% CO_2. HCO_3^- was calculated from P_{CO_2} determined on venous blood and intracellular pH from DMO distribution in the muscle.

exchange of extracellular hydrogen ion for intracellular sodium and potassium and renal compensation would act to increase extracellular bicarbonate and restore the normal bicarbonate concentration ratio.

Fig. 6 shows the blood values we have obtained in rats over periods of time up to 18 days. By 18–24 hours, renal activity is playing a significant role; by 3–5 days, in the rat, compensation is maximum. When the extracellular-intracellular bicarbonate concentration ratio has been restored and renal compensation has increased the extracellular bicarbonate level still more, intracellular bicarbonate also increases, and in the final steady state both intracellular and extracellular compensation have occurred, with pH in both compartments being restored toward the original value.

Skeletal muscle CO_2 buffer curves   Rats on 10% CO_2

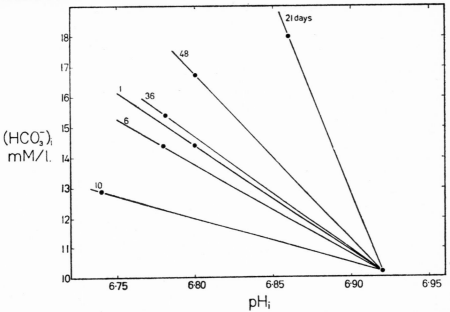

$(HCO_3^-)_i$ mM/l.

pH$_i$

Fig. 5. Skeletal muscle CO_2 buffer curves determined at 1, 5, 10, 36 and 48 hours, and after 21 days in rats breathing 10% CO_2.

We can identify at least three overlapping stages then in the buffering of CO_2 by the body. These are

(1) Chemical buffering and distribution.
(2) Ion exchange between intracellular and extracellular fluids.
(3) Renal compensation.

In the first phase, bicarbonate is largely limited to that volume in ready diffusion equilibrium with blood. This phase is essentially complete in 15–20 minutes under normal conditions of tissue perfusion and gives us the initial "steady state". In the second phase, skeletal and cardiac muscle bicarbonate may decrease while extracellular bicarbonate concentration continues to increase. In the rat, this phase is complete in 24–36 hours. In the third phase, both intracellular and extracellular bicarbonate increase to their final steady-state value. This requires 3–5 days with alveolar CO_2 tensions of 60–120 torr in the rat.

Plasma Values. Rats Breathing 5, 10, 15% CO_2

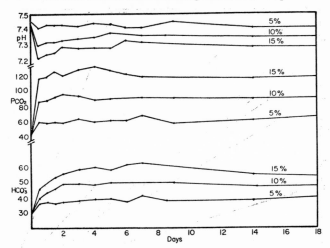

Fig. 6. Plasma values on rats breathing 5, 10, or 15% CO_2 for periods up to 18 days.

This division of CO_2 buffering into three overlapping phases again emphasizes the fact that the admonition against attempting to delineate time independent values for buffer capacity of tissues *in vivo,* applies in modified form to use of hypercapnia as well as hypocapnia. We have illustrated this influence of time with changes in buffer capacity of blood, skeletal muscle, cerebrospinal fluid, and cardiac muscle. The data in Table 5 illustrate the influence of the composition of one body fluid compartment on the buffer capacity of a second compartment with which it exchanges ions. The data in the first 2 lines were obtained on dogs before and after 1½ hours of breathing 15% CO_2. The *in vivo* CO_2 buffer value of skeletal muscle was 19 sl. When the experiments were repeated with the addition of an intravenous infusion of $NaHCO_3$ solution to maintain extracellular pH constant, intracellular HCO_3^- increased more than in the previous experiments and buffer value increased to 140 sl (lines 3 and 4 of Hypercapnia). The first 2 lines under hypocapnia are data from an experiment in which a dog was mildly hyperventilated (P_{CO_2} decreased from 52 to 33 torr). Muscle CO_2 buffer value was 17 sl. In similar experiments, except that HCl was infused intravenously to maintain extracellular pH constant, there was a larger decrease in intracellular (HCO_3^-) and buffer value was 80 sl. These data

Table 5. Effect of Changes in Extracellular Fluid Composition on
Buffer Capacity of Intracellular Fluid

| | Extracellular | | | (Skeletal Muscle) Intracellular | |
	pH	HCO_3^- mM/l	P_{CO_2} torr	pH	HCO_3^- mM/l
			Hypercapnia		
1.	7.34	23.3	45	6.98	12.7
	6.98	26.4	114	6.75	17.1
				$\beta = 19$ sl	
2.	7.37	25.3	46	6.96	11.6
	7.37	65.8	117	6.87	24.2
				$\beta = 140$ sl	
			Hypocapnia		
3.	7.29	24.1	52	7.00	14.4
	7.43	20.9	33	7.13	12.2
				$\beta = 17$ sl	
2.	7.36	26.5	46	6.96	11.7
	7.34	14.8	27	7.01	7.7
				$\beta = 80$ sl	

1. Clancy & Brown
2. Brown, Kim & Moorehead
3. Brown & Goott

indicate that the composition of extracellular fluid has a significant influence on the *in vivo* CO_2 buffer value of skeletal muscle.

BONE

In the discussion thus far we have spoken primarily about buffer capacity of soft tissues. The possibility that bone serves as a source of buffer has intrigued investigators for many years. Bergstrom & Wallace (1954) and Bergstrom & Ruva (1960) have determined the effects of acidosis on bone sodium. In both instances plasma sodium decreased markedly, and it is difficult to assign the loss of bone sodium to the acidosis per se rather than to the decrease in extracellular sodium. There was a decrease in bone sodium in both sets of experiments. Nichols (1958) reported that bone CO_2 decreased in his rats breathing 24% CO_2 for 48 hours, and he suggested that bone

E. B. BROWN, JR.

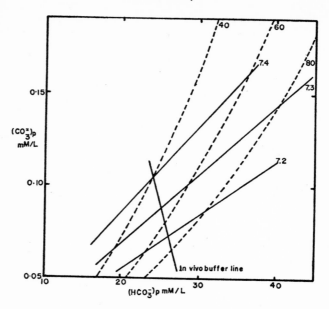

Fig. 7. The initial "steady-state" *in vivo* CO_2 buffer curve of blood plotted on a carbonate-bicarbonate diagram. Note that with increasing P_{CO_2} and $(HCO_3)p$, the $(CO_3^=)p$ decreases.

CO_2, which is largely in the form of carbonate, was in equilibrium with ECF carbonate rather than bicarbonate or CO_2 tension.

If we set the buffer equations for the first and second dissociation constants of H_2CO_3 equal to each other and solve for carbonate in terms of bicarbonate, we can plot a graph as shown on Fig. 7. Now, if we construct a normal *in vivo* CO_2 buffer curve on this graph, it is apparent that in the initial uncompensated state of respiratory acidosis, extracellular carbonate concentration decreases. However, as compensation occurs, extracellular carbonate increases. Within a few hours, compensation has developed to the place where carbonate concentration has again been restored to its original value. From this point on carbonate concentration in the extracellular fluid exceeds the original value, and if Nichols' theory is correct, bone should become a store for CO_2. Fig. 8 shows actual data from our rats breathing 10% CO_2 with respect to time at which these changes occurred. Freeman & Fenn (1953) found no increase in bone CO_2 in rats breathing 20%

Rats on 10% CO₂

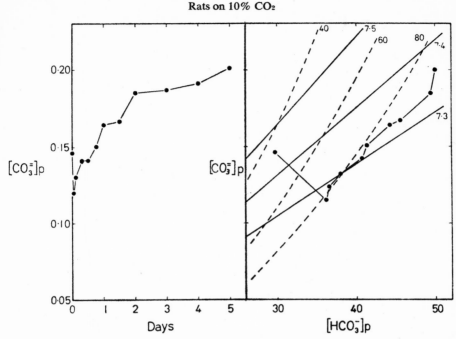

Fig. 8. The left panel shows calculated plasma carbonate concentration (mM/L), in rats breathing 10% CO_2. Within 24 hours $(CO_3^=)p$ has returned to control level and thereafter it is elevated above normal. The panel on the right shows these data plotted on $(CO_3^=) - (HCO_3^-)$ diagram.

CO_2 for periods up to 6 hours, but after 6–11 days bone had become an important store for CO_2 amounting to 30–70 per cent of the total body increase. Data are not available to delineate precisely the changes in bone as a function of time, but if further studies validate Nichols' hypothesis, perhaps a fourth phase of CO_2 uptake or loss with a change in CO_2 tension must be added to the picture. At any rate, if this hypothesis is valid, it further emphasizes the importance of time in determining *in vivo* buffering. This biphasic response of bone as a CO_2 store is reminiscent of the biphasic buffer capacity of skeletal muscle.

332   E. B. BROWN, JR.

REFERENCES

Bergstrom, W. H. & Ruva, F. D. (1960) Changes in bone sodium during acute acidosis in the rat. *Amer. J. Physiol. 198,* 1126–1128.
Bergstrom, W. H. & Wallace, W. M. (1954) Bone as a sodium and potassium reservoir. *J. clin. Invest. 33,* 867–873.
Bleich, H. L., Berkmann, P. M. & Schwartz, W. B. (1964) The response of cerebrospinal fluid composition to sustained hypercapnia. *J. clin. Invest. 43,* 11–16.
Brackett, N. C., Cohen, J. J. & Schwartz, W. B. (1965) Carbon dioxide titration curve of normal man. Effect of increasing degrees of acute hypercapnia on acid-base equilibrium. *New Engl. J. Med. 272,* 6–12.
Brody, Henry (1930) The carbon dioxide dissociation curve of frog heart muscle. *Amer. J. Physiol. 93,* 190–196.
Brown, E. B., Jr. (1950) Changes in brain pH response to CO_2 after prolonged hypoxic hyperventilation. *J. appl. Physiol. 2,* 549–552.
Brown, E. B., Jr. (1966) Detection and quantitation of metabolic acidosis and alkalosis. *Ann. N. Y. Acad. Sci. 133,* 118–124.
Brown, E. B., Jr. & Clancy, R. L. (1965) *In vivo* and *in vitro* CO_2 blood buffer curves. *J. appl. Physiol. 20,* 885–889.
Clancy, R. L. & Brown, E. B., Jr. (1966) *In vivo* CO_2 buffer curves of skeletal and cardiac muscle. *Amer. J. Physiol. 211,* 1309–1312.
Cohen, J. J., Brackett, N. C. & Schwartz, W. B. (1964) The nature of the carbon dioxide titration curve in the normal dog. *J. clin. Invest. 43,* 777–786.
Engel, K., Kildeberg, P. & Winters, R. W. (1969) Quantitative displacement of blood acid-base status in acute hypocapnia. *Scand. J. clin. Lab. Invest. 23,* 5–17.
Fenn, W. O. (1961) Carbon dioxide and intracellular homeostasis. *Ann. N. Y. Acad. Sci. 92,* 547–558.
Fenn, W. O. (1928) The carbon dioxide dissociation curve of nerve and muscle. *Amer. J. Physiol. 85,* 207–223.
Freeman, F. H. & Fenn, W. O. (1953) Changes in carbon dioxide stores of rats due to atmospheres low in oxygen or high in carbon dioxide. *Amer. J. Physiol. 174,* 422–430.
Furusawa, K. & Kerridge, P. M. T. (1927) The hydrogen ion concentration of the muscles of the cat. *J. Physiol. (Lond.) 63,* 33–41.
Giebisch, G., Berger, L. & Pitts, R. F. (1955) Extrarenal response to acute acid-base disturbances of respiratory origin. *J. clin. Invest. 34,* 231–245.
Ichiyanagi, K., Masuko, K., Nishisaka, N., Matsuki, M., Horikawa, H. & Watanabe, Reiko (1969) Acid-base changes of arterial plasma during exogenous and endogenous hypercapnia in man. *Resp. Physiol. 7,* 310–325.
Kazemi, H., Shannon, D. C. & Carvallo-Gil, E. (1967) Brain CO_2 buffering capacity in respiratory acidosis and alkalosis. *J. appl. Physiol. 22,* 241–246.
Kjällquist, A., Nardini, M. & Siesjö, B. K. (1969) The regulation of extra- and intracellular acid-base parameters in the rat brain during hyper- and hypocapnia. *Acta physiol. scand. 76,* 485–494.
Lee, J. E., Chu, F., Posner, J. B. & Plum, F. (1969) Buffering capacity of cerebrospinal fluid in acute respiratory acidosis in dogs. *Amer. J. Physiol. 217,* 1035–1038.
Lloyd, B. B. & Michel, C. C. (1966) A theoretical treatment of the carbon dioxide dissociation curve of true plasma *in vitro. Resp. Physiol. 1,* 107–120.

Martin, E. D., Scamman, F. L., Attebery, B. A. & Brown, E. B., Jr. (1967) Time related adjustments in acid-base status of extracellular and intracellular fluid in chronic respiratory acidosis. USAF School of Aerospace Medicine, Brooks AFB, Texas. SAM-TR-67-116.

Michel, C. C. (1968) The buffering behavior of blood during hypoxaemia and respiratory exchange: Theory. Resp. Physiol. 4, 283–291.

Michel, C. C., Lloyd, B. B. & Cunningham, D. J. C. (1966) The in vivo carbon dioxide dissociation curve of true plasma. Resp. Physiol. 1, 121–137.

Nichols, G. (1958) Serial changes in tissue carbon dioxide content during acute respiratory acidosis. J. clin. Invest. 37, 1111–1122.

Peters, J. P. & Van Slyke, D. D. (1931) Quantitative Clinical Chemistry. Williams and Wilkins, Baltimore.

Roos, A. & Thomas, L. J., Jr. (1967) The in vivo carbon dioxide dissociation curves of true plasma. Anesthesiology 28, 1048–1063.

Prys-Roberts, C., Kelman, G. R. & Nunn, J. F. (1966) Determination of the in vivo carbon dioxide titration curve of anesthetized man. Brit. J. Anaesth. 38, 500–509.

Prys-Roberts, C. (1968) In vivo CO_2 dissociation curves of mixed venous and arterial blood in anesthetized man. Brit. J. Anaesth. 40, 802.

Shaw, L. A. & Messer, A. C. (1932) The transfer of bicarbonate between the blood and tissues caused by alterations of carbon dioxide concentrations in the lungs. Amer. J. Physiol. 100, 122–136.

Solberg, L., Lindholm, R. & Brown, E. B., Jr. (1960) Unsteady state studies on CO_2 uptake; including HCO3 deficit and the mechanisms of its production. Unpublished summer research project report. Univ. of Minn. Med. School.

Van Slyke, Donald D. (1922) On the measurement of buffer values and on the relationship of buffer value to the dissociation constant of the buffer and the concentration and reaction of the buffer solution. J. biol. Chem. 52, 525–570.

Van Slyke, D. D. & Cullen, G. E. (1917) Studies of Acidosis I. The bicarbonate concentration of the blood plasma; its significance, and its determination as a measure of acidosis. J. biol. Chem. 30, 289–346.

Wallace, W. M. & Lowry, O. H. (1942) An in vitro study of carbon dioxide equilibria in mammalian muscle. J. biol. Chem. 144, 651–655.

Woodbury, J. W. (1965) Regulation of pH. In Physiology and Biophysics, ed. Ruch, T. C. & Patton, H. D. W. B. Saunders Co., Philadelphia.

DISCUSSION

KRUHØFFER

I would like to comment on the use or misuse of the word buffer capacity. As long as we are speaking about plasma there is no problem. Even in the case of whole blood the term may be applicable in its strict physico-chemical sense if the pH changes inside and outside the erythrocytes can be assumed to be parallel. If the use of the term is to be extended to systems including also interstitial and intracellular fluids, I think that an essential condition is again that the same pH shift occurs in all phases of the system during the "titration". CO_2 titrations of such complex systems are, however, more a matter of registering the movement of hydrogen ions and bicarbonate between the various compartments and with knowledge of the pH shift in only one of these, the plasma. I don't think we should go on using the word "whole body buffer capacity" in the sense it has been used here. This criticism obviously does not affect the value of the work in characterizing important dynamic properties of the body.

SIESJÖ

Apparently when you go up to very long periods of hypercapnia there is a very high buffer capacity with an almost complete pH regulation in the intracellular space in the muscle after many days. In another slide there was a marked effect of the extracellular bicarbonate concentration on the intracellular bicarbonate concentration. What was the duration of that experiment?

BROWN

Two hours.

SIESJÖ

We have used the buffer capacity expression before for tissues, but that was at the time when we thought that the permeability of the membranes to hydrogen ions and bicarbonate ions was very low. Our own experiments, Dr. Brown's experiments, and Dr. Woodbury's experiments seem to show that there is an appreciable permeability to hydrogen and bicarbonate ions, and then I think we would only confuse the issue by using the buffer capacity expression. The buffer capacity should be something which we use for a system which we have in isolation and which does not change with time. I wonder if we couldn't simply express our acid-base results as the change in pH for a given change in Pco_2?

BROWN

I agree fully that the term has become almost meaningless and that this thing we call buffer capacity, which is simply a measure of the accumulation of bicarbonate in a place in response to a change in Pco_2, is also a function of time. Therefore it is completely meaningless to the chemist. Conceptionally I think we still need some kind of expression to describe it. I will ask for a name that we could use to refer to these relative changes when we are looking at one tissue compared with another at any particular time.

J. W. WOODBURY

I disagree entirely with these objections. It may be confusing to use the phrase "buffer value", but the number which has the units of Slykes (the slope of the CO_2 titration curve at a specified time) and which I call buffer value (Woodbury 1965) is a useful number. A measurement of the apparent buffer value at a specified time can be compared meaningfully with what you expect on a physico-chemical basis. This difference or ratio is a measure of the ability of the tissue to compensate for acid-base changes above and beyond the innate physico-chemical buffer value. It seems to me it would be ridiculous to express these data in any other way simply because the term "buffer value" is objectionable. This is the abstraction from data of a number which represents the ability of the cells to regulate their pH, and whether it is due to active transport or to physico-chemical buffering is as important as a measure of ability to resist pH changes.

ASTRUP

I also have the opinion that the term buffer capacity is not a good one and we have never used it. I don't think it is very useful. What Dr. Brown has described, that is mainly the movements of bicarbonate ions, and this is of course very valuable, but I am afraid that it confuses many people to use the word buffer capacity.

Woodbury, J. W. (1965) Regulation of pH. In *Physiology and Biophysics,* ed. Ruch, T. C, & Patton, H. D., Chapter 46. W. B. Saunders, Philadelphia.

KRUHØFFER

As I said, I think it is valuable to speak of buffer capacity in the case of isolated plasma and the term may perhaps also be appropriate for titrations of whole blood. However, I decline the use of the expression in connection with titrations on complex systems including also tissues, because buffer capacity certainly has a definite meaning in a physico-chemical sense. Suppose you have a liter of plasma and you are trying to determine the slope by increasing the CO_2 tension and measuring the pH in the plasma. If somebody were going to fool you and were e. g. secretly adding some lactic acid then it would not be a true buffer capacity that you were measuring. It is something of this kind you are up against when you determine so-called whole body buffer capacity.

LASSEN

We must realize that blood *in vivo* and blood *in vitro* are exactly the same blood. And it strikes me as being a very useless term to speak of blood *in vivo* contra *in vitro*. It is only when it has passed around the tissue these changes occur. I should like very much never to see the comparison of *in vivo* and *in vitro* curves.

BROWN

I think that from a clinical standpoint, a very pragmatic standpoint, this difference is important, and we were in trouble for a long time because we didn't recognize it. I think one has to admit that the *in vivo* slope is important, and that the blood *in vivo* is not the same as *in vitro*, because in spite of the fact that you have the same amount of buffer you have a dilution through a much larger volume. The net effect is that which you would have if you had an amount of blood with a membrane and about three times the additional volume through which the buffer was distributed. It therefore makes the blood literally a different fluid *in vivo* as opposed to *in vitro*.

J. W. WOODBURY

I would like to confirm what Dr. Brown said. Blood *in vivo* is blood diluted by the extracellular space, otherwise it is the same. To get back to this buffering value or capacity business. I feel strongly that the $[HCO_3^-]$ – pH diagram and CO_2 titration curves are the most useful way of expressing acid-base data. I had the occasion to study seriously this matter six years ago, when I wrote a chapter on the subject, and starting from other premises I concluded that this is really the best way of presenting acid-base data. However, since "buffer capacity" or value is objectionable, maybe we can solve the problem by calling the same thing the "pH regulatory coefficient" or some similar impressive term. The term does need to be short.

COHEN

We seem to be more in agreement than we appear. We agree on the physiology, but I wonder if we are not just getting hooked on semantics. We are hooked on the difference between CSF as a simple buffer and CSF as a fluid buffered by the body. The use of the word as illustrated by "buffer capacity" is quite important and a useful fiction illustrating the body's ability by one mechanism or another to buffer a fluid.

SEVERINGHAUS

I would like to support the idea that we use the term buffering. However, I suggest that two modifiers be used: chemical buffering and physiological buffering, the latter including all the homeostatic mechanisms we are discussing.

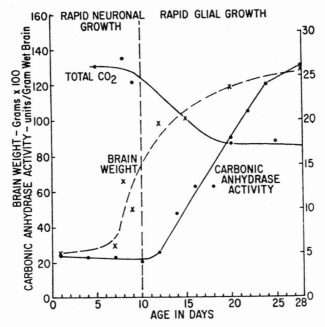

D. WOODBURY

I would like to change the subject completely and return to a discussion of
the possible role of glial cells in acid-base regulation in the CNS. This
subject has been neglected in this conference, mainly because so little is
known about this role. This can best be discussed in connection with the
data shown in this figure. Dr. Withrow and I studied the changes in total
CO_2 content in brain and plasma during maturation. These results, together
with data on brain carbonic anhydrase activity with age done by Dr.
Karler and myself, are shown in this figure. Similar changes with age have
been described by Millichap. Brain total CO_2 content is higher than plasma
total CO_2 in young animals and remains high until about the 9th day after
birth, then decreases rapidly until the 21st day at which time the rate of
decrease is reduced. Adult values are reached after about the 35th day.
In the adult, total CO_2 in brain is about half the plasma value. Carbonic
anhydrase activity in contrast is very low in the neonatal period. After
10 days of age, activity increases rapidly until 21 days of age. After this
time, the activity continues to increase, but at a much slower rate, for the
rest of the life of the rats. Electron microscopic and other studies have
shown that the rat brain contains no or few glial cells in the first 10 days
of life, but that after this time glial cells proliferate rapidly for the next
10 to 15 days and more slowly thereafter.

Since Giacobini (1962) demonstrated that brain carbonic anhydrase is
located predominantly in glial cells, it is evident that the rapid increase in
brain carbonic anhydrase activity between 10 and 25 days after birth is due
to growth of glial cells. This also corresponds to the time when total CO_2
content of the brain decreases. Since the total CO_2 content is high in the
brain at a time when no or only a few glial cells are present (up to 10 days
after birth) it is evident that the high total CO_2 is present in the neurons.
The decrease to the adult value, however, requires the presence of glial cells
containing carbonic anhydrase. Evidently, by some as yet unknown mechanism, carbonic anhydrase in glial cells regulates the exit of CO_2 from
neurons. Since the CSF total CO_2 of the neonatal animals does not appear
to be elevated, their high brain total CO_2 content would appear to be due
to increased amounts of bicarbonate. These studies emphasize the impor-

---

Giacobini, E. (1962) A cytochemical study of the localization of carbonic anhydrase in
the nervous system. *J. Neurochem. 9*, 169–177.

tance of elucidating the role of glial cell carbonic anhydrase in the regulation of acid-base metabolism in the brain and the nature of metabolically produced CO_2 in neurons. Such studies are continuing in our laboratory.

SEVERINGHAUS
Dr. Siesjö, how much did the CO_2 content increase when you inhibited carbonic anhydrase in rats at a constant tissue Pco_2?

SIESJÖ
Approximately 2 mMol/kg tissue water (Kjällquist *et al.* 1969).

SEVERINGHAUS
One may speculate that the rise is due to an increase in carbonic acid concentration. I would like to ask Dr. D. Woodbury whether he thinks that the 5 to 6 mMol/kg H_2O increase which he finds could be due to a higher metabolic rate in the growing brain?

D. WOODBURY
It is not likely since the metabolic rate is lower in the growing brain than in the adult. Also the increased total CO_2 content in the brain of young rats appears to be due to increased amounts of bicarbonate concentration since plasma CO_2 is approximately the same in the infant as in the adult. However, the possibility that the increased amount is all carbonic acid cannot be ruled out.

SEVERINGHAUS
Is there any evidence regarding the diffusion distances and the blood supply to these brains, which might suggest that it is more difficult for metabolically produced CO_2 to get into the blood?

D. WOODBURY
I don't know, it is a possibility but there are no data available to prove it. However, I think it is more likely that the lack of carbonic anhydrase is the reason for the high values of CO_2 in the brain.

SIESJÖ
Dr. Severinghaus, before we studied the effect of acetazolamide on the bicarbonate concentration in the brain we analysed the effect of acetazolamide on the relation between blood and tissue CO_2 tensions (Brzezinsky

et al. 1967). In the later communication (Kjällquist *et al.* 1969) we could thus conclude that the intracellular bicarbonate increased in spite of a normal CO_2 tension and a pH shift in the alkaline direction should result. However, since the tissue lactate and pyruvate concentrations were decreased we had to conclude that the results were equally compatible with an acid shift. This brought us to the same point as you in that we had to wonder if there is not a disequilibrium between CO_2 and H_2CO_3 with a relative increase in the latter when acetazolamide is given.

SEVERINGHAUS

I also find pH decreasing, but interpret this as due to accumulation of H_2CO_3, H^+ and HCO_3^- without an increase in P_{CO_2}, due to inhibition of the dehydration of metabolically produced H_2CO_3 into CO_2.

HORNBEIN

Dr. Severinghaus, I didn't understand the explanation you were offering to Dr. Weyne's observation that brain bicarbonate after sustained metabolic acidosis essentially was unaltered. It would seem to me that the ventilatory responses would tend to have accentuated the difference rather than have masked it. Hyperventilation should have produced an even lower bicarbonate in these animals than if the P_{CO_2} had been held constant.

Kjällquist, Å., Nardini, M. & Siesjö, B. K. (1969) The effect of acetazolamide upon tissue concentrations of bicarbonate, lactate and pyruvate in the rat brain. *Acta physiol. scand.* 77, 241–251.

Brzezinsky, J., Kjällquist, Å. & Siesjö, B. K. (1967). Mean carbon dioxide tension in the brain after carbonic anhydrase inhibition. *J. Physiol. (Lond.).* 188, 13–23.

Kjällquist, Å., Nardini, M. & Siesjö, B. K. (1969) The effect of acetazolamide upon tissue concentrations of bicarbonate, lactate and pyruvate in the rat brain. *Acta physiol. scand.* 77, 241–251.

Hydrogen Ion Distribution and Regulation in Various Rat Tissues

C. D. Withrow, Trudy Elsmore[1], J. A. Williams[2] & D. M. Woodbury[3]

The distribution of hydrogen ions (H⁺) between blood and various tissue fluid compartments has been vigorously studied in recent years, primarily because of rapid advancement in acid-base methodology. The results of most tissue studies suggest that H⁺ are not in electrochemical equilibrium across membranes, and that perhaps a transport system for H⁺ is responsible for the maintenance of the gradients (Woodbury 1965). Little is known, however, about the nature of the supposed H⁺ transport system. Furthermore, even the concentration of H⁺ has not been accurately measured in many tissues. Finally, electrochemical gradients for H⁺ have not been determined directly except in a few instances (Waddell & Bates 1969). The present work was thus undertaken to measure H⁺ concentrations and electrical gradients concurrently in tissues exposed to a variety of experimental conditions; to determine H⁺ distribution in some tissues not heretofore investigated; and to investigate to a limited extent the nature of the proposed H⁺ transport systems.

METHODS

Most blood acid-base values were measured at 37° C with an Instrumentation Laboratory, Boston, S-123, pH – pCO_2 apparatus. Blood values

Department of Pharmacology, College of Medicine, University of Utah, Salt Lake City, Utah 84112, U. S. A.

[1] Present address: Department of Cell Biology and Pharmacology, University of Maryland, Baltimore, Maryland.

[2] Post-doctoral Fellow NIH (1F2 AM40, 018–01) of National Institute of Arthritis and Metabolic Diseases, U. S. P. H. S.

[3] Research Career Awardee (5–K6–NS–13838) of National Institute of Neurological Diseases and Stroke, U. S. P. H. S.

in the smooth muscle experiments (Table 4) were obtained from blood pH measurements and total plasma CO_2 concentrations determined with a Fisher Scientific Co., Pittsburgh, clinical gas partitioner.

Tissue extracellular space values were determined by use of either ^{3}H- or ^{14}C-labeled inulin. Values used for the experiments reported here were as follows (per cent): skeletal muscle *in vivo* = 10.1; liver *in vivo* = 9.6; diaphragm *in vitro* = 18.6; jejunum *in vivo* = 20.7; and uterus *in vivo* = 36.1.

Intracellular acid-base parameters were derived from the distribution of 5,5–dimethyl–2, 4- oxazolidinedione (DMO) according to the suggestions of Waddell & Butler (1959).

Electrolyte analyses were done with an Instrumentation Laboratory, Boston, internal standard flame photometer.

Membrane potentials were measured with a glass micropipette filled with 3 M KCl titrated to pH = 2 with HCl.

The *in vitro* diaphragm experiments were done by the method published by Relman *et al.* (1961).

Electrochemical potentials were calculated from the formula: H^+ electrochemical gradient = 61 (pHi – pHo) – (Em or $E_K{}^+$). A positive sign for the values found indicates that the H^+ gradient is into cells; hence H^+ gradients greater than zero must be achieved by extrusion of H^+ from intracellular into extracellular fluids.

Details of most experimental methods for isotope measurements, electrolyte analyses, and potential recording have been reported previously (Williams *et al.* 1970).

RESULTS

Table 1 summarizes measured electrochemical gradient data for muscle and liver from rats subjected to three different experimental conditions.

It is clear that H^+ in both tissues is always distributed against an electrochemical gradient in the direction that cells contain too little H^+. Another obvious point from the data in Table 1 is that muscle and liver react differently to the various experimental manipulations. After CO_2 and ouabain treatment, and after 24-hour nephrectomy, the electrochemical gradient for H^+ became more positive in liver. In muscle, CO_2 treatment caused little change in the H^+ gradient, while 24-hour nephrectomy and ouabain adminis-

Table 1. Electrochemical potentials for H^+ measured in rat skeletal muscle and liver *in vivo*.[1]

Muscle

	4% CO_2	40% CO_2	1-hour Nephrectomy	24-hour Nephrectomy	Control	Ouabain 10 mg/kg
Resting potential, mV	−92.3±.8[1]	−83.1±.8	−90.9±.6	−77.3±.9	−90.6±.5	−65.1±.6
Blood pH	7.43±.03	6.75±.02	7.45±.01	7.34±.02	7.43±.02	7.27±.01
Intracellular pH	7.06±.02	6.52±.03	6.99±.02	7.04±.03	6.98±.02	6.81±.03
Electrochemical potential, mV	+ 69.8	+ 69.1	+ 62.9	+ 58.9	+ 63.2	+ 37.1

Liver

	4% CO_2	40% CO_2	1-hour Nephrectomy	24-hour Nephrectomy	Control	Ouabain 10 mg/kg
Resting potential, mV	−45.6±.4	−37.2±.5	−43.1±.3	−47.6±.4	−43.8±.4	−47.9±.6
Blood pH	7.43±.03	6.75±.02	7.45±.01	7.34±.02	7.43±.02	7.27±.01
Intracellular pH	7.23±.02	6.84±.01	7.20±.02	7.29±.02	7.23±.02	7.14±.04
Electrochemical potential, mV	+ 33.4	+ 42.7	+ 27.9	+ 44.6	+ 31.6	+ 40.0

[1] All values are means ± S. E., with the exception that the electrochemical gradients were calculated from average values as indicated in the text.

tration clearly made the gradient less positive. In animals given a high CO_2 concentration, both muscle and liver cells were depolarized. However, 24-hour nephrectomy and treatment with ouabain produced a significant depolarization of muscle cells, but the same treatments caused the membrane potential to become more negative in liver cells of the same animals. The mechanisms underlying the hyperpolarization of liver cells in contrast to muscle cells have been discussed elsewhere (Williams *et al.* 1970) and will not be considered further here. Regardless of the mechanisms involved, the rising H^+ electrochemical gradient in liver, in face of an increased electrical gradient forcing H^+ into cells, suggests that liver cells respond to acid challenges by an increase in the outward movement of H^+ ions. In muscle, the depolarization observed in all experiments would increase the movement of H^+ from cells and thus decrease the electrochemical gradient. However, in the nephrectomy studies and in the CO_2 experiments, the muscle electrical gradient decreases more than the observed fall in electrochemical gradient. Thus, in two of three experimental situations, muscle exhibits a homeostatic mechanism that cannot be accounted for by changes in the membrane potential alone.

Table 2. Electrochemical potentials calculated for skeletal muscle from rats treated *in vivo* with ouabain and challenged with acid loads.

	Saline			
	Control	NH$_4$Cl 6 mEq/kg	12% CO$_2$	24% CO$_2$
E$_K$+, mV	−95.3[1]	−84.0	−92.0	−84.7
Blood pH	7.46±.01[2]	7.22±.03	7.08±.02	6.90±.02
Intracellular pH	6.96±.02[2]	6.88±.03	6.73±.04	6.60±.02
Electrochemical potential, mV	+64.9[3]	+63.3	+70.7	+66.4

	Ouabain, 20 mg/kg			
	Ouabain	Ouabain + 6 mEq/kg NH$_4$Cl	Ouabain 12% CO$_2$	Ouabain 24% CO$_2$
E$_K^+$, mV	−67.7	−64.1	−63.5	−60.9
Blood pH	7.38±.02	7.09±.01	7.02±.01	6.84±.01
Intracellular pH	6.95±.02	6.87±.01	6.69±.02	6.61±.03
Electrochemical potential, mV	+41.6	+50.7	+43.5	+46.9

[1] E$_K^+$ calculated from average muscle cell and ECF K$^+$ values. [2] All values are means ± S. E. [3] Calculated from average pH and E$_K^+$ potential values.

The results given in Table 2 for the saline-treated group confirm the muscle findings in Table 1, namely, that the change in the total electrochemical gradient is always less than that predicted from the electrical gradient alone, and, in fact, the gradient increases in two of the three experiments. Or, stated in another way, changes in the muscle electrochemical H$^+$ gradient during acidosis cannot be accounted for if it is assumed that H$^+$ is passively distributed across cell membranes. A second finding given in Table 2 is that ouabain does not appear to affect the ability of the cell to handle additional acid loads, since the change in H$^+$ electrochemical gradient produced by ouabain alone is not decreased by CO$_2$ or NH$_4$Cl treatment.

The *in vitro* experiments summarized in Table 3 show that muscle can increase its electrochemical gradient even when changes in membrane potential are prevented during ouabain treatment and/or acidosis. *In vitro*, ouabain treatment appears to prevent the marked rise in electrochemical gradients observed in control tissues during a carbonic acid or a low-bicarbonate acidosis.

Table 3. Electrochemical potentials calculated with data obtained from rat diaphragm incubated *in vitro* with ouabain and challenged with acid loads.[1])

	Saline		
	Control	Low HCO$_3$ (5.1 mM/1)	High CO$_2$ (pCO$_2$ = 90 mm Hg)
E_K^+, mV	−84.7[1])	−80.7	−83.9
Bath pH	7.46±.01	6.85±.01	7.02±.01
Intracellular pH	7.21±.02	6.88±.03	6.91±.02
Electrochemical gradient, mV	+69.5	+82.7	+77.2
	80 mg/1 Ouabain		
E_K^+, mV	−70.0	−71.5	−73.2
Bath pH	7.48±.02	6.86±.01	6.96±.01
Intracellular pH	7.30±.02	6.75±.01	6.75±.02
Electrochemical gradient, mV	+59.0	+64.9	+60.4

[1]) See footnotes to Table 2 for explanation of the derivation of values given here.

The acid-base data given in Table 4 are difficult to analyse because a calculation of H$^+$ electrochemical gradients is not possible in all cases. In normal animals, membrane potential values of approximately 42 mV (Casteels & Huriyama 1965) and 60 mV (Burnstock *et al.* 1963) for uterus and jejunum, respectively, have been reported. By use of these values and the extracellular and intracellular pH's given in Table 4, it can be shown that H$^+$ is distributed against an electrochemical gradient in both uterus and jejunum. How well this gradient is preserved in acidosis and alkalosis cannot be surmised from the data here. However, if H$^+$ were passively distributed, for example, in the uterus of animals given 7.5 mM/kg NH$_4$Cl, the membrane potential would have to be approximately + 17 mV. Similar calculations for other cases indicate that it is not likely that H$^+$ is passively distributed in any of the situations studied.

DISCUSSIONS AND CONCLUSIONS

Previous work from our laboratory (Withrow & Woodbury 1964) and the experiments of Keynes (1965) suggested that Na$^+$ and H$^+$ might compete for a common site for extrusion from cells. Since ouabain is a potent inhibitor of Na$^+$ transport, the ouabain experiments reported here were done to determine how Na$^+$ transport inhibition might affect acid-base balance.

Table 4. Extracellular and intracellular acid-base values of rats exposed to various acid-base distortions.

	CO$_2$					NH$_4$Cl (mM/kg)		NaHCO$_3$ (mM/kg)	
	Hyperventilation to 40 % CO$_2$					4.0	7.5	2.5	9.5
	(12)[1]	(6)	(12)	(7)	(6)	(12)	(7)	(12)	(6)
Plasma									
pH	7.60[2]	7.26	7.09	6.81	6.62	7.31	7.16	7.53	7.84
	.02	.03	.02	.01	.02	.02	.03	.03	.04
pCO$_2$ (mm Hg)	20.3	51.8	86.2	169.5	256.8	26.7	28.2	30.1	19.7
	1.0	4.5	3.4	4.0	8.2	1.5	2.6	2.1	2.0
HCO$_3^-$ (mM/l)	19.0	22.1	25.0	26.3	25.6	13.2	10.1	24.1	31.9
	0.6	0.4	0.5	0.4	1.2	0.3	1.0	0.5	0.5
Tissues									
Skeletal Muscle pH$_i$	7.23	6.80	6.81	6.74	6.38	6.88	6.81	7.00	7.25
	.03	.03	.03	.03	.05	.06	.06	.03	.04
Jejunum pH$_i$	7.30	7.04	7.02	6.89	6.77	7.21	7.01	7.26	7.34
	.03	.03	.03	.02	.06	.03	.10	.03	.11
Uterus pH$_i$	7.49	7.01	7.14	6.99	6.72	7.15	6.78	7.09	7.14
	.06	.15	.04	.04	.05	.05	.09	.07	.19

[1]) Number in parentheses denotes number of animals in each group.
[2]) All values are means ± S. E.

In *in vivo* experiments with skeletal muscle, ouabain clearly reduced the electrochemical gradient for H$^+$. In most experiments, both in normal and in acid-challenged rats (Table 2), the change in the total H$^+$ gradient is about the same as the change in the electrical gradient. Because the changes in electrical gradients are almost certainly due to inhibition of Na$^+$ transport by ouabain, these data suggest that ouabain does not affect H$^+$ regulation, except indirectly. The lack of an effect of a marked depolarization of muscle on transmembrane H$^+$ distribution has been reported before (Kostyuk & Sorokina 1961), and was attributed to the fact that it appears that a considerable time is necessary to change intracellular H$^+$ concentration. The present results were obtained in acute experiments, and it is possible that not enough time was allowed for equilibration. On the other hand, in some ouabain-treated animals (Table 1) and in *in vitro* acid-challenge experiments (Table 3), the change in total H$^+$ electrochemical gradient is more than can be accounted for by changes in the membrane potential. Further, the finding that ouabain prevents the acid-induced rise in electrochemical gradients *in vitro* (Table 3) also suggests that it affects H^+ movements directly. Thus, the relationships between Na^+ and H^+ movements are still not clear. It is quite likely that chronic experiments might be of value for settling this question.

The various acid-base distortions have different effects on the H^+ electrochemical gradient. CO_2 has relatively little effect on transmembrane potentials, but high concentrations markedly change pH both inside and outside cells. NH_4Cl and $NaHCO_3$ raise and lower, respectively, extracellular H^+ much more rapidly than they affect intracellular H^+, particularly when ventilation is regulated, but the two drugs do not cause large changes in membrane potential. Nephrectomy of 24-hour duration results in a rise in extracellular H^+ and K^+, thus causing a change in both the chemical and electrical gradient for H^+. It is therefore difficult to make general statements about the regulation of H^+ gradients in tissues; however, some definite points are suggested by the data presented above.

First, the observation was made that in every tissue studied and in every experimental situation, H^+ was always distributed against an electrochemical gradient. Because the tissue studied represented several cell types – high membrane potential, excitable cells (skeletal muscle), low membrane potential, excitable cells (smooth muscle), low membrane potential, nonexcitable cells (liver) – it can probably be concluded that H^+ is generally out of electrochemical equilibrium in tissues.

Second, severe carbonic and noncarbonic acid distortions never eliminated the H^+ electrochemical gradient. In fact, acidosis, in many experiments in muscle and always in liver, caused the H^+ gradient to become more positive. Therefore, it appeared that the H^+ regulatory system is not easily compromised and may consist of a homeostatic mechanism which is stimulated to extrude H^+ from cells. The purpose of the homeostatic mechanism seems to be to keep cell pH constant, rather than to maintain a constant H^+ electrochemical gradient.

Finally, it is clear that intracellular acid-base regulation is a complex interaction of changes in both the electrical and chemical H^+ gradients and that the interaction differs from tissue to tissue. There is, therefore, much additional work needed concerning the nature of H^+ transport in tissue. Of particular importance are answers to the questions of how cellular mechanisms respond to chronic acid-base distortions, and of which factors stimulate, inhibit, or qualitatively modify the exchange of H^+ between intracellular and extracellular fluids.

ACKNOWLEDGMENTS

Experimental work supported by U. S. Public Health Service program project grant 5–P01–NS–04553 from the National Institute of Neurological Disease and Stroke, U. S. P. H. S.

REFERENCES

Burnstock, G., Holman, M. E. & Prosser, C. L. (1963) Electrophysiology of smooth muscle. *Physiol. Rev. 43*, 482–527.

Casteels, R. T. & Kuriyama, H. (1965) Membrane potential and ionic content in pregnant and non-pregnant rat myometrium *J. Physiol. 177*, 263–287.

Keynes, R. D. (1965) Some further observations on the sodium efflux in frog muscle. *J. Physiol. 178*, 305–325.

Kostyuk, P. G. & Sorokina, Z. A. (1961) On the mechanism of hydrogen ion distribution between cell protoplasm and the medium. In *Membrane Transport and Metabolism,* ed. Kleinzeller, A. & Kotyk, A., pp. 193–203. Academic Press, New York.

Relman, A. S., Gorham, G. W. & Levinsky, N. G. (1961) The relation between external potassium concentration and the electrolyte content of isolated rat muscle in the steady state. *J. clin. Invest. 40*, 386–393.

Waddell, W. J. & Butler, T. C. (1959) Calculation of intracellular pH from the distribution of 5,5–dimethyl–2, 4–oxazolidinedione (DMO). Application to skeletal muscle of the dog. *J. clin. Invest. 38*, 720–729.

Waddell, W. J. & Bates, R. G. (1969) Intracellular pH. *Physiol. Rev. 49*, 285–329.

Williams, J. A., Withrow, C. D. & Woodbury, D. M. (1970) Effects of ouabain and diphenylhydantoin on transmembrane potentials, intracellular electrolytes, and cell pH of rat muscle and liver *in vivo*. Submitted to *J. Physiol. (Lond.)*.

Withrow, C. D. & Woodbury, D. M. (1964) Direct and indirect effects of desoxycorticosterone (DOC) on skeletal muscle electrolyte and acid-base metabolism. In *Hormonal Steriods: Biochemistry, Pharmacology and Therapeutics:* Proc. 1st Int. Cong. on Hormonal Steroids, Vol. I, pp. 503–513. Academic Press, New York.

Woodbury, J. W. (1965) Regulation of pH. In *Physiology and Biophysics,* 19th ed., ed. Ruch, T. C. & Patton, H. D., pp. 899–934. W. B. Saunders, Philadelphia and London.

DISCUSSION

SEVERINGHAUS

When the rat diaphragm was soaked *in vitro* with ouabain you still had sizable sodium potentials. Is this a matter of time or doesn't ouabain completely inhibit the pump?

WITHROW

I don't know the answer to your question. With these doses of ouabain the intracellular sodium concentration doubles within the one hour that one works with the tissue, but, as you pointed out, a sizable sodium potential remains.

SEVERINGHAUS

What if you wait a day or two?

WITHROW

With ouabain you don't have this option, because the duration of action is so short. I don't know if anyone has been able to maintain inhibition that long.

SEVERINGHAUS

If ouabain stops active Na pumping and thus permits the battery to run down can we then draw any conclusions about the hydrogen and sodium gradients and the potential? Perhaps each species reaches equilibrium at different rates due to differing permeabilities.

WITHROW

The problem is that the sodium battery seems to be running down, but the H^+ battery seems to be increasing in activity slightly. We have the consistent finding that when you challenge ouabain-treated animals with massive H^+ loads the electrochemical gradient for H^+ goes up.

MINES

It seems to me that even though the sodium-potassium pump may be completely inhibited, I haven't seen any really solid evidence that the hydrogen ion pump is tightly linked in this case to the sodium-potassium pump. It seems to me that the evidence that was shown means that there may be a possibility of having a hydrogen ion regulating pump which is not necessarily dependent on a functional sodium-potassium pump.

WITHROW

We got interested in the Na^+ – H^+ problem because when you make an animal chronically deficient with potassium there are three consistent observations: (1) an extracellular alkalosis (2) an intracellular acidosis and (3) an intracellular accumulation of sodium. If one assumes that there is a coupled sodium-potassium pump and if one also makes the assumption that hydrogen ions are being extruded by the same mechanism, then a lowering of the extracellular potassium concentration would raise the intracellular sodium concentration and also increase intracellular hydrogen ion concentration. It would also be consistent with the fact that intracellular potassium concentration goes down. The first time we gave the high doses of ouabain we saw changes in he hydrogen ion concentration of 0.2 pH unit and I should mention that Grayman *et al.* (1968) found that incubation of the isolated frog brain with ouabain *in vitro* causes an intracellular acidosis. However, I must say that if one considers absolute changes in the concentrations of hydrogen ion in our experiments the data are disappointing. If you start looking at the electrochemical gradients, the data become a little more convincing.

MINES

Then the next step is perhaps to try to swamp the ability to pump hydrogen ions out in some other way? You mentioned sodium loading.

WITHROW

This is why we have gone to *in vitro* frog sartorius preparations which we can load with sodium. We are looking at the effect of temperature and on the effects of elevated and lowered external potassium on Na^+ and H^+ in the cells of this preparation. There are data in literature, particularly by the Relman group in Boston (Hudson & Relman 1962), which show that

Grayman, G., Bradbury, M. V. & Kleeman, C. R. (1968) Intracellular pH of the amphibian brain incubated in vitro. *Life Sci. 7*, 499–504.

Hudson, J. B. & Relman, A. S. (1962) Effects of potassium and rubidium on muscle cell bicarbonate. *Amer. J. Physiol. 203*, 209–214.

if you raise extracellular potassium, then you can actually get an intracellular alkalosis.

CAMERON

I have some provisional results on the intracellular pH of the isolated frog brain *in vitro*. If this is incubated in a fluid of raised potassium concentration there is a significant increase in the pH of the intracellular fluid measured by the DMO technique. It would appear that brain resembles muscle under these circumstances.

KRUHØFFER

Dr. J. W. Woodbury, there were no large pH changes here, but may we ask on the basis of the permeability coefficients that you estimated, and the intracellular buffer capacity that we could make a guess of, how long time it would take for us to have a change in the pH of 0.1 after completely stopping the hydrogen pump.

J. W. WOODBURY

Assuming the flux of HCO_3^- is 2×10^{-12} moles/cm^2 $\times$ sec, the same as that of Na^+ in frog muscle, a fiber radius of 40μ, and an internal buffer value of 40 slykes, then slightly over one hour would be required to change the pH_i by 0.1 pH units.

SEVERINGHAUS

When you use ouabain I think there is also a large intracellular movement of water which must bring anions with it. Whether it is chloride or bicarbonate depends on their permeabilities. Therefore the resulting change in hydrogen ion concentration may be influenced more by this movement than by the active transport of hydrogen.

Bicarbonate, Chloride and Lactate in Brain During Acid-Base Alterations

J. Weyne & I. Leusen

In recent years the acid-base balance of brain and cerebrospinal fluid (CSF) has been studied by many authors, and different mechanisms have been proposed to explain the changes observed in CSF in respiratory and non-respiratory acidosis and alkalosis.

During metabolic acid-base changes in blood it was observed that the pH and the bicarbonate concentration ($[HCO_3^-]$) in CSF are only very slightly influenced in acute conditions (cf. De Bersaques 1955, De Bersaques & Leusen 1954, Robin *et al.* 1958, Leusen 1965). More prolonged changes in plasma $[HCO_3^-]$ are reflected in the CSF (de Thurzo & Katzenelbogen 1935, Fencl *et al.* 1966, Chazan *et al.* 1969) but the pH appears to be also very well maintained within normal range in these conditions. Similar observations were made in clinical studies (for the literature cf. Mitchell 1966).

More rapid changes are observed to occur, on the other hand, in the $[HCO_3^-]$ of CSF during respiratory changes of the acid-base equilibrium. These changes, which are rather moderate in acute conditions, become progressively more pronounced with time. The increased hydrogen ion concentration ($[H^+]$) seen in CSF in acute respiratory acidosis as a result of the increased carbon dioxide tension (P_{CO_2}), is thus progressively normalized by an elevation of the $[HCO_3^-]$ (Swanson & Rosengren 1962, Bleich *et al.* 1964, Reichart *et al.* 1965, Lee *et al.* 1969). In respiratory alkalosis a slow but progressive decrease of $[HCO_3^-]$ in CSF is observed which progressively normalizes the pH which is shifted by the lowered P_{CO_2}. In acute experiments this decrease concords with an increase of the lactate concentration in CSF (Van Vaerenbergh *et al.* 1965, Plum & Posner 1967) while in more pro-

Laboratory of Normal and Pathological Physiology, State University of Ghent, De Pintelaan 115, B-9000 Ghent, Belgium.

longed conditions an increase of the chloride concentration ($[Cl^-]$) is observed (Severinghaus *et al.* 1963).

All these observations indicate that modifications of $[HCO_3^-]$ in the CSF are not simply related to modifications of the $[HCO_3^-]$ in blood plasma.

Since CSF has no intrinsic capacity to form bicarbonate, the changes which occur in $[HCO_3^-]$ must be derived elsewhere. Blood and brain must thus be considered as potential sources.

Active mechanisms involving blood-brain barrier activity have been advanced for the regulation of $[HCO_3^-]$ and $[H^+]$ in CSF and extracellular fluid of the brain by Pappenheimer, Severinghaus and Mitchell (Severinghaus *et al.* 1963, Fencl *et al.* 1966). Such mechanisms would maintain the pH in the extracellular fluid of the central nervous system constant within a very narrow range. This hypothesis, however, was not generally accepted (cf. Loeschcke 1965), and more recently the theory was advanced by Siesjö & Kjällquist (1969) that $[HCO_3^-]$ in brain extracellular fluid and CSF is controlled in a passive way by the double action of plasma $[HCO_3^-]$ and the electrical potential difference between plasma and CSF which varies in function of plasma pH (Held *et al.* 1964, cf. Kjällquist 1970).

Another possibility which must be considered is that the changes in brain extracellular fluid and CSF are more directly related to changes which occur primarily in the brain tissue itself. Such an exchange mechanism was suggested by Swanson & Rosengren (1962) to explain the compensatory modifications occurring in CSF $[HCO_3^-]$ during hypocapnia and hypercapnia. Others, however, did not agree with the suggestion of primary brain regulation of CSF $[HCO_3^-]$ (cf. Severinghaus 1965).

However, the possible role of brain tissue, or at least of some of its cell types in the buffering of brain extracellular fluid and CSF, merits a close examination. Indeed, brain tissue shows important buffering capacities towards CO_2 as has been demonstrated *in vivo* and *in vitro* (Brodie & Woodbury 1958, Nicholls 1958, cf. Pontén 1966), and the presence of carbonic anhydrase in glial structures together with important intracellular chloride concentrations (Koch *et al.* 1962, Reed *et al.* 1964) allows consideration of the possibility of rapid buffering and exchange mechanisms such as are present in the erythrocytes.

The possible influence of the brain tissue on the CSF composition has been clearly indicated by the observations made on the lactate concentration during hyperventilation. Thus it was found that an intense hyperventilation is accompanied by an important elevation of the lactate levels in CSF. Infusion experiments during identical time intervals have shown that this elevation is not due to exchange with the lactate of the blood, which is also elevated in these conditions (Van Vaerenbergh *et al.* 1965). On the other hand, a more rapid and more important increase of the lactate concentration was observed in brain tissue itself (Leusen & Demeester 1966, Leusen *et al.* 1967) suggesting that the increase of lactate in CSF results directly from diffusion out of the brain. During prolonged hyperventilation, an equilibrium of the lactate concentration in CSF with the brain tissue lactate was found to occur after 3 to 6 hours (Plum & Posner 1967).

In the experiments to be described, the bicarbonate concentration of brain was examined in various conditions in which the bicarbonate concentration in blood was changed.

1. BICARBONATE CONCENTRATION DURING ACUTE P_{CO_2} CHANGES: THE CO_2 DISSOCIATION CURVE

The variations of [HCO_3] in plasma, brain and muscle in control anaesthetized and curarized rats exposed for 20 minutes to different P_{CO_2} levels are summarized in Fig. 1. Different carbon dioxide tension values were realized by appropriate ventilation patterns as described elsewhere (Weyne *et al.* 1970a, b). At the end of the exposure period, arterial blood was anaerobically sampled and the brain was frozen and analysed as described (Weyne *et al.* 1968, 1970a, b). In other rats, the adductor muscle of the thigh was frozen a few instants after exposure by crushing between 2 large aluminium tongs chilled in liquid nitrogen (cf. Wollenberger *et al.* 1960) and the muscle tissue was analysed as brain. All concentrations determined in the tissue were corrected for the trapped blood. The blood content of the frozen brain tissue was determined by measuring the haemoglobin content and, for muscle tissue, by comparing the radioactivity 30 minutes after i. v. injection of Cr^{51} labelled erythrocytes. Water content was determined by drying tissue to constant weight at 105° C, and for plasma a water content of 93 per cent was assumed.

From these data the mean [HCO_3] in the brain water (including intracellular and large cavity fluid) was calculated as described by Pontén (1966) (cf. Weyne *et al.* 1968). For muscle tissue, intracellular [HCO_3] and pH

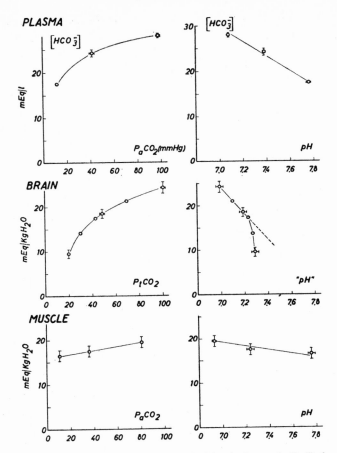

Fig. 1. Left panels: Bicarbonate concentrations in blood plasma (mEq/l), brain (mEq/kg H_2O) and muscle (mEq/kg intracellular H_2O) at different CO_2 tensions maintained during 20 minutes in anaesthetized and curarized rats (mean ± S. E. M.). The panels on the right side illustrate the [HCO₃] data in function of blood pH, composite brain pH and intracellular pH of muscle.

were calculated assuming P_{CO_2} in the tissue equal to Pa_{CO_2} and using appropriate values for s and pK (cf. Clancy & Brown 1966). The Cl⁻ space was used as a measure of the extracellular space; in that calculation, however, an intracellular [Cl⁻] of 1/24th of the extracellular [Cl⁻] was assumed (cf. Graham *et al.* 1967).

The left panels of Fig. 1 indicate the respective [HCO₃] increases with increasing P_{CO_2} in the blood plasma, brain water and muscle intracellular

23*

water. The very important HCO_3^- formation with carbon dioxide tension rise in brain is manifest. Such relationships between $[HCO_3^-]$ and P_{CO_2} are also observed *in vitro,* in which case the effect is entirely due to physicochemical mechanisms. Control experiments show that P_{CO_2} and $[HCO_3^-]$ in blood plasma and total brain CO_2 do not vary between 20 and 50 minutes after a step change in P_{CO_2}.

2. DISPLACEMENTS OF THE CO_2 DISSOCIATION CURVE

It is necessary to distinguish between CO_2 dissociation curves obtained *in vivo* and curves obtained *in vitro.* Different results can be obtained due to other factors *in vivo* than pure physicochemical buffering. Factors of interest are transport of HCO_3^- and H^+ ions between compartments within the body or within the tissues and reaction of bicarbonate with organic acids. The action of such factors on $[HCO_3^-]$ results in a disturbance of the normal relationship between $[HCO_3^-]$ and P_{CO_2}. This is illustrated by a displacement of the CO_2 dissociation curve. Such an effect can be easily studied in a Davenport diagram relating $[HCO_3^-]$ to pH. Such diagrams are presented in the right panels of Fig. 1.

a. *Acute hyperventilation*

In blood plasma and muscle, a linear relation between $[HCO_3^-]$ and pH is observed during acute modification of P_{CO_2}. In brain, a marked change of the slope of the curve towards the "pH" axis occurs during intense hypocapnia (Weyne *et al.* 1968) (Fig. 2). A similar change in slope is seen in the P_{CO_2}/pH diagram. These findings indicate a smaller increase of composite pH in brain during intense hypocapnia *in vivo* than expected from determination of the CO_2 buffer capacity *in vitro.* In the same experimental conditions there is an almost exponential rise of the brain tissue lactate (Leusen & Demeester 1966, Leusen *et al.* 1967, cf. Bain & Klein 1949). Such a change in the slope of the brain $[HCO_3^-]$/pH curve during acutely induced intense hyperventilation was also observed after prolonged hypercapnia and hyperventilation (Weyne *et al.* 1968). In these conditions, brain lactate also increased in function of increasing brain composite pH (Weyne *et al.* 1970a).

b. *Acute hypoxia*

The influence of lactate formation on brain $[HCO_3^-]$ is further illustrated by

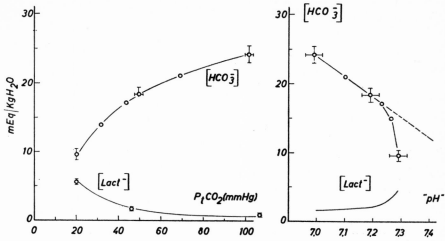

Fig. 2. Left panels: Bicarbonate and lactate concentrations in brain (mEq/kg H_2O) at different CO_2 tensions maintained during 20 minutes in anaesthetized and curarized rats (mean ± S .E. M.). The panel on the right side illustrates [HCO_3^-] and lactate in function of composite brain pH.

the results of experiments in which anaesthetized and curarized rats were artificially ventilated during 20 minutes with a hypoxic gas mixture (7% O_2 in nitrogen) (Fig. 3). During hypoxemia, brain [HCO_3^-] was found to be several mEq/kg H_2O lower than in the normoxic brains at the two P_{CO_2} levels studied. Such a "non-respiratory" fall of brain [HCO_3^-] during hypoxia was also reported for cat brain (Swanson 1966). In these experiments brain lactate markedly increased to the same level as when Pa_{CO_2} is lowered to about 12 mm Hg during intense hyperventilation with air (Leusen & Demeester 1966, Leusen *et al.* 1967).

c. *Prolonged hypercapnia and hyperventilation*

During prolonged hypercapnia and hypocapnia, compensatory adaptations, e. g. by renal mechanisms, contribute to shift the CO_2 dissociation curve so that blood pH tends to normalize. Whereas these mechanisms are rather slow in man and dog and require several days to attain a steady state (cf. Schwartz *et al.* 1965, Engel *et al.* 1968), it is seen in the rat that plasma [HCO_3^-] increases rapidly during hypercapnia and reaches a steady state within 24 hours (Warren *et al.* 1970, cf. Levitin *et al.* 1958). In brain, shifts of the CO_2

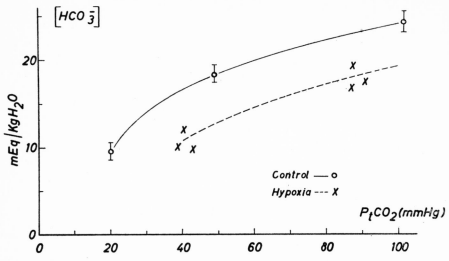

Fig. 3. Bicarbonate concentrations in brain (mEq/kg H_2O) at different CO_2 tensions maintained during 20 minutes in anaesthetized and curarized rats (X: values found during ventilation with a hypoxic gas mixture; O: values found during ventilation with 20 % O_2).

dissociation curve have been demonstrated after prolonged respiratory acidosis and alkalosis (Brown 1950, Kazemi *et al.* 1967, Weyne *et al.* 1968).

To study the influence of a prolonged hypercapnia and hypocapnia on the CO_2 dissociation curves, unanaesthetized rats were maintained during $6 \pm \frac{1}{2}$ and $24 \pm \frac{1}{2}$ hours in a small chamber through which 12% CO_2 in air or 10% O_2 in nitrogen was flushed. After this exposure period the rats were anaesthetized, curarized and artificially ventilated during 20 minutes. In individual animals of each group different Pa_{CO_2} levels were realized and arterial blood, muscle and brain tissue sampled and analysed.

The acid-base parameters of blood illustrate after 6 and 24 hours the influence of the compensatory reactions occurring during prolonged respiratory acidosis and alkalosis (Fig. 4). "Standard" plasma [HCO_3^-] is higher after 6 and 24 hours hypercapnia than after 6 and 24 hours hypocapnia. The CO_2 dissociation curves illustrate the higher [HCO_3^-] at each P_{CO_2} after hypercapnia. The CO_2 dissociation curve of control animals, studied together with the 24-hour group, lies between the curves of the hypercapnic and hypocapnic animals. As a consequence, a lower pH is obtained in blood at each

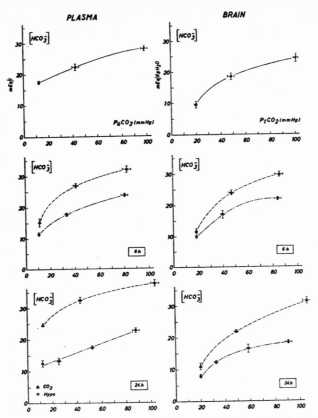

Fig. 4. Bicarbonate concentrations in blood plasma (mEq/l) and brain (mEq/l kg H₂O) at different CO_2 tensions maintained during 20 minutes in anaesthetized and curarized rats. 2 upper panels: data in normal control rats. 2 middle panels: data in rats after 6 hours hypercapnia (– – – –) or hypoxic hyperventilation (– · – · –). 2 lower panels: data in rats after 24 hours hypercapnia (– – – –) or hypoxic hyperventilation (– · – · –).

imposed P_{CO_2} after prolonged hypocapnia and a higher pH after prolonged hypercapnia.

Essentially the same alterations are observed in the [HCO₃] of the combined water phase of the brain, where also two CO_2 dissociation curves are obtained. The similarity of the compensatory mechanisms of brain and blood during prolnged hypercapnia and hypocapnia in the rat is thus striking.

d. *Prolonged non-respiratory variations in blood*

During primary alteration of [HCO₃] in the blood, CSF [HCO₃] remains very stable in the initial period. In the brain too, [HCO₃] is not altered by an acute change of plasma [HCO₃] during 1 and 6 hours (Swanson 1966, Siesjö & Pontén 1966, Weyne *et al.* 1968). We have further investigated the CO_2 dissociation curve of brain *in vivo* when changes in blood [HCO₃] are produced by i. v. infusion of HCl or $NaHCO_3$ solutions during 25 minutes, 6 hours and 24 hours (Weyne *et al.* 1970b). The *in vivo* CO_2 dissociation curves were determined by maintaining the rats after anaesthesia and curarization for 20 minutes at different P_{CO_2} levels. The shifts induced in the CO_2 dissociation curve of the blood were very similar to the changes obtained during prolonged hypercapnia and hypocapnia (Fig. 5). The relation between [HCO₃] and imposed P_{CO_2} found in the brain water shows that the CO_2 dissociation curve of the brain is not modified after 6 hours infusion despite the marked shift in the blood.

After 24 hours, the CO_2 dissociation curves of the brains of the acidotic and alkalotic animals show a small difference. At identical P_{CO_2}, brain [HCO₃] is approximately 1.5 mEq/kg H_2O higher after $NaHCO_3$ infusion than after the HCl infusion, which represents a statistically significant difference. It is obvious that this non-respiratory difference of brain [HCO₃] observed after 24-hour infusion is out of proportion to the differences found after prolonged periods of hypercapnia and hypocapnia, while the differences in blood plasma can be directly compared. Measurements of the P_{CO_2} in arterial blood during the 24-hour infusion period indicate, moreover, that the small changes in brain [HCO₃] between the two groups of animals can in fact be related to small differences in carbon dioxide tension.

e. *Prolonged hypercapnia combined with HCl infusion and prolonged hyperventilation combined with $NaHCO_3$ infusion*

In order to dissociate [HCO₃] changes in blood and brain, combined experiments were carried out in rats in which respiratory and non-respiratory changes were simultaneously induced. Unanaesthetized rats were maintained during $6 \pm \frac{1}{2}$ hours in a chamber flushed with 12% CO_2 in air or with 10% O_2 in nitrogen. Via a small plastic tubing, the animals kept in hypercapnia received simultaneously a HCl solution while the hypoxic hyperventilating rats were infused with a $NaHCO_3$ solution. After this exposure period the animals were anaesthetized, curarized and artificially ventilated during 20 minutes with air containing CO_2 in order to realize an arterial P_{CO_2} of $\pm$ 80 mm Hg. The results are illustrated in the two lower panels

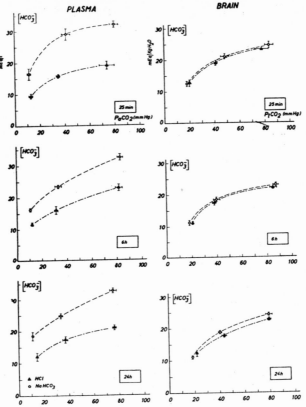

Fig. 5. Bicarbonate concentrations in blood plasma (mEq/l) and brain (mEq/kg H_2O) at different CO_2 tensions maintained during 20 minutes in anaesthetized and curarized rats. 2 upper panels: data obtained in animals infused with HCl ($-\cdot - \cdot -$) or $NaHCO_3$ solutions ($- - -$) during 25 minutes prior to the end of the experiment. 2 middle panels: data obtained in animals infused during 6 hours prior to the end of the experiment. Anaesthesia was induced about 1 hour before the end of the experiment. Infusion started with a large dose during 25 minutes as in the first group followed by a slow infusion. 2 lower panels: data obtained in animals infused during 24 hours prior to the end of the experiment. Further procedure as in the preceding group.

of the left part of Fig. 6 and compared with the results after simple hypercapnia and hypocapnia (upper panels). Due to overcompensation by the infusions, a non-respiratory decrease of plasma [HCO₃] was realized in the hypercapnic rats and an increase in the hypocapnic animals. Despite the reverse of the shift between the two CO_2 dissociation curves in the blood,

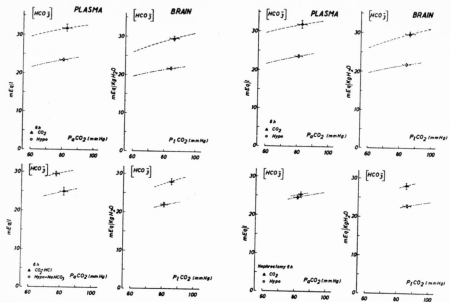

Fig. 6. Bicarbonate concentrations in blood plasma (mEq/l) and brain (mEq/kg H_2O) at identical high CO_2 tensions maintained during 20 minutes in anaesthetized and curarized rats. *Left part* lower panels: data obtained in animals after 6 hours hypercapnia combined with a HCl infusion (– · – · –) and after 6 hours hypoxic hyperventilation combined with a $NaHCO_3$ infusion (– – – –). Anaesthesia was induced about 1 hour prior to the end of the experiment. Upper panels: data in animals after 6 hours hypercapnia and hypoxic hyperventilation (cf. Fig. 4). *Right part* lower panels: data obtained in nephrectomized animals after 6 hours hypercapnia and 6 hours hypoxic hyperventilation. Upper panels: data obtained in control rats after 6 hours hypercapnia and 6 hours hypoxic hyperventilation (cf. Fig. 4).

the shift of [HCO₃⁻] in the brain was identical as in simple hypercapnia and hypocapnia.

f. *Prolonged hypercapnia and hyperventilation in nephrectomized rats*

Rats were bilaterally nephrectomized under ether anaesthesia. About 1 hour after nephrectomy, they were kept for $6 \pm \frac{1}{2}$ hours in a hypercapnic atmosphere (12% CO_2 in air) or in 10% O_2 in nitrogen, provoking a hypocapnia by hyperventilation. After this exposure period the [HCO₃⁻] in brain was investigated as in the previous series of experiments. The results are illustrated in the two lower panels of the right part of Fig. 6 and (upper panels). In the nephrectomized rats very similar [HCO$_3^-$] concentrations were observed at constant P$_{CO_2}$ in the plasma after 6 hours hypercapnia and hypocapnia, while the brain [HCO$_3^-$] still showed a manifest difference between the two groups of animals.

3. MODIFICATIONS OF THE CHLORIDE CONCENTRATIONS DURING ACID-BASE DISTURBANCES AND THEIR RELATION TO [HCO$_3^-$].

a. *Modifications of [Cl$^-$] in blood plasma and brain*

Our results show no changes in [Cl$^-$] of brain and plasma when P$_{CO_2}$ is altered during a short period of 20 minutes. A constant [Cl$^-$] in blood plasma was also found by Cohen *et al.* (1964) and the underlying mechanisms were discussed by Böning (1968). A constant brain [Cl$^-$] during acute alteration of P$_{CO_2}$ was also reported by Woodbury *et al.* (1958).

Marked differences are seen, however, in the mean [Cl$^-$] of blood plasma of rats maintained for some time in an altered acid-base status. After prolonged hypocapnia, [Cl$^-$] in brain is also increased in comparison to the values found in the rats kept in hypercapnia. After 6 hours the differences were 10.0 mEq/l and 1.5 mEq/kg H$_2$O respectively in blood plasma and brain. After 24 hours they were respectively 14.0 mEq/l and 4.7 mEq/kg H$_2$O.

In the experimental groups in which non-respiratory modifications of the acid-base balance were produced by HCl or NaHCO$_3$ infusion, differences of 11.5, 8.4 and 9.0 mEq/l were found in blood plasma respectively after 25 minutes, 6 hours and 24 hours, the HCl infused animals showing the higher concentrations. In the brain no difference is observed after 25 minutes infusion, whereas after 6 and 24 hours differences of 1.8 and 2.6 mEq/kg H$_2$O were found.

After nephrectomy the [Cl$^-$] of brain and plasma showed no changes between the hypercapnic and the hypocapnic rats.

After 6 hours hypercapnia with simultaneous HCl infusion, brain [Cl$^-$] was the same as in the rats which had 6 hours hyperventilation combined with a NaHCO$_3$ infusion. In the blood a very slightly higher value was observed in the acidotic animals.

b. *Relationship between the variations of [Cl$^-$] and [HCO$_3^-$]*

Acute alterations of the bicarbonate concentrations in plasma and brain as an adaptation to acutely imposed changes in the carbon dioxide tension realizing the CO_2 dissociation curve *in vivo,* occur without modifications of the chloride concentrations. When more prolonged respiratory changes in acid-base balance are maintained, our results suggest that the alterations of $[HCO_3]$ in the plasma are compensated by reciprocal variations of $[Cl^-]$. After prolonged hypercapnia and hypocapnia, a difference is also seen in brain $[Cl^-]$ which is opposite to the differences found in $[HCO_3]$. There is, however, no simple quantitative relation between the changes of both electrolytes. Indeed, the changes in $[Cl^-]$ appear to be less important than the alterations found in $[HCO_3]$ at a given P_{CO_2}. It must be considered, moreover, that the differences in the actual $[HCO_3]$ of the brain during the steady period of hypercapnia and hypocapnia are in fact more important because differences in P_{CO_2} will determine still lower or higher bicarbonate concentrations on the dissociation curves.

In the nephrectomized animals, identical $[Cl^-]$ concentrations were found in brain and plasma after 6 hours hypercapnia and hypocapnia, whereas a significant difference in the brain $[HCO_3]$ occurred. In these nephrectomized rats the difference in the actual $[HCO_3]$ in brain in steady state was also greater than the shift measured at identical P_{CO_2}.

On the other hand, in the infusion experiments a difference in brain $[Cl^-]$ is already seen after 6 hours without any change of the $[HCO_3]$.

The results in the combination experiments recall the results in the nephrectomized rats; $[Cl^-]$ in brain is equal for both groups, whereas a great difference in $[HCO_3]$ exists at identical P_{CO_2} which represents an even greater difference in the actual $[HCO_3]$ in the steady state.

It can be concluded that these results do not indicate a close relation between the variations of $[Cl^-]$ and $[HCO_3]$ in the brain in the different series of experiments.

c. *Relationship between the variations of* $[Cl^-]$ *in brain and in blood plasma*

The actual values of the mean concentrations of $[Cl^-]$ in plasma, plasma water and brain water for the different series of experiments are represented in the first 3 columns of Table 1. The last column represents the variation in the brain water as percentage of the change in the plasma water. In series F and G the differences of $[Cl^-]$ between the 2 groups of rats are not significant neither in plasma nor in brain. In the other conditions marked differences exist in plasma. Our data illustrate that in the brain water modifications

Table 1.

		Cl^- Plasma mEq/l	Cl^- Plasma-water mEq/kg	Cl^- Brain-water mEq/kg	Cl^- Space %	$\dfrac{Cl^- \text{ brain} \times 100}{Cl^- \text{ plasma}}$
A 6 h.	CO_2(1)	99.7	107.2	35.0	33	13 %
	Hyp(2)	109.7	118.0	36.4	31	
B 24 h.	CO_2	93.0	100.0	35.0	35	32 %
	Hyp	106.7	114.7	39.7	35	
C 25 min.	HCl(3)	113.0	121.5	34.8	29	0 %
	$NaHCO_3$ (4)	101.5	109.1	34.8	32	
D 6 h.	HCl	108.4	116.6	34.1	29	20 %
	$NaHCO_3$	100.0	107.5	32.3	30	
E 24 h.	HCl	108.1	116.2	35.7	31	27 %
	$NaHCO_3$	99.1	106.6	33.1	31	
F 6 h.	CO_2 + HCl	104.2	112.0	34.9	31	
	Hyp + $NaHCO_3$	101.8	109.5	34.8	32	
G 6 h.	CO_2 + nephr(5)	101.8	109.5	36.9	34	
	hyp + nephr	102.3	110.0	36.7	33	

(1) hypercapnia; (2) hypocapnia; (3) HCl infusion; (4) $NaHCO_3$ infusion; (5) nephrectomy.

of [Cl^-] in the same direction as in plasma occur if sufficient time is allowed. When in the plasma a marked difference is upheld during 25 minutes by infusion (series C), no difference appears in brain; after 6 hours respiratory and nonrespiratory acid-base alterations, (series A and D), however, the changes in the brain water represent respectively 13 per cent and 20 per cent of the changes in the plasma water. After 24 hours the differences in the brain water are increased respectively to 32 per cent and 27 per cent of the differences found in the plasma water (series B and E).

The conventionally calculated Cl^- space in brain occupies 29–35 per cent; the observations are thus compatible with the existence of a Cl^- space in the brain which has almost equilibrated with plasma after 24 hours. Siesjö & Pontén (1966) reported equilibration after 6 hours during administration of $NaHCO_3$ and NH_4Cl. The difference in the plasma [Cl^-] in their experiments, however is twice as large as in our experiments. Our results are compatible with the data of Vernadakis & Woodbury (1965) showing equilibration of Cl^- between blood and brain after 18 hours in adult rats.

4. INTERPRETATION OF THE PRESENT RESULTS

a. *Nature of the alterations of* [HCO_3^-] *in brain during acute changes of* P_{CO_2}

The evolution of the CO_2 dissociation curve in brain is conformable to the presence of other buffer systems than bicarbonate, as has been deduced previously from studies *in vivo* and *in vitro* by many authors (cf. Siesjö 1962, 1965). When with our data a CO_2 buffer capacity of the brain is calculated from the slope of the [HCO_3^-]/pH (slykes) or log P_{CO_2}/pH (β) curves at the lower pH values, one obtains a value of 28.5 slykes or $\beta = 1.6$ for the normal rats, which is slightly higher than Pontén's value of $\beta = 1.4$ (1966). Recently Kjällquist *et al.* (1969) calculated for the intracellular phase of brain a buffer capacity $\beta = 2.3$.

At very low carbon dioxide tensions the decrease of [HCO_3^-] is drastically accentuated *in vivo,* as indicated above, by the metabolic formation of non-carbonic acids which form a barrier against further alkalinisation of the tissue. Formation of lactic acid probably represents the important factor of this mechanism (cf. Weyne *et al.* 1970a, Leusen *et al.* 1967).

In our data a transport of HCO_3^- in exchange for Cl^- between total brain (including CSF) and blood seems to have no part in acute CO_2 buffering *in vivo.* Local shifts of Cl^- and HCO_3^- between compartments within the brain cannot be excluded. Swanson & Rosengren (1962) suggested such a possible exchange between the unbuffered CSF and the highly buffered brain tissue.

b. *Nature of the displacement of the* CO_2 *dissociation curve*

A displacement of the CO_2 dissociation curve can be due to many factors. Possibilities which can be considered are: (a) reactions of the bicarbonate with non-carbonic acids, (b) changes in the concentration or in pK of the CO_2 buffer, both variations leading to a different CO_2 buffer capacity, (c) exchange of HCO_3^- between the buffer system in a compartment and an external system.

In the brain such displacements are observed in acute conditions during severe hyperventilation and during hypoxia. The influence of severe hyperventilation is illustrated by a change in slope of the *in vivo* [HCO_3^-]/ pH curve which becomes much steeper. Such a change during acute intense hyperventilation was not a common observation in blood and muscle in our different groups of experiments, whereas it was always observed in the brain tissue. During hypoxia an almost parallel shift of the CO_2 dissociation curve is seen illustrating the decrease of $[HCO_3^-]$. The $[HCO_3^-]/$ pH or log $P_{CO_2}/$ pH curves are shifted but show an unchanged slope. Both effects in brain are brought in relation with an increased lactate concentration. The nature of the increased lactate concentration in brain during acute hyperventilation is still controversial; possible mechanisms have been discussed (Leusen & Demeester 1966, Weyne *et al.* 1970a).

The shifts of the CO_2 dissociation curve after prolonged hypercapnia and hypocapnia probably cannot be related to a different lactate concentration. Brain lactate was only slightly elevated after 24 hours in our experimental conditions of hypoxic hyperventilation, and this rise was insufficient to explain the depression of the CO_2 dissociation curve in the hypocapnic animals. It certainly gives no explanation for the elevation of the dissociation curve in the hypercapnic rats; as indicated above, the dissociation curve of control animals was found to lie between the curves of the hypercapnic and hypocapnic rats.

It was suggested that the displacement of the CO_2 dissociation curve in the brain might be related to changes in organic brain buffers (Kazemi *et al.* 1967). Fig. 7 represents the individual values of log $P_{CO_2}/$ pH in blood and brain of two groups of anaesthetized rats artificially ventilated for 20 minutes at different P_{CO_2} after 24 hours hypercapnia or hypocapnia. Carbon dioxide tension values imposed were higher than 30 mm Hg to minimize the possible interference of important lactic acid formation.

If a regression line is calculated (least squares), one observes a slightly lower buffer capacity of the brain after hypercapnia than after hypocapnia (18.5 vs 24.1 slyke; $\beta = 1.30$ vs $\beta = 1.55$). This indicates that the elevated CO_2 dissociation curve of the brain after prolonged hypercapnia cannot be explained by an increased buffer capacity. The calculated *in vivo* buffer capacity of the blood did not show a significant difference after 24 hours hypercapnia or hypocapnia. The *in vitro* buffer capacity calculated after equilibration of blood with 2 gas mixtures with a P_{CO_2} of about 30 and 60 mm Hg, however, is significantly greater after 24 hours hypoxic hyperventilation ($\beta = 2.1$; 43 slyke) than after 24 hours hypercapnia ($\beta = 1.6$; 38.5 slyke). Direct determination of the haemoglobin concentration demonstrated a 13 per cent higher value after hypoxia (16.8 g $\pm$ 0.4/100 ml) than after hypercapnia (14.7 $\pm$ 0.3/100 ml) explaining the effect.

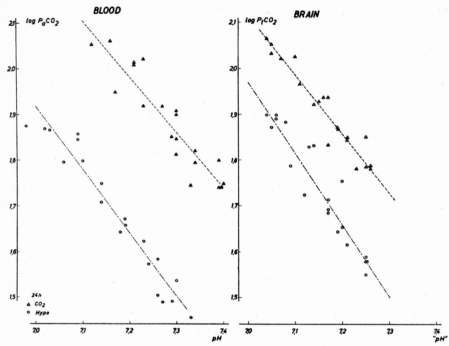

Fig. 7. Relation between log P_{CO_2} and pH in blood and brain at different CO_2 tensions maintained during 20 minutes in anaesthetized and curarized rats. Each symbol represents a single observation in one animal. △ rats maintained 24 hours in 12–13% CO_2 in air before the experiment. ○ rats maintained 24 hours in 9–10% O_2 in N_2 before the experiment.

A third mechanism to be considered is the possibility of an addition of HCO_3^- to the brain system during prolonged hypercapnia and a withdrawal of HCO_3^- during prolonged hypocapnia. As our curves are calculated for the total brain water phase, this should mean a transport between the central nervous system as a whole and blood. A possible mechanism could be an exchange of HCO_3^- for Cl^-. It is known that in the CSF the variations of $[HCO_3^-]$ are almost balanced by variations of $[Cl^-]$ (cf. Bleich *et al.* 1964, Fencl *et al.* 1966) and an identical relation between $[HCO_3^-]$ and $[Cl^-]$ has been proposed for brain extracellular fluid (Fencl *et al.* 1966). There is however no simple relation for the total brain water phase between the alterations of $[HCO_3^-]$ and $[Cl^-]$ in our different experiments (cf. supra). Comparison of changes of $[Cl^-]$ and $[HCO_3^-]$ in prolonged conditions neces-

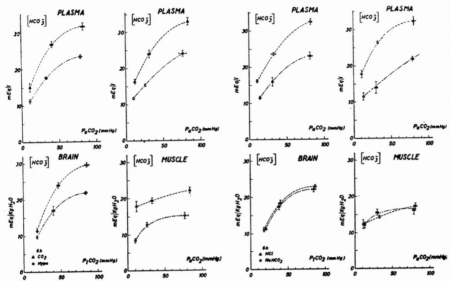

Fig. 8. Displacements of the CO_2 dissociation curves of muscle and brain compared to the displacement of the CO_2 dissociation curve of blood plasma. *Left part:* Bicarbonate concentration at different CO_2 tensions maintained during 20 minutes in anaesthetized and curarized rats after 6 hours hypercapnia or hypoxic hyperventilation. Left panels: plasma and brain (cf. Fig. 4). Right panels: plasma and intracellular space of muscle. *Right part:* Data obtained after 6 hours HCl or $NaHCO_3$ infusion. Left panels: plasma and brain (cf. Fig. 5). Right panels: plasma and intracellular space of muscle.

sistates a steady state. In control experiments Pa_{CO_2} was measured in non-anaesthetized rats repeatedly during several hours of HCl and $NaHCO_3$ infusion and in an atmosphere of 12% CO_2 in air or 10% O_2 in nitrogen. Approximated P_{CO_2} values were respectively 30 and 40 and 25 and 90 mm Hg. From Figs. 4 and 5 the steady-state $[HCO_3]$ can be assumed in the different conditions. This yields the conclusion that the relative variations of $[HCO_3]$ and $[Cl^-]$ in brain are very dissimilar during metabolic and respiratory disturbances.

Recently Siesjö & Kjällquist (1969) introduced the theory that transport of HCO_3 between blood and brain extracellular fluid is controlled by the $[HCO_3]$ gradient and by the potential difference between CSF and blood which varies in function of blood pH. Measurements of the time course of changes in CSF composition itself have not been made in the experiments

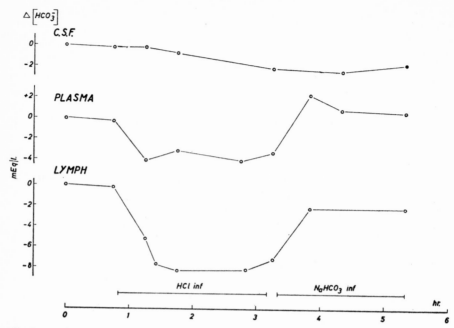

Fig. 9. Alterations of bicarbonate concentrations (mEq/l) in cerebrospinal fluid, blood plasma and hindlimb lymph during i. v. infusion of HCl (HCl inf.) and NaHCO₃ (NaHCO₃ inf.) solutions in an anaesthetized dog.

which are described here. The changes observed in brain, however, agree largely with the observations reported on CSF in comparable conditions.

It is striking that, if increased lactate is excluded, displacement of the CO_2 dissociation curve of the brain in our experiments occurs in all conditions in which a different P_{CO_2} is upheld for some time. The slight dissociation between the two curves after 24 hours infusion with HCl or NaHCO₃ can, in fact, also be related to a small difference of P_{CO_2} during the infusion period.

From the results of our experiments it can hardly be decided whether brain [HCO₃⁻] is controlled by P_{CO_2} or by an interaction of the bicarbonate concentration and the pH working through a D. C. potential. Very striking is the observation that the variations in the intracellular phase of skeletal muscle during acid-base disturbances are qualitatively the same as in brain. This is illustrated in Fig. 8 in which displacements of the CO_2 dissociation curves of muscle and brain are compared when in the plasma comparable changes are produced for 6 hours by hypercapnia or hypocapnia or by infusion of HCl or $NaHCO_3$ solutions (left & right part of Fig. 8).

These observations raise the question whether changes in brain are not related to more universal characteristics of biological membranes. The influence of external pH on the membrane potential of muscle is still controversial, but in the experiments in which a depolarization of the membrane was found during acidosis (increasing the influx of HCO_3^-, cf. the brain model), the $\triangle$ P. D./$\triangle$ pH was smaller than the variation reported by several authors for the CSF-blood potential.

In contrast with the lack of equilibration of plasma and intracellular $[HCO_3^-]$ in these experiments, extracellular $[HCO_3^-]$ in muscle is accepted to change quickly. It is generally considered that the capillary wall in muscle is freely permeable to HCO_3^- and that the steady state distribution of HCO_3^- between plasma and intracellular fluid is governed by a Donnan equilibrium. Fig. 9 summarizes the alteration of $[HCO_3^-]$ at fairly constant P_{CO_2} in hindlimb lymph and CSF during step changes of plasma $[HCO_3^-]$ by i. v. infusion of HCl or $NaHCO_3$ solutions in a typical experiment on a dog. Provided changes in lymph and CSF reflect changes in extracellular fluid in these conditions, this illustrates the very different behaviour of brain extracellular fluid and limb extracellular fluid.

REFERENCES

Bain, J. A. & Klein, J. R. (1949) Effect of carbon dioxide on brain glucose, lactate, pyruvate and phosphates. *Amer. J. Physiol. 158*, 478–484.

Bleich, H. L., Berkman, P. M. & Schwartz, W. B. (1964) The response of cerebrospinal fluid composition to sustained hypercapnia. *J. clin. Invest. 43*, 11–16.

Böning, D. (1968) Veränderungen der CO_2-bindingskurve des Blutes bei akuter respiratorischer Acidose und ihre Ursachen. *Pflügers Arch. ges. Physiol. 302*, 133–148.

Brodie, D. A. & Woodbury, D. M. (1958) Acid-base changes in brain and blood of rats exposed to high concentrations of carbon dioxide. *Amer. J. Physiol. 192*, 91–94.

Brown, E. B. Jr. (1950) Changes in brain pH response to CO_2 after prolonged hypoxic hyperventilation. *J. appl. Physiol. 2*, 549–552.

Chazan, J. A., Appleton, F. M., London, A. M. & Schwartz, W. B. (1969) Effects of chronic metabolic acid-base disturbances on the composition of cerebrospinal fluid in the dog. *Clin. Sci. 36*, 345–358.

Clancy, R. L. & Brown, E. B. Jr. (1966) *In vivo* CO_2 buffer curves of skeletal and cardiac muscle. *Amer. J. Physiol. 211*, 1309–1312.

Cohen J. J., Brackett, N. C. Jr. & Schwartz, W.B . (1964) The nature of the carbon dioxide titration curve in the normal dog. *J. clin. Invest. 43*, 777–786.

De Bersaques, J. (1955) pH et CO_2 du sang et du liquide céphalorachidien dans l'acidose et l'alcalose métabolique. *Arch. int. Physiol. 63*, 1–6.

De Bersaques, J. & Leusen, I. (1954) Acid-base equilibrium between blood and cerebrospinal fluid. *J. Physiol (Lond.) 126*, 14P.

De Thurzo, E. & Katzenelbogen, S. (1935). Alkali reserve in blood and in cerebrospinal fluid in experimental acidosis. *Arch. Neurol. Psychiat. (Chic.) 33*, 786–790.

Engel, K., Dell, R. B., Rahill, W. J., Denning, C. R. & Winters, R. W. (1968) Quantitative displacement of acid-base equilibrium in chronic respiratory acidosis. *J. appl. Physiol. 24*, 288–295.

Fencl, V., Miller, T. B. & Pappenheimer, J. R. (1966) Studies on the respiratory response to disturbances of acid-base balance, with deductions concerning the ionic composition of cerebral interstitial fluid. *Amer. J. Physiol. 210*, 459–472.

Graham, J. A., Lamb, J. F. & Linton, A. L. (1967) Measurement of body water and intracellular electrolytes by means of muscle biopsy. *Lancet ii*, 1172–1176.

Held, D., Fencl, V. & Pappenheimer, J. R. (1964) Electrical potential of cerebrospinal fluid. *J. Neurophysiol. 27*, 942–959.

Kazemi, H., Shannon, D. C. & Carvallo-Gil, E. (1967) Brain CO_2 buffering capacity in respiratory acidosis and alkalosis. *J. appl. Physiol. 22*, 241–246.

Kjällquist, A. (1970) The CSF/blood potential in sustained acid-base changes in the rat. With calculations of electrochemical potential differences for H^+ and HCO_3^-. *Acta physiol. scand. 78*, 85–93.

Kjällquist, A., Nardini, M. & Siesjö, B. K. (1969) The regulation of extra- and intracellular acid-base parameters in the rat brain during hyper- and hypocapnia. *Acta physiol. scand. 76*, 485–494.

Koch, A., Ranck, J. B. Jr. & Newman, B. L. (1962) Ionic content of the neuroglia. *Exp. Neurol. 6*, 186–200.

Lee, J. E., Chu, F., Posner, J. B. & Plum, F. (1969) Buffering capacity of cerebrospinal fluid in acute respiratory acidosis in dogs. *Amer. J. Physiol. 217*, 1035–1038.

Leusen, I. (1965) Aspects of the acid-base balance between blood and cerebrospinal fluid. In *Cerebrospinal Fluid and the Regulation of Ventilation*, ed. Brooks, C. McC., Kao, F. F. & Lloyd, B. B. Blackwell Scientific Publ., Oxford.

Leusen, I. & Demeester, G. (1966) Lactate and pyruvate in the brain of rats during hyperventilation. *Arch. int. Physiol. 74*, 25–34.

Leusen, I., Lacroix, E. & Demeester, G. (1967) Lactate and pyruvate in the brain of rats during changes in acid-base balance. *Arch. int. Physiol. 75*, 310–324.

Levitin, H., Branscome, W. & Epstein, F. H. (1958) The pathogenesis of hypochloremia in respiratory acidosis. *J. clin. Invest. 37*, 1667–1675.

Loeschcke, H. H. (1965) Discussion. In *Cerebrospinal Fluid and the Regulation of Ventilation*, ed. Brooks, C. McC., Kao, F. F. & Lloyd, B. B., p. 259. Blackwell Scientific Publ., Oxford.

Mitchell, R. A. (1966) Cerebrospinal fluid and the regulation of respiration. In *Advances in Respiratory Physiology*, ed. Caro, C. G. Edward Arnold Publishers Ltd., London.

Nichols, G. Jr. (1958) Serial changes in tissue carbon dioxide content during acute respiratory acidosis. *J. clin. Invest. 37*, 1111–1122.

Plum, F. & Posner, J. B. (1967) Blood and cerebrospinal fluid lactate during hyperventilation. *Amer. J. Physiol. 212*, 864–870.

Pontén, U. (1966) Acid-base changes in rat brain tissue during acute respiratory acidosis and baseosis. *Acta physiol. scand. 68*, 152–163.

Reed, D. J., Woodbury, D. M. & Holtzer, R. L. (1964) Brain edema, electrolytes, and extracellular space: Effect of triethyl tin on brain and skeletal muscle. *Arch. Neurol. 10*, 604–616.

Reichart, E., Saunier, C., Schibi, M. & Colas, T. (1965) Hypercapnie aiguë experimentale chez le chien, variations de l'équilibre acido-basique dans le sang artériel et le liquide céphalorachidien. *C. R. Soc. Biol. (Paris) 160*, 352–357.

Robin, E. D., Whaley, R. D., Crump, C. H., Bickelmann, A. G. & Travis, D. M. (1958) Acid-base relations between spinal fluid and arterial blood with special reference to control of ventilation. *J. appl. Physiol. 13*, 385–392.

Schwartz, W. B., Brackett, N. C. Jr. & Jordan, J. J. (1965) The response of extracellular hydrogen ion concentration to graded degrees of chronic hypercapnia: the physiological limits of the defense of pH. *J. clin. Invest. 44*, 291–301.

Severinghaus, J. W. (1965) Electrochemical gradients for hydrogen and bicarbonate ions across the blood-CSF barrier in response to acid-base balance changes. In *Cerebrospinal Fluid and the Regulation of Ventilation*, ed. Brooks, C. McC., Kao, F. F. & Lloyd, B. B. Blackwell Scientific Publ., Oxford.

Severinghaus, J. W., Mitchell, R. A., Richardson, R. W. & Singer, M. M. (1963) Respiratory control at high altitude suggesting active transport regulation of CSF pH. *J. appl. Physiol. 18*, 1155–1166.

Siesjö, B. K. (1962) The bicarbonate/carbonic acid buffer system of the cerebral cortex of cats, as studied in tissue homogenates. I. The amount of carbon dioxide bound at different carbon dioxide tensions. With a critique of the application of chloride space measurements to the study of the acid-base metabolism of the brain. *Acta neurol. scand. 38*, 98–120.

Siesjö, B. K. (1965) Active and passive mechanisms in the acid-base metabolism of brain tissue. In *Cerebrospinal Fluid and the Regulation of Ventilation*, ed. Brooks, C. McC., Kao, F. F. & Lloyd, B. B. Blackwell Scientific Publ., Oxford.

Siesjö, B. K. & Kjällquist, A. (1969) A new theory for the regulation of the extracellular pH in the brain. *Scand. J. clin. Lab. Invest. 24*, 1–9.

Siesjö, B. K. & Pontén, U. (1966) Acid-base changes in the brain in nonrespiratory acidosis and alkalosis. *Exp. Brain Res. 2*, 176–190.

Swanson, A. G. (1966) The role of bicarbonate in brain buffering. *Trans. Amer. neurol. Ass. 91*, 344–345.

Swanson, A. G. & Rosengren, H. (1962) Cerebrospinal fluid buffering during acute experimental respiratory acidosis. *J. appl. Physiol. 17*, 812–814.

Van Vaerenbergh, P. J. J., Demeester, G. & Leusen, I. (1965) Lactate in cerebrospinal fluid during hyperventilation. *Arch. int. Physiol. 73*, 738–747.

Vernadakis, A. & Woodbury, D. M. (1965) Cellular and extracellular spaces in developing rat brain. Radioactive uptake studies with chloride and insulin. *Arch. Neurol. 12*, 284–293.

Warren, J., Luke, R. G., Kashgarian, M. & Levitin, H. (1970) Micropuncture studies of chloride and bicarbonate absorption in the proximal renal tubule of the rat in respiratory acidosis and in chloride depletion. *Clin. Sci. 38*, 375–383.

Weyne, J., Demeester, G. & Leusen, I. (1968) Bicarbonate and chloride shifts in rat brain during acute and prolonged respiratory acid-base changes. *Arch. int. Physiol.* *75*, 415–433.

Weyne, J., Demeester, G. & Leusen, I. (1970a) Effects of carbon dioxide, bicarbonate and pH on lactate and pyruvate in the brain of rats. *Pflügers Arch. ges. Physiol. 314*, 292–311.

Weyne, J., Pannier, J. L., Demeester, G. & Leusen, I. (1970b) Bicarbonate and chloride of rat brain during infusion induced changes in bicarbonate concentration of blood. *Pflügers Arch. ges. Physiol.* In press.

Wollenberger, A., Ristau, O. & Schoffa, G. (1960) Eine einfache Technik der extrem Schnellen Abkühlung grözerer Gewebstücke. *Pflügers Arch. ges. Physiol. 270*, 399–412.

Woodbury, D. M., Rollins, L. T., Gardner, M. D., Hirschi, W. L., Hogan, J. R., Rallison, M. L., Tanner, G. S. & Brodie, D. A. (1958) Effects of carbon dioxide on brain excitability and electrolytes. *Amer. J. Physiol. 192*, 79–90.

DISCUSSION

SØRENSEN

I must object to your statement that it is a generally accepted view that bicarbonate changes in plasma are not reflected in brain or CSF. I don't think very many of us here would accept that view. I don't understand for instance the experiment where you found no change in the CO_2-dissociation curve for plasma, but a marked difference in the CO_2-dissociation curves for brain. What was the plasma pH under those two circumstances? From all we have heard in the last couple of days, it has little meaning just to consider concentration changes in the two compartments without considering the simultaneous potential changes. For the same reason it is difficult to see from your data that there should be any general difference between the situations during metabolic acid-base changes and during respiratory acid-base changes. I would like to challenge another of your statements: You claim that anaerobic glycolysis is responsible for the reduction of the bicarbonate concentration in brain during hypocapnia. It is very likely that it is the case, but you can only claim that the changes in lactate concentration are suggestive evidence. As long as you haven't shown a change in production rate, you cannot provide conclusive proof. The increase in lactate concentration in brain could just as well be due to a change in the elimination of lactate. We know that the production rate of lactate increases during hypocapnia but I don't think that your experiments proved that by themselves.

WEYNE

Regarding your first objection: Several authors have shown that acute changes of plasma bicarbonate concentration obtained by i. v. infusion of NH_4Cl or HCl, and $NaHCO_3$ or Na_2CO_3, are not accompanied by similar changes of the bicarbonate concentration in CSF. The results I presented illustrate the effect of infusion of HCl and $NaHCO_3$ during approximately 2 hours, and I think they are in good agreement with the data of the literature (Robin et al. 1958, de Bersaques 1955, Posner et al. 1965, Manfredi 1962).

Robin, E. D., Whaley, R. D., Crump, C. H., Bickelmann, A. G. & Travis, D. M. (1958) Acid-base relations between spinal fluid and arterial blood with special reference to control of ventilation. *J. appl. Physiol. 13*, 385–392.

de Bersaques, J. (1955) pH et Pco$_2$ du sang et du liquide céphalo-rachidien dans l'acidose et l'alcalose métabolique. *Arch. internat. Physiol. 63*, 1–6.

During prolonged exposure, changes in plasma are certainly reflected in the CSF.

Your second point concerns the possible effect of the potential difference between blood and CSF. Our results give changes of bicarbonate content in the whole brain tissue including intra- and extracellular compartments. Direct correlation with potential changes has not been attempted. Concerning the challenge about the influence of glycolysis on brain bicarbonate concentration: It is very difficult to measure a production of lactate by the brain of the rat *in vivo,* but incubated brain tissue always reacts with an increase of the ractate production during alkalosis (Leusen *et al.* 1967, Weyne *et al.* 1970). This certainly does not prove that *in vivo* the increased lactate concentration in the brain during cerebral alkalosis is also only related to a direct influence of pH on lactate production. The important regulating influence of Pco_2 and $[H^+]$ on cerebral vascular resistance certainly has to be considered. An increased lactate concentration could be related to an increased production enhanced by hypoxia (Leusen & Demeester 1966, Weyne *et al.* 1970). Hypoxia is however not the only way by which a reduced cerebral blood flow during cerebral alkalosis could elevate lactate concentration. It could also be an accumulation of lactate due to a decreased cerebral blood flow and a decrease in the elimination of lactate from the brain (Hohorst *et al.* 1968). Anyway, the parallelism between the increase in lactate concentration and the accelerated decrease of the bicarbonate concentration during acute hyperventilation is at least striking and suggests – together with the hypoxia data – the possibility of titration of bicarbonate by lactic acid.

Posner, J. B., Swanson, A. G. & Plum, F. (1965) Acid-base balance in cerebrospinal fluid. *Arch. Neurol. 12,* 479–496.

Manfredi, F. (1962) Acid-base relations between serum and cerebrospinal fluid in man under normal and abnormal conditions. *J. Lab. clin. Med. 59,* 128–136.

Leusen, I., Lacroix, E. & Demeester, G. (1967) Lactate and pyruvate in the brain of rats during changes in acid-base balance. *Arch. internat. Physiol. Biochem. 75,* 310–324.

Weyne, J., Demeester, G. & Leusen, I. (1970) Effects of carbon dioxide, bicarbonate and pH on lactate and pyruvate in the brain of rats. *Pflügers Arch. ges. Physiol. 314,* 292–311.

Leusen, I. & Demeester, G. (1967) Lactate and pyruvate in the brain of rats during changes in acid-base balance. *Arch. internat. Physiol. Biochem. 75,* 310–324.

Hohorst, H. J., Betz, E. & Weidner, A. (1968) Relation between energy-rich substrates, tissue redox changes, and EEG during and after hypoxia. *Scand. J. clin. Lab. Invest., Suppl. 102, III B.*

SIESJÖ

Are you all the time referring to total tissue bicarbonate concentrations or did you also measure the CSF concentrations? In other words, can you partition the ions between the extra- and intracellular spaces?

WEYNE

The data I presented here were all from the whole frozen brain including extracellular fluid. The muscle data I presented were intracellular data.

FENCL

Dr. Weyne, wouldn't it be more meaningful to present the changes in the "CO_2 dissociation curves" of brain in relation to the composition of CSF, instead of relating them to the composition of plasma? In the case of the muscle, the latter is all right, however. I think that all of us agree that the cells in the brain are exposed to an extracellular fluid which is not an ultrafiltrate of plasma; the cerebral extracellular fluid, in the various acid-base conditions, is rather similar to, or perhaps even identical with, the steady-state CSF in a given acid-base condition. In metabolic acid-base disturbances, CSF and cerebral ISF are better protected against the changes occurring in the composition of blood, than they are in the disturbances of respiratory origin. Wouldn't this explain the difference you showed between the effect of bicarbonate administration and CO_2 inhalation on the "CO_2 dissociation curves" of brain?

WEYNE

Analysing CSF is the only way to get some insight in the composition of the brain interstitial fluid, but it needs a steady state, which might not be achieved after 20 minutes step change in ventilation. We did not measure in the rat changes in CSF and in the brain tissue simultaneously. We did, however, some experiments measuring HCO_3^-, Cl^-, and lactate concentration in the CSF of rabbits after 20 minutes and 6 hours hypercapnic or hypoxic hyperventilation. As in the brain tissue of the rat, after 20 minutes one observes in the CSF of the rabbit an increase of the $[HCO_3^-]$ during hypercapnia and a decrease during hypocapnia; these variations are not compensated by a significant modification of $[Cl^-]$. After 6 hours the changes in $[HCO_3^-]$ are much more pronounced and accompanied by opposite changes in the Cl^- concentration.

PLUM

In animals maintained with metabolic acidosis for 24 hours didn't you find any bicarbonate depletion in brain despite the bicarbonate depletion in blood?

WEYNE

After 24 hours there was a small difference in brain [HCO₃] between HCl and NaHCO$_3$ infused rats. But it was out of proportion with the differences observed in the brain during respiratory acid-base changes although the changes in the blood in respiratory and non-respiratory acid-base changes can directly be compared.

PLUM

If your animals hyperventilated due to the HCl infusion, then from the bicarbonate data that you showed their brains would have been intensely alkalotic.

WEYNE

We have measured arterial Pco_2 during the infusion of HCl and NaHCO$_3$ in some experiments. During several hours there was only a small difference: Pco_2 was about 5 mm Hg lower in the HCl infused rats than in NaHCO$_3$ infused rats. Differences in bicarbonate concentration in the brain and in Pco_2 are thus in the same direction and both are rather small.

SEVERINGHAUS

I want to also caution about interpolation from CSF HCO$_3^-$ to extracellular fluid bicarbonate. Fig. 1 compares the changes in pH measured with a pH electrode on the cortex and the changes measured in bulk CSF during hypoxia in dogs. pH on the cortex fell more during hypoxia than CSF pH. Therefore hypoxia increased the gradient between pH on the cortex surface and that in bulk CSF.

SØRENSEN

To me it looks more as if the electrode on the cortex generates a considerable difference between the CSF and cortex.

Relationship of ECF and CSF pH during hypoxia in dogs.

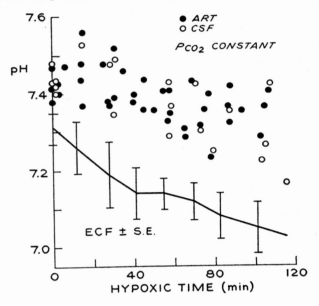

SEVERINGHAUS

Yes, the prehypoxic control state at time zero showed a difference between the pH in CSF and the pH measured on the cortex.

SØRENSEN

As far as I can see, those two lines run parallel. I would deduce that it is the electrode which creates a difference in pH on the cortex and in CSF.

SEVERINGHAUS

The difference between them during hypoxia is greater than it was during the control, as you can see.

SØRENSEN

That is what I can't see.

SIESJÖ

I should like to recall two previous communications from our laboratory in which we studied the effect of nonrespiratory acidosis and alkalosis (6 hrs) upon the plasma, the CSF and the tissue bicarbonate concentrations in rats (Siesjö & Pontén 1966, Pontén & Siesjö 1967). The CSF results obtained were in very good agreement with those obtained by others on other animals, or on patients (see paper by Fencl, this symposium). However, although there were marked differences in the CSF bicarbonate concentration between the acidotic and alkalotic groups, there were very small, if any, differences in the tissue bicarbonate concentrations, and these differences could be ascribed to differences in the CO_2 tensions (6–8 mm Hg).

Siesjö, B. K. & Pontén, U. (1966) Acid-base changes in the brain in nonrespiratory acidosis and alkalosis. *Exp. Brain Res. 2,* 176–190.

Pontén, U. & Siesjö, B. K. (1967) Acid-base relations in arterial blood and cerebrospinal fluid of the unanesthetized rat. *Acta physiol. scand. 71,* 89–95.

Control of Glycolysis and Oxidative Metabolism in Tissues*

John R. Williamson,** *John B. Clark,† William J. Nicklas†† &*
Brian Safer††

The purpose of this paper will be to review the general control features of carbohydrate utilization as they apply to a variety of tissues with different relative contents of mitochondria. Analogies may be drawn between these tissues and the heterogeneous cell types comprising nervous tissue. Although the scope of the treatment will be fairly broad, the examples taken for discussion will be highly selective, and details of all the possible control interactions will not be fully described. Three major topics will be covered. First, the nature of the principal feedback interactions between cytoplasmic and mitochondrial metabolic events will be described in relation to the functional activity of the tissue. Secondly, the time constants of some of the activational and deactivational processes will be illustrated by specific examples. Thirdly, general aspects of the control of the utilization of pyruvate and cytoplasmic reducing equivalents by mitochondria, and how these may affect the tissue lactate to pyruvate ratio, will be discussed. An attempt will be made to relate the conclusions to what is presently known about the control of energy metabolism in brain.

GENERAL CONCEPT OF FEEDBACK INHIBITIONS

Fig. 1 illustrates the types of feedback which may be observed by operation of a metabolic switch. A stimulus (e.g. increased release of a hormone,

From the Johnson Research Foundation, University of Pennsylvania, Philadelphia, Pennsylvania 19104, U. S. A.
 * Supported by grants from the U. S. Public Health Service (GM 12202) and the American Heart Association.
** Established Investigator of the American Heart Association.
 † M. R. C. Travelling Fellow, on leave of absence from the Biochemistry Department, St. Bartholomew's Hospital Medical College, University of London, Charterhouse Square, London, E.C.1, England.
†† N.I.H. Postdoctoral Fellow.

Metabolic Switch With Feedback

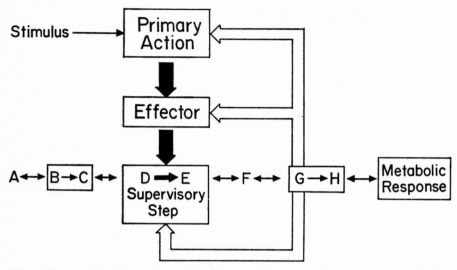

Fig. 1. Generalized scheme of metabolic feedback. Solid arrows represent an activation and the open arrows an inhibition. The letters A→B – – – H represent intermediates of a metabolic pathway, and steps shown in a box represent physiologically irreversible reactions.

membrane depolarization) generally elicits a specific primary action. This produces a change in the concentration of one or more intracellular chemical intermediates which regulate the activity of a key control site (supervisory step) of a metabolic pathway (e.g. ADP activation of phosphofructokinase). In Fig. 1 the metabolic pathway is depicted by the sequence of intermediates A - - - - -H. Most metabolic sequences are composed of reversible and essentially irreversible steps. With reversible reactions, the rate of the forward and back reactions is generally much faster than the net flux through the pathway, and reversible steps rarely function as control sites except for occasional instances when one of the substrates is present in the tissue at concentrations far below the Km for the enzyme. On the other hand, irreversible steps are far displaced from equilibrium, and unless there is a specific allosteric interaction, the forward flux is relatively independent of the product concentration. Most irreversible enzymes are capable of rapid changes of activity by modifiers which act allosterically on the active site (i.e., their binding to the enzyme induces a conformational change of the protein structure which results in an alteration of the kinetic properties of the enzyme, e.g. change of the Km for a substrate). The so-called supervisory step of a metabolic sequence is normally the first irreversible step unique to that pathway, and flux through this step controls the over-all flux through the pathway, thereby eliciting the metabolic response to the primary stimulus. Feedback may be of several types, usually complementing each other. Thus, the effect of the stimulus on the site of primary action may be antagonized directly by the secondary release of another hormone as a result of the metabolic activity (e.g. insulin counteraction of the effects of glucagon or catecholamines on the adenyl cyclase system). Alternatively, the concentration of the effector compound may be decreased by its interaction with later steps of the same or another pathway (e.g. phosphorylation of ADP by P-glyceric kinase and pyruvate kinase, or by the respiratory chain). Thirdly, the supervisory step of the metabolic pathway may be directly inhibited by an accumulated product of later steps of the pathway or its ancilliary reactions (e.g. ATP and citrate inhibition of phosphofructokinase). Finally, a supply of substrate to the metabolic pathway has to be assured, and this may occur by breakdown of stored carbohydrate or lipid reserves.

The various activational processes and their feedback inhibitions have characteristic time constants for a particular tissue, so that reserves of high energy phosphate compounds may first have to be called upon before a new balance is reached in the steady state between the rate of utilization of ATP and its rate of production by increased metabolic activity. Often, the perturbations of metabolite levels between two steady states may be relatively small even with a large flux change (Helmreich & Cori 1965), but in the transition phase big variations can be observed because of the temporary imbalance between the effects of activational stimulae and their regulatory feedback inhibitions. Knowledge of the kinetic change of metabolite levels in the transition phase, therefore, is very important for an identification of control sites and the nature of the chemical modifiers in a metabolic pathway.

METABOLIC EFFECTS OF ELECTRICAL DISCHARGE OF THE MAIN ORGAN OF ELECTROPHORUS ELECTRICUS

The electric organ of the eel remains excitable and capable of electric discharge for some time after dissection (Keynes & Martins-Ferreira 1953).

It is a highly homogenous tissue, being composed of numerous layers of electroplates placed end to end like the cells of an accumulator. As with muscle and nerve, membrane depolarization, consequent to discharge, is associated with a reversal of polarity, due to an entry of Na^+ ions into the electroplates and exit of K^+ ions. The ionic gradients are subsequently restored by activation of the sodium pump. The energy demands are initially met from the phosphagen reserves, which are then restored by increased metabolic activity (Aubert et al. 1964). The tissue is very low in cytochromes, has a poor capacity for oxidative phosphorylation (Chance et al. 1964), but is rich in glycogen and glycolytic enzymes (Maitra et al. 1964). Therefore, it offers distinct advantages for studies of the feedback control properties of the glycolytic pathway.

Sections of the dissected organ about 8 cm long were placed in a specially constructed guillotine with Ag-AgCl electrodes at both end surfaces of the section (Williamson et al. 1967a). Electrical discharge of the organ was elicited by pulses (40–60 volts, 0.1 msec duration, 100 per sec) from a stimulator. The duration of the discharge was 1 to 2 msec and the output, 20 to 40 volts. Slices of the section, each about 2 mm thick, were cut during both discharge and recovery phases and fell directly into liquid freon maintained at $-140°$. Weighed aliquots were extracted with perchloric acid, and the extracts were neutralized with potassium carbonate and analyzed for metabolic intermediates by enzyme fluorometric assays (Williamson 1965).

The kinetic changes in the levels of inorganic phosphate, creatine phosphate, ATP, ADP and AMP in an electric organ section during and after a 60 sec discharge period are shown in Figs. 2 and 3. Rapid utilization of the creatine-P reserves began during the discharge period and continued during the early phase of the recovery period, causing a marked depletion of the creatine-P level. Only after the second minute of recovery was there a net synthesis of creatine-P. The changes of inorganic phosphate essentially mirrored those of the creatine-P. Despite the large decrease of phosphagen reserve, the ATP level changed very little. The changes of ADP and AMP were much larger because of their lower initial tissue content and increased most dramatically immediately after the discharge period. A return to the resting levels occurred after 5 minutes of recovery. Although in this case the discharge stimulus was a relatively large one because of its long duration (probably longer than the eel would normally maintain in vivo), it is clear

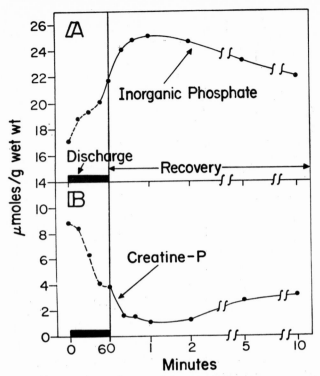

Fig. 2. Kinetics of inorganic phosphate (P_i) and creatine phosphate (creatine-P) changes in the main electric organ of *Electrophorus* during discharge and recovery. Each *point* represents analysis of a tissue slice cut from the section and rapidly frozen at the time indicated.

that increased glycolytic activity could not keep up with the energy demands on the tissue. This is partly due to the capacity of the organ for glycolysis being too small for the rate of energy expenditure. Thus, the rate of creatine-P utilization during stimulation was about 12 μmoles/g wet wt/min, while the maximum rate of glycolysis observed (5 μmoles lactate/g wet wt/min) would only provide 7.5 μmoles/g wet wt/min of ATP synthesis (Williamson *et al.* 1967a, 1967b). However, another reason for the transient energy imbalance is the slow onset of glycogenolysis.

This is revealed by the data shown in Fig. 4. Like many other tissues, glycogen phosphorylase exists in two forms in the electric organ. In the resting state, most of the enzyme is present as phosphorylase *b* which is

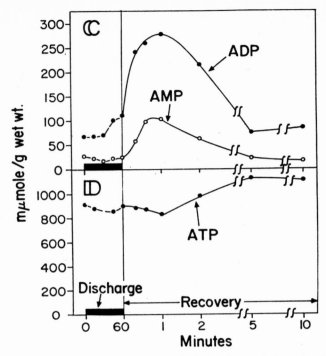

Fig. 3. Kinetics of the changes in the levels of ATP, ADP and AMP in the main electric organ of *Electrophorus* during discharge and recovery. The eel section used was the same as that of Fig. 2.

relatively inactive at the low AMP and high ATP concentrations prevailing in the tissue (Krebs *et al.* 1966). Phosphorylation to phosphorylase *a* produces an active form of the enzyme which is not dependent on the AMP concentration. Dephosphorylation of phosphorylase *a* is catalyzed by phosphorylase phosphatase, and metabolite feedback is mediated by glucose, glycogen and glucose-6-P, which are activators, and P_i and fructose-1, 6-di-P which are inhibitors of the phosphatase (Holmes & Mansour 1968). The enzyme catalyzing the activation of phosphorylase, phosphorylase *b* kinase, also exists in an inactive dephosphorylated form and an active phosphorylated form, the latter being distinguished by a greater activity at pH 6.8 (where the nonactivated enzyme has very low activity) than at pH 8.2 where the nonactivated enzyme is almost fully active (Posner *et al.* 1965). Thus, the ratio of phosphorylase *b* kinase activity measured at pH 6.8 relative

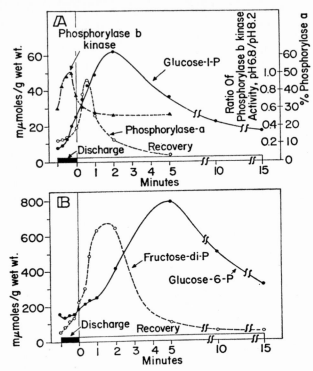

Fig. 4. Comparison of changes in the levels of phosporylase *a,* phosphorylase *b* kinase (activity at pH 6.8 compared with that at pH 8.2), glucose-1-P, glucose-6-P, and fructose-1,6-di-P in an electric organ section stimulated to discharge for 60 sec and followed by a 15 min recovery period.

to that at pH 8.2 gives a measure of the activity of the more active form. As shown in Fig. 4A, this activity increased immediately after the onset of discharge, reached a peak after 30 to 45 sec, and subsequently declined before the end of the discharge period. However, activation of phosphorylase *b* kinase was not associated with an immediate increase of phosphorylase *a*. In fact, there was a delay of 15 to 30 sec before phosphorylase *a* activity started to increase appreciably, and peak activity was not reached until shortly after the end of the discharge period. Glucose-1-P, the first intermediate of glycogen breakdown, also showed a lag before increasing gradually to levels 8-fold higher than resting values, the peak being observed after about 2 min of recovery.

25*

The sharp but distinct peaks in the activities of phosphorylase *b* kinase and phosphorylase *a* after the onset of discharge illustrate two phenomena. First, that the impulse resulting in activation of the phosphorylase cascade of enzymes (Helmreich 1969) is very transient, and does not coordinate with the duration of discharge. This must mean that it is subject to strong negative feedback influences, so that only a limited amount of substrate from the glycogen reserves becomes available to the glycolytic enzymes. Unfortunately, neither the initiating factor nor the details of possible changes in activity of phosphorylase *b* kinase phosphatase or phosphorylase phosphatase are known for the electric organ. Cyclic AMP levels do not change after discharge (Williamson *et al.* 1967a). However, there is growing evidence from work with skeletal and cardiac muscle that changes of calcium ion concentration are involved early in the activation process (Drummond *et al.* 1969, Namm *et al.* 1968). Secondly, it is apparent that each activation step has its own time constant, thereby imposing a lag between the initiation of discharge and the supply of substrate to the glycolytic enzymes.

Measurements of the kinetics of the changes of each of the glycolytic intermediates (Williamson *et al.* 1967a) reveal that not only is the release of hexose units from glycogen highly controlled, but so also is their usage. The flow of substrate in the glycolytic pathway is regulated principally by phosphofructokinase, a highly irreversible enzyme which phosphorylates fructose-6-P to fructose-1, 6-di-P by the conversion of ATP to ADP. Phosphofructokinase functions as the supervisory step in the glycolytic sequence, since it also controls hexokinase activity by regulation of the glucose-6-P levels, hexokinase being product inhibited (Rose & Rose 1969).

Fig. 4B shows the changes in the tissue levels of glucose-6-P and fructose-1, 6-di-P. Fructose-6-P levels were about one third as great as those of glucose-6-P, and showed similar kinetics. Initially, the fructose-1, 6-di-P levels were very low, but unlike those of glucose-6-P, they started to increase immediately after the onset of discharge, continued to increase sharply during the first minute of the recovery period, peaked after 2 min, and subsequently decreased rapidly. Glucose-6-P levels, on the other hand, increased relatively little both during and immediately after discharge, but subsequently increased greatly even when the levels of both glucose-1-P and fructose-1, 6-di-P were falling. Maximum levels of glucose-6-P and fructose-6-P were reached after about 5 min of recovery. It is apparent that control at the phosphofructokinase step has imposed a phase shift on the accumu-

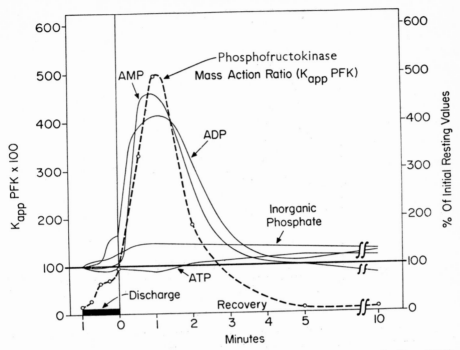

Fig. 5. Comparison of changes in the phosphofructokinase mass action ratio (K_{app} PFK) with the percentage changes of ATP, ADP, AMP, and inorganic phosphate in the main electric organ of *Electrophorus* during discharge and recovery. The *curves* shown are based on the analytical data presented in Figs. 2–4.

lation-depletion curves of the glycolytic intermediates. The large increase of fructose-1, 6-di-P levels followed by a rapid depletion out of phase with the hexose-P levels is indicative of a transient activation of phosphofructokinase which did not correspond with the supply of substrate from glycogen.

Phosphofructokinase activity is controlled by rather different mechanisms than those responsible for the interconversion of phosphorylase *a* and *b*. The purified enzyme from a variety of sources (Rose & Rose 1969) has been shown to be inhibited by ATP and citrate, while ADP, AMP, P_i, fructose-6-P and fructose-1, 6-di-P are activators. However, it may be noted that phosphorylase *b*, like phosphofructokinase, is inhibited by ATP and activated by AMP (Morgan & Parmeggiani 1964).

Fig. 5 shows the relationship of the relative activity changes of phosphofructokinase in the electric organ during the discharge and recovery period,

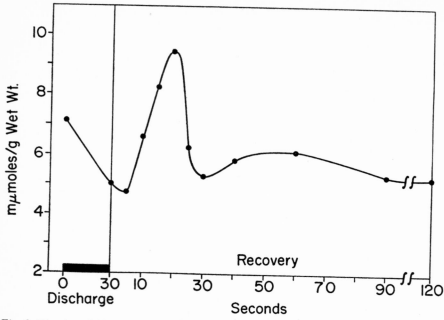

Fig. 6. Kinetics of NADH changes in the main electric organ of *Electrophorus* during a 30 sec period of discharge and a 2 min period of recovery.

compared with the percentage changes of the adenine nucleotide levels. The activity of phosphofructokinase was not measured directly, since enzyme activity measurements made on tissue extracts bear little or no relation to the actual net velocity of the enzyme *in situ*. Alternatively, because phosphofructokinase is normally about five orders of magnitude displaced from equilibrium, relative *in situ* activity changes can be estimated from changes of the mass action ratio; fructose-di-P × ADP/fructose-6-P × ATP (Williamson 1966a, Williamson *et al.* 1967a). This gives a measure of the change of the rate constant of phosphofructokinase provided the aldolase rate constant remains approximately the same. The data in Fig. 5 suggest that phosphofructokinase activity increases almost immediately after the onset of discharge, rises to a peak after one minute of recovery, and subsequently declines rapidly. The kinetics of the percentage changes of AMP, ADP, P_i and ATP indicate that phosphofructokinase activity is controlled mainly by changes of the AMP and ADP levels. Thus, the activity of the supervisory

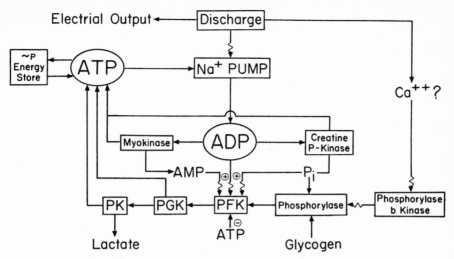

Fig. 7. Scheme indicating the main feedback pathways between electrical activity and control of glycogenolysis in the main electric organ of *Electrophorus*. Abbreviations used are: P_i, inorganic phosphate; PK, pyruvate kinase; PGK, phosphoglycerate kinase; PFK, phosphofructokinase.

step of glycolysis (phosphofructokinase) is apparently delicately and synchronously controlled by the energy state of the tissue.

The rapid increase in the rate of triose-P production shortly after the end of the discharge period, due to the high phosphofructokinase activity, causes a perturbation of the glyceraldehyde-3-P dehydrogenase equilibrium, and a transient increase of the NADH levels in the tissue (Fig. 6). Rather similar responses were obtained by Aubert *et al.* (1964), using the tissue fluorescence technique to monitor reduction changes of the pyridine nucleotides. These studies reveal that the cycle of pyridine nucleotide reduction can be used as a kinetic index of increased glycolytic activity.

The probable events occurring when the electric organ is caused to discharge are summarized in Fig. 7. The current associated with discharge is caused by Na^+ ions entering the electroplates. Energy is subsequently expended from creatine-P reserves to restore the ionic gradients and permit continuous discharge. Replenishment of the high energy phosphate reserves occurs by increased glycogenolysis, but only after a distinct lag. Separate chemical signals induce the initiation of glycogen breakdown by activation of phosphorylase *b* kinase, and its conversion to pyruvate and lactate by ac-

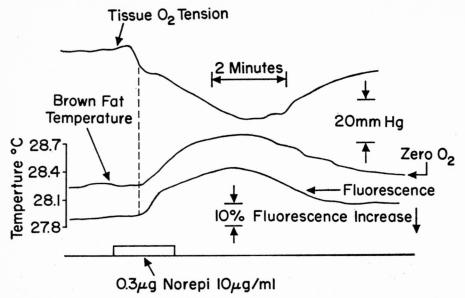

Fig. 8. Effect of intravenous infusion of norepinephrine (Norepi) on the oxygen tension, temperature and pyridine nucleotide fluorescence of interscapular brown fat of the normal hamster *in vivo*.

tivation of phosphofructokinase. The former conversion may be mediated by local changes of Ca^{++} concentration (Rasmussen & Tenenhouse 1968, Bradham et al. 1970), while phosphofructokinase activation is brought about initially by the rise of inorganic phosphate and subsequently by ADP and AMP. While the creatine phosphate store remains, large increases of ADP are prevented by the high activity of creatine phosphokinase, but when these are diminished, ADP accumulates and a limited further supply of ATP is yielded by the adenylate kinase reaction. Increased flux through the phosphofructokinase step is self-limited by the phosphorylation of ADP at later steps in the glycolytic pathway, and phosphofructokinase activity is diminished when the ATP/ADP ratio is restored. Creatine phosphate levels are replenished by a prolonged, slower rate of glycolysis in the later phase of the recovery process.

METABOLIC EFFECTS OF NOREPINEPHRINE IN BROWN ADIPOSE TISSUE

Brown fat represents an opposite extreme compared with electric organ tissue in that it has a low glycolytic activity but a very high respiratory activity (Joel 1965). In the experiment shown in Fig. 8, the interscapular brown fat of a normal anaesthetized hamster was exposed *in vivo,* and recordings were made of the tissue pyridine nucleotide fluorescence (lower trace), temperature (center trace), and oxygen tension (upper trace). The paper by Prusiner *et al.* (1968a) may be consulted for further technical details. Norepinephrine (0.3 μg) was infused into the external jugular vein over the time interval shown. Twenty-five seconds after the beginning of infusion, the tissue oxygen tension started to fall from an initial level of 60 mm Hg and reached a minimum value of 30 mm Hg after about 3 min. Since norepinephrine has a vasodilator rather than a vasoconstrictor effect on the blood vessels supplying the interscapular brown fat, the fall of the tissue oxygen tension denotes an increased respiratory activity. Increased oxygen consumption following norepinephrine addition has been amply confirmed in studies with isolated brown fat cells (Fain *et al.* 1967, Prusiner *et al.* 1968b, Williamson 1970a). Shortly after the onset of the decrease of tissue oxygen tension, the temperature of the brown fat started to increase (thermogenesis) and the tissue fluorescence level decreased, denoting an oxidation of the pyridine nucleotides. The whole effect of the norepinephrine infusion was transient, and baseline levels of the different parameters were reached after about 6 min. These results demonstrate that in a tissue of high mitochondrial content, the characteristic response of the pyridine nucleotide system is towards an oxidation with increased metabolic activity associated with active respiration. For a review of the control of energy metabolism in brown adipose tissue see Williamson *et al.* (1970).

METABOLIC EFFECTS OF EPINEPHRINE IN PERFUSED RAT HEART

The kinetics of the various metabolic events following epinephrine addition to cardiac muscle have been studied in detail by a number of groups (Williamson 1966a, Williamson & Jamieson 1966, Drummond *et al.* 1966, Robison *et al.* 1965, Namm & Mayer 1968). Heart, like brain, has a good capacity for both glycolysis and oxidative metabolism. Studies by Safer & Hoffmann (1970), employing the tissue pyridine nucleotide fluorescence technique in perfused rat heart, have indicated that of the total pyridine nucleotide fluorescence increase observed in the fully reduced state, about half is derived from the mitochondrial space and about half from the cytoplasmic space. In Fig. 9A, the kinetics of the pyridine nucleotide

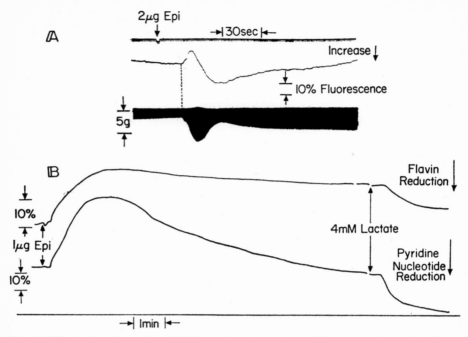

Fig. 9. Effects of epinephrine (Epi) in perfused rat heart. The top tracings (A) show the effect of 2 μg epinephrine added to a normal heart on the pyridine nucleotide fluorescence (366 nm excitation, 460 nm emission) and force of contraction. The bottom tracings (B) show the effect of 1 μg epinephrine on the flavin fluorescence (436 nm excitation, 540 nm emission) and pyridine nucleotide fluorescence (366 nm excitation, 460 mm emission) of a glycogen depleted heart perfused without substrate.

fluorescence change observed after addition of 2 μg epinephrine to a perfused rat heart (upper trace) is compared with the contractile response (lower trace). Coincident with the onset of the increased force of contraction, the fluorescence level decreased, indicating an oxidation of pyridine nucleotide. After a few seconds, the fluorescence change reversed, and a slow cycle of pyridine nucleotide reduction occurred. From the results of a number of studies (Williamson & Jamieson 1965, 1966, Chance et al. 1965), we have interpreted the biphasic fluorescence response as revealing an early oxidation of the mitochondrial pyridine nucleotide system caused by the increased production of ADP due to the increased contractile work of the heart, followed by a burst of glycogenolysis which produces a large reduction of the cytoplasmic pyridine nucleotide system. For comparison, the effects of epinephrine on flavin and pyridine nucleotide fluorescence changes in a glycogen depleted rat heart perfused without substrate are shown in Fig. 9B. Unlike the pyridine nucleotides, fluorescent flavoproteins are primarily located in the mitochondria, and the intensity changes prior to the first phosphorylation site are caused mainly by oxidation-reduction changes of lipoic dehydrogenase (Scholz et al. 1969). Since the flavin of lipoic dehydrogenase is in equilibrium with the mitochondrial NAD pool (Hassinen & Chance 1968), flavin fluorescence changes can be used as a monitor of the mitochondrial NAD oxidation-reduction state. Fig. 9B shows that when neither glucose nor glycogen are available as fuels in the perfused rat heart, epinephrine produces only an oxidation of the mitochondrial pyridine nucleotide pool. This response is similar to the effect of norepinephrine on brown adipose tissue, and is analogous to the effects observed on adding ADP to isolated rat heart mitochondria (Klingenberg et al. 1959, LaNoue et al. 1970).

The above results show that the effects of epinephrine in mediating the inotropic response and increased respiratory activity of the heart are temporally separated from the effects on glycogenolysis. This conclusion is further substantiated by the data shown in Fig. 10. Here, it is seen that the increase of tissue cyclic AMP levels paralleled the increased force of contraction, peak values being reached 10 sec after epinephrine administration, but the interconversion of phosphorylase b to a was delayed by a few seconds. Unlike the electric organ tissue, cyclic AMP has been shown to mediate the activation of phosphorylase b kinase in heart (Robison et al. 1968), and the phosphorylated active form of this enzyme subsequently phosphorylates phosphorylase b to a.

Catecholamines, histamine and electrical stimulation result in an increased rate of cyclic AMP formation in brain (Rall & Kakiuchi 1966, Kakiuchi & Rall 1968, Kakiuchi et al. 1969), and presumably the rise of cyclic AMP is responsible for activation of phosphorylase b kinase and the initiation of glycogenolysis in brain, as in heart. The metabolism of these two tissues is rather similar except for the inability of unconditioned brain to utilize ketone bodies and fatty acids as metabolic fuels. Control of glycolysis appears to be much the same as shown by the similar patterns of metabolite changes induced by anoxia in mouse brain (Lowry et al. 1964, Lowry & Passonneau 1964) and rat heart (Williamson 1966b). Furthermore, a recent study of the oxidation-reduction transitions of cytochromes and pyridine nucleotides in

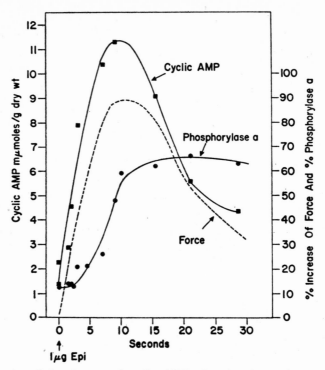

Fig. 10. Kinetics of the changes of cyclic AMP, phosphorylase *a* levels and force of contraction following addition of 1 μg epinephrine to perfused rat hearts. Each *point* represents analyses performed on individual hearts after rapid freezing at the time intervals shown.

isolated rat superior cervical ganglion upon electrophysiological stimulation (Brauser *et al.* 1970) has demonstrated biphasic effects of the NAD systems very similar to those observed in the normal heart after epine-phrine addition. Coincident with the onset of stimulation (6 cps for 40 sec) pyridine nucleotide oxidation and cytochrome *b* oxidation were observed. However, whereas cytochrome *b* showed only a cycle of oxidation followed by a return to the baseline shortly after cessation of the stimulation, the pyridine nucleotide system responded by a large cycle of reduction, following the initial oxidation with a delay of about 10 sec. These studies may be inter-preted as indicating an altered redox state of the mitochondrial respiratory chain due to more active electron transport, analogous to a state 4 to 3 transition (Chance & Williams 1955), as more ADP becomes available to the mitochondria as a result of an increased rate of ATP use in maintaining ionic gradients. Activation of glycogenolysis, aerobic glycolysis and increase of the cytoplasmic NADH/NAD ratio occurs after a short delay. Thus, in nervous tissue as in electric organ and heart, the endogenous high energy phosphate reserves are utilized first in response to an increased work load, and chemical signals in the form of ADP, AMP and P_i are transmitted simultaneously to the mitochondria (causing increased respiration) and cytoplasm (causing phosphofructokinase activation). If the increased rate of energy expenditure is small, increased glycolysis from glucose is probably sufficient to provide the mitochondria with substrate (together with fatty acids when available), perturbations of metabolite levels are minimal and the characteristic response of the mitochondrial respiratory chain carriers is towards an oxidation (Williamson & Jamieson 1965). With more severe energy stresses, independent signals (e.g. from cyclic AMP and/or Ca^{++}) activate phosphorylase b kinase to mobilize the glycogen reserve, and increase the substrate supply. This system seems to be less delicately controlled, so that larger changes of the metabolic intermediates occur and the characteristic response of the pyridine nucleotides is a cycle of cytoplasmic NAD reduction and a corresponding increase of the lactate to pyruvate ratio.

TRANSPORT OF REDUCING EQUIVALENTS FROM CYTOPLASM TO MITOCHONDRIA

Brain tissue normally relies almost exclusively on carbohydrate as a metabolic fuel. The major control mechanisms regulating the breakdown of glycogen and its metabolism by aerobic glycolysis have been discussed in some detail. Some metabolic properties of mitochondria will now be discussed which have a particular bearing on the lactate to pyruvate ratio. Aerobic glycolysis produces stoichiometric amounts of pyruvate and NADH. If lactate is not to accumulate, these compounds must be oxidized by the mitochondria in equivalent amounts. Reduced pyridine nucleotides as such are not readily oxidized by mammalian mitochondria (Lehninger et al. 1960). Instead, the reducing equivalents of NADH are transported by the reduced partner of suitable NAD-linked dehydrogenase substrate redox couples. Of the various H-shuttles which have been proposed (Borst 1963), the one with the most experimental support is the malate-aspartate cycle, depicted in Fig. 11. The vertical lines represent the inner mitochondrial membrane, with the cytoplasmic space to the left and the mitochondrial matrix space to the right.

JOHN R. WILLIAMSON ET AL.

Hydrogen Transport Shuttle

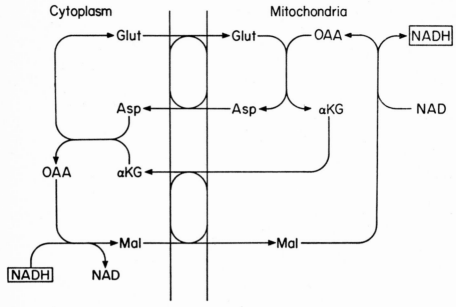

Fig. 11. Scheme of the malate-aspartate shuttle for the transport of reducing equivalents across the mitochondrial membrane.

Cytoplasmic NADH reduces oxalacetate to malate, which enters the mitochondria in exchange for α-ketoglutarate (Klingenberg 1970). Intramitochondrial malate is oxidized to oxalacetate with the production of NADH in the mitochondrial space. Oxalacetate at physiological concentrations is relatively impermeable to the mitochondrial membrane, but its transamination with glutamate to yield aspartate and α-ketogluarate removes this difficulty. Oxalacetate is regenerated in the cytoplasm by a reverse transamination step. As shown in Fig. 11, although the net effect of the cycle is to transfer NADH across the mitochondrial membrane, this process involves an influx of malate and glutamate into the mitochondria and efflux of aspartate and α-ketoglutarate. Each of these anions is transported by special carrier systems subject to a variety of controls (Klingenberg 1970, Chappell 1969).

Although no physiological mechanisms have so far been shown to affect the anion transport processes in the intact tissue, control of the H-shuttle represents a possible way of regulating the proportion of pyruvate formed

Table 1. *Effects of Amino-oxyacetic Acid (AOA) in Perfused Hearts from Normal and Hyperthyroid Rats*

Rat hearts were perfused as described by Williamson (1962). Rats were made hyperthyroid by daily subcutaneous injections of 100 μg/100 g body wt of triiodothyronine (cytomel).

Condition of animal	Substrate	Amino-oxyacetic acid	No of expts	Metabolic changes		
				Glucose	Lactate	Pyruvate
				μmoles/g dry wt/hr		
Normal	5 mM glucose plus	0	6	-320 ± 9	$+ 54\pm 6$	
	10 munits/ml insulin	0.4	5	-382 ± 12	$+171\pm21$	
Normal	5 mM L(+)Lactate	0	7		-276 ± 7	
		0.2	7		-173 ± 15	
Normal	10 mM Pyruvate	0	2		$+180$	-765
		0.4	2		$+186$	-757
Hyperthyroid	5 mM glucose plus	0	9	-400 ± 7	$+154\pm 6$	
	10 munits/ml insulin	0.4	7	-437 ± 20	$+297\pm 8$	
Hyperthyroid	10 mM Pyruvate	0	4		$+288\pm31$	-909 ± 60
		0.4	4		$+228\pm13$	-903 ± 43

from glucose which is oxidized to CO_2 by mitochondria, or reduced to lactate by lactate dehydrogenase. Thus, if the transport of NADH from cytoplasm to mitochondria is inhibited, NADH will tend to accumulate in the cytoplasm and increase the rate of reduction of pyruvate to lactate. The lactate to pyruvate ratio would increase, and this change would be independent of the oxygen tension of the tissue. This type of effect is illustrated in Table 1, which shows the effect of amino-oxyacetic acid, an inhibitor of glutamate-oxalacetate transaminase (Roberts *et al.* 1964), on substrate utilizations by perfused hearts from both normal and hyperthyroid rats. The rationale for using this compound is that by inhibiting the transaminase step, the malate-aspartate NADH transport shuttle will be inhibited. Hyperthyroid rats have increased mitochondrial α-glycerophosphate oxidase activity, and so if the α-glycerophosphate NADH transport shuttle is operative in the intact heart, it would be expected that amino-oxyacetic acid should be less effective in hearts from hyperthyroid rats than from normal rats. The data show that with glucose as substrate, amino-oxyacetic acid had little effect on glucose uptake with both normal and hyperthyroid hearts, but more than doubled the rate of lactate formation in both groups. The rate of aerobic glycolysis was greater with hyperthyroid than normal hearts, which is opposite to what is expected if more efficient mechanisms were operating for the transport of reducing equivalents into mitochondria. The lactate to pyruvate ratio in the perfusion medium (not shown) increased dramatically from 5 to about 450 in normal hearts and from 5 to 250 in hyperthyroid hearts after amino-oxyacetic acid addition. With lactate as sole substrate, its uptake was inhibited 40 per cent by amino-oxyacetic acid in normal hearts. On the other hand, pyruvate uptake and the conversion of pyruvate to lactate were not markedly affected by amino-oxyacetic acid in either group. An inhibition of oxygen consumption and production of $^{14}CO_2$ from ^{14}C-glucose by amino-oxyacetic acid and hydroxylamine (another transaminase inhibitor) has also been observed in brain cortex slices (Haber 1965).

Although amino-oxyacetic acid is an artificial cell poison, its use in the above experiments demonstrates (1) that a transaminase step is involved in the transport of reducing equivalents from cytoplasm to mitochondria, (2) that the α-glycerophosphate shuttle appears not to be a major pathway for H-transport in the intact organ, and (3) that interference with the malate-aspartate shuttle is a very effective means of increasing the tissue lactate to pyruvate ratio. Since transport of metabolic anions across the mitochondrial membrane is dependent on cation movements (Papa *et al.* 1969), it is entirely conceivable that changes of the cation balance in nerve and brain cells due to altered electrical activity could affect the rate of transport of reducing equivalents into mitochondria, and hence the lactate to pyruvate ratio.

REGULATION OF PYRUVATE UTILIZATION

Pyruvate dehydrogenase is subject to a wide variety of controls. An inhibition of pyruvate oxidation in tissues such as brain, which have a low pyruvate carboxylase activity, will result in an increase of the intracellular pyruvate concentration, causing a competition with the H-shuttle for NADH produced at the glyceraldehyde-3-P dehydrogenase step of glycolysis. Thus, an inhibition of pyruvate oxidation could be associated with an increased rate of lactate formation but a fall of the lactate to pyruvate ratio. Two types of mechanisms are known to control pyruvate dehydrogenase activity (Fig. 12).

PYRUVATE DEHYDROGENASE CONTROL

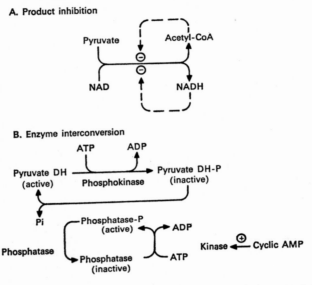

Fig. 12. Scheme showing postulated controls of the activity of pyruvate dehydrogenase. The positive sign represents an activational effect.

The first is through product inhibition by NADH and acetyl-CoA (Garland & Randle 1964, Bremer 1969, Wieland *et* al. 1969). Wieland *et al.* (1969) report a *Km* for pyruvate of 20 μM and *Ki* value of 29 μM for acetyl-CoA for the pig heart enzyme. The second mechanism has been discovered very recently (Reed 1969, Wieland & Siess 1970) and involves the interconversion of pyruvate dehydrogenase between active and inactive forms. This process is analogous to the sequence of events resulting in the interconversion of the two forms of phosphorylase and glycogen synthetase (Helmreich 1969). In the case of pyruvate dehydrogenase, phosphorylation of the enzyme leads to a loss of activity. Dephosphorylation is catalyzed by a phosphatase which apparently can exist also in phosphorylated (active) and nonphosphorylated (inactive) forms (Wieland & Siess 1970). Phosphorylation of the phosphatase is catalyzed by a kinase which itself is activated by cyclic AMP. Activation of this nonspecific kinase may be a primary effect of cyclic AMP in a number of tissues (Miyamoto *et al.* 1969, Walsh *et al.* 1968, Corbin & Krebs 1969, Kuo & Greengard 1969, Bishop & Larner 1969, Langan 1968).

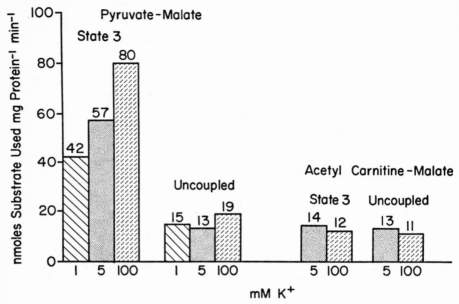

Fig. 13. The effect of K+ on the uptakes of pyruvate and acetylcarnitine by rat brain mitochondria in the ADP stimulated and uncoupled states. Rat brain mitochondria (1 mg protein/ml) were suspended in media containing (a) 1 or 5 mM KCl, 225 mM mannitol, 75 mM sucrose, 10 mM phosphate-tris, 10 mM Tris-Cl, 50 μM EDTA pH 7.4, or (b) 100 mM KCl, 75 mM mannitol, 25 mM sucrose, 10 mM phosphate-tris, 10 mM Tris-Cl, 50 μM EDTA pH 7.4. Malate was present at a final concentration of 1 mM, pyruvate between 0.5 and 1 mM, and acetylcarnitine at 12 mM. State 3 was induced by the presence of 10 mM ADP and uncoupling by the addition of FCCP (7 nmoles/mg protein). In all cases the reaction was initiated by the addition of mitochondria. The incubations were run at 28° C and samples were removed 2, 4, 8, 10 min after the addition of mitochondria. These samples were quenched in 18% perchloric acid, neutralized, centrifuged to remove protein and perchlorate, and the supernatants assayed for pyruvate or carnitine respectively.

Recent studies from our laboratory have described an unusual K+ effect on the utilization of pyruvate by rat brain (mainly glia) mitochondria (Clark 1970). Fig. 13 shows the rate of pyruvate utilization by brain mitochondria incubated in the presence of malate and different K+ concentrations from 1 to 100 mM. In state 3 (i. e., active respiration induced by ADP), pyruvate uptake increased from 42 to 80 mμ/moles/mg protein/min with increasing K+ concentration. In the uncoupled state (i. e., no respiratory control), pyruvate uptake was inhibited at both low and high K+ concentrations. On the other

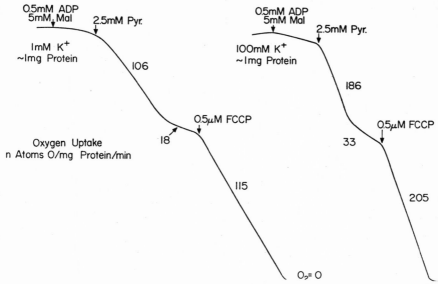

Fig. 14. Effect of K+ on the oxygen uptake of rat brain mitochondria using pyruvate-malate as substrate. Rat brain mitochondria (approximately 1 mg protein, prepared according to the method of Clark & Nicklas (1970), were suspended in a final volume of 1 ml of media containing (a) 1 mM KCl, 225 mM mannitol, 75 mM sucrose, 10 mM phosphate-tris, 10 mM Tris-Cl, 50 μM EDTA pH 7.4, or (b) 100 mM KCl, 75 mM mannitol, 25 mM sucrose, 10 mM phosphate-tris, 10 mM Tris-Cl, 50 μM EDTA pH 7.4. State 3 respiration was initiated by the addition of ADP and pyruvate-malate, and oxygen uptake was measured by an oxygen electrode. The numbers associated with each of the curves represent the oxygen uptake in natoms oxygen/mg protein/min.

hand, with acetylcarnitine instead of pyruvate as a source of acetyl units in the presence of malate, there was no effect of either K+ or uncouplers on the rate of acetylcarnitine utilization. A polarographic trace of the oxygen concentration in the mitochondrial suspension (Fig. 14) shows that with pyruvate and malate as substrates, an increase of the K+ concentration from 1 mM to 100 mM increased the rate of oxygen consumption from 106 to 186 mμatoms/mg protein/min in state 3, and from 18 to 33 mμatoms/mg protein/min in state 4 (i. e., controlled respiration in the absence of ADP). Addition of uncoupler increased respiration to values slightly higher than the state 3 rates both at low and high K+ concentrations. Thus, in the uncoupled state, pyruvate uptake is inhibited but respiration is not. This effect is interpreted as due to a loss of intramitochondrial K^+ in the uncoupled state. Measurements of acetyl-CoA and NADH levels in brain mitochondria incubated under different conditions showed that neither the K^+ stimulation of pyruvate uptake nor the inhibition by uncoupling agents could be explained by product inhibition due to NADH and acetyl-CoA. These data suggest that in rat brain, pyruvate oxidation is controlled primarily by interconversion of the active and inactive forms of pyruvate dehydrogenase.

Glutamate along with γ-aminobutyric acid have been implicated as neurochemical transmitters, and it is of interest that addition of K^+ ions to rat brain mitochondria incubated in the presence of malate, glutamate and pyruvate resulted in a switch from 50 per cent pyruvate and 50 per cent glutamate metabolism to a situation where 90 per cent of the respiration could be accounted for as pyruvate oxidation (Nicklas et al. 1970). A similar effect of K^+ in increasing glucose oxidation at the expense of amino acid metabolism has also been observed in brain slices (Berl et al. 1968, 1970). The effect of K^+ in stimulating the respiration of brain slices is well documented. Sattin & Rall (1967) found that exposure of guinea pig cortical slices to 40 mM KC1 resulted in a large increase of cyclic AMP levels, so that it is conceivable that K^+ effects on pyruvate oxidation are mediated by the effect of cyclic AMP in stimulating pyruvate dehydrogenase phosphatase (cf. Fig. 12). It remains to be seen whether adenyl cyclase activity is present in preparations of rat brain mitochondria.

Further work is needed to evaluate the physiological significance of the K^+ effect on brain mitochondria, particularly as it is unlikely that the intramitochondrial K^+ concentration would be subject to wide variations in vivo. However, more sensitive modulations of pyruvate dehydrogenase activity by relatively small changes of K^+ concentration may be effected by changes of the cyclic AMP concentration resulting from the sensitivity of adenyl cyclase to cations (e. g. Drummond & Duncan 1970).

EFFECTS OF pH ON GLYCOLYSIS

The respiration rate of brain slices increases over the pH range from 6 to 9, and falls off sharply in more alkaline medium (Canzanelli et al. 1939). Aerobic glycolysis (i. e., lactate production from glucose in the presence of oxygen) apparently increases with increasing pH over the physiological pH range (Domonkos & Huszák 1959, Scheuer & Berry 1967). However, it is clear that there is no direct correlation between the pH of the medium buffer and the intracellular pH, although they probably change in the same direction. The effects of pH on glycolysis have been extensively studied in erythrocytes (for review see Williamson 1970b), where an increase of glycolysis and lactate to pyruvate ratio also occurred with increasing alkalinity. The increased rate of glycolysis was caused by an activation of phosphofructokinase due to a release of inhibition by ATP and decrease of the K_m for fructose-6-P at higher pH values.

Recent results from Dr. Siesjö's laboratory (Granholm & Siesjö 1969, Granholm et al. 1969) have shown that hyperventilation of rats, which results in diminished arterial pCO_2 values and a rise of pH, causes an increased lactate to pyruvate ratio, and an increased reduction of pyridine nucleotides, but little change of the ATP/ADP or creatine-P/creatine ratios in cortical tissue. The increased pH associated with hyperventilation produces an increased rate of aerobic glycolysis in the rat brain, as well as in human brain (Cohen et al. 1968). The increased ratios of lactate to pyruvate and cytoplasmic NADH/NAD observed during hyperventilation and hypocapnia, therefore, are probably related directly to the stimulation of phosphofructokinase by the rise of pH, and are not indicative of local tissue hypoxia. Under extreme conditions of diminished cerebral blood flow during hyperventilation, local areas in the brain may be inadequately oxygenated, in which case a partial reduction of the mitochondrial NAD pool and decreased creatine-P/creatine ratios would be observed.

SUMMARY

The general features of a metabolic switch where feedback interactions circumscribe the duration and strength of a metabolic stimulus are described. Key control steps in the utilization of carbohydrate by tissues are glycogen phosporylase and phosphofructokinase. The basic kinetic control features of glycogenolysis, glycolysis and mitochondrial respiration are illustrated by examples from the main electric organ of Electrophorus electricus (low mitochondrial content), hamster brown fat (very high mitochondrial content) and perfused rat heart (average mitochondrial content). Although these tissues differ greatly in their function and the type of work performed (ion pumping, heat production and contraction), the studies reveal that the cyto-plasmic glycolytic system and the mitochondrial respiratory chain respond in a characteristic manner to an increased energy expenditure by the tissue. Thus, analogies may be drawn between various tissues which are more amenable to experimental investigation than brain, in order to arrive at an understanding of the basic control features of common metabolic pathways.

The characteristic response of the glycolytic pathway to an increased con-centration of ADP, AMP and inorganic phosphate is an activation of phos-phofructokinase, which is revealed by a marked increase of its mass action ratio (fructose-1,6-di-P $\times$ ADP/fructose-6-P $\times$ ATP). Initiation of glycogen mobilization is achieved by other messengers (e. g. cyclic AMP or Ca^{++}) which are released by the action of the primary stimulus on the tissue. Phos-phorylation of the various enzymes in the activation sequence resulting in the production of glucose-1-P from glycogen imposes a time lag in the supply of substrate to the glycolytic enzymes. During this time a depletion of tissue high energy phosphate stores may occur if ATP generation by oxidative phosphorylation is not sufficiently rapid. The pulse of increased glycogenol-ysis causes a transient reduction of the cytoplasmic pyridine neucleotide pool and and increase of the lactate to pyruvate ratio.

The characteristic response of the mitochondria to an increased concen-tration of ADP and inorganic phosphate is an increased respiratory activity, and an oxidation of the mitochondrial pyridine nucleotides, fluorescent flavoproteins and cytochrome b. In tissues having both a high glycolytic activ-ity and high mitochondrial respiration, such as heart and brain, the charac-teristic responses of the cytoplasmic and mitochondrial enzyme systems towards suitable primary stimulae may be distinguished kinetically by direct observation of the tissue pyridine nucleotide fluorescence changes. Oxidation of the mitochondrial NAD pool occurs initially, followed by a reduction of the cytoplasmic NAD pool.

Factors controlling the rate of transport of reducing equivalents from cytoplasm to mitochondria and the rate of oxidation of pyruvate by pyruvate dehydrogenase are discussed in relation to their effect on the tissue lactate to pyruvate ratio. It is concluded that large variations in the lactate to pyru-vate ratio can occur, in response to physiological stimulae, which are inde-pendent of the state of oxygenation of the tissue.

REFERENCES

Aubert, X., Chance, B. & Keynes, R. D. (1964) Optical studies of biochemical events in the electric organ of *Electrophorus. Proc. roy. Soc. B. 160*, 211–245.

Berl, S., Nicklas, W. J. & Clarke, D. D. (1968) Compartmentation of glutamic acid metabolism in brain slices. *J. Neurochem. 15*, 131–140.

Berl, S., Nicklas, W. J. & Clarke, D. D. (1970) Compartmentation of citric acid cycle metabolism in brain: labeling of glutamate, glutamine, aspartate and gaba by several radioactive tracer metabolites. *J. Neurochem. 17*, 1009–1016.

Bishop, J. S. & Larner, J. (1969) Presence in liver of a 3′,5′-cyclic AMP stimulated kinase for the I form of UDPG-glycogen glucosyltransferase. *Biochim. biophys. Acta 171*, 374–377.

Borst, P. (1963) Hydrogen transport and transport metabolites. In *Funktionelle und Morphologische Organisation der Zelle*, pp. 137–158. Springer-Verlag, New York.

Bradham, L. S., Holt, D. A. & Sims, M. (1970) The effect of Ca^{2+} on the adenyl cyclase of calf brain. *Biochim. biophys. Acta 201*, 250–260.

Brauser, B., Bücher, Th. & Dolivo, M. (1970) Redox transitions of cytochromes and pyridine nucleotides upon stimulation of an isolated rat ganglion. *FEBS Letters 8*, 297–300.

Bremer, J. (1969) Pyruvate dehydrogenase, substrate specificity and product inhibition. *Europ. J. Biochem. 8*, 535–550.

Canzanelli, A., Greenblatt, M., Rogers, G. A. & Rapport, D. (1939) The effect of pH changes on the *in-vitro* O_2 consumption of tissues. *Amer. J. Physiol. 127*, 290–295.

Chance, B. & Williams, G. R. (1955) Respiratory enzymes in oxidative phosphorylation. III. The steady state. *J. biol. Chem. 217*, 409–427.

Chance, B., Lee, C.-P. & Oshino, R. (1964) The electron transport components of the main organ of *Electrophorus Electricus. Biochim. biophys. Acta 88*, 105–111.

Chance, B., Williamson, J. R., Jamieson, D. & Schoener, B. (1965) Properties and kinetics of reduced pyridine nucleotide fluorescence of the isolated and *in vivo* rat heart. *Biochem. Z. 341*, 357–377.

Chappell, J. B. (1969) Transport and exchange of anions in mitochondria. In *Inhibitors: Tools in Cell Research*, ed. Bücher, Th. & Sies, H., pp. 335–350. Springer-Verlag, New York.

Clark, J. B. (1970) Effect of potassium (K^+) ions on respiration of rat brain mitochondria. *Fed. Proc. 29*, 471 Abs.

Clark, J. B. & Nicklas, W. J. (1970) The metabolism of rat brain mitochondria: preparation and characterization. *J. biol. Chem.* In press.

Cohen, P. J., Alexander, S. C. & Wollman, H. (1968) Effects of hypocarbia and of hypoxia with normocarbia on cerebral blood flow and metabolism in man. *Scand. J. clin. Lab. Invest.*, Suppl. 102, IV, A.

Corbin, J. D. & Krebs, E. G. (1969) A cyclic AMP-stimulated protein kinase in adipose tissue. *Biochem. biophys. Res. Commun. 36*, 328–336.

Domonkos, J. & Huszák, I. (1959) Effect of hydrogen-ion concentration on the carbohydrate metabolism of brain tissue. *J. Neurochem. 4*, 238–243.

Drummond, G. I. & Duncan, L. (1970) Adenyl cyclase in cardiac tissue. *J. biol. Chem. 245*, 976–983.

Drummond, G. I., Duncan, L. & Hertzmann, E. (1966) Effect of epinephrine on phosphorylase *b* kinase in perfused rat hearts. *J. biol. Chem. 241*, 5899–5903.

Drummond, G. I., Harwood, J. P. & Powell, C. A. (1969) Studies on the activation of phosphorylase in skeletal muscle by contraction and by epinephrine. *J. biol. Chem.* *244*, 4235–4240.

Fain, J. N., Reed, N. & Saperstein, R. (1967) The isolations and metabolism of brown fat cells. *J. biol. Chem. 242*, 1887–1894.

Garland, P. B. & Randle, P. J. (1964) Control of pyruvate dehydrogenase in perfused rat heart by the intracellular concentration of acetyl-coenzyme A. *Biochem. J. 91*, 6C–7C.

Granholm, L. & Siesjö, B. K. (1969) The effects of hypercapnia and hypocapnia upon the cerebrospinal fluid lactate and pyruvate concentrations and upon the lactate, pyruvate, ATP, ADP, phosphocreatine and creatine concentrations of cat brain tissue. *Acta physiol. scand. 75*, 257–266.

Granholm, L., Lukjanova, L. & Siesjö, B. K. (1969) The effect of marked hyperventilation upon tissue levels of NADH, lactate, pyruvate, phosphocreatine, and adenosine phosphates of rat brain. *Acta physiol. scand. 77*, 179–190.

Haber, B. (1969) The effect of hydroxylamine and aminooxyacetic acid on the cerebral *in vitro* utilization of glucose, fructose, glutamic acid, and γ-aminobutyric acid. *Canad. J. Biochem. 43*, 865–876.

Hassinen, I. & Chance, B. (1968) Oxidation-reduction properties of the mitochondrial flavoprotein chain. *Biochem. biophys. Res. Commun. 31*, 895–900.

Helmreich, E. (1969) Control of synthesis and breakdown of glycogen, starch and cellulose. In *Comprehensive Biochemistry*, ed. Florkin, M. & Stotz, E. H., Vol. 17, pp. 17–92. Elsevier Publishing Co., New York.

Helmreich, E. & Cori, C. F. (1965) Regulation of glycolysis in muscle. *Adv. Enzyme Regul. 3*, 91–107.

Holmes, P. A. & Mansour, T. E. (1968) Glucose as a regulator of glycogen phosphorylase in rat diaphragm. II. Effect of glucose and related compounds on phosphorylase phosphatase. *Biochim. biophys. Acta 156*, 275–284.

Joel, C. D. (1965) The physiological role of brown adipose tissue. In *Handbook of Physiology*, ed. Renold, A. E. & Cahill, G. F. Jr., Sec. 5, pp. 59–85. American Physiological Society, Washington, D. C.

Kakiuchi, S. & Rall, T. W. (1968) The influence of chemical agents on the accumulation of adenosine 3′,5′-phosphate in slices of rabbit cerebellum. *Molec. Pharmacol. 4*, 367–378.

Kakiuchi, S., Rall, T. W. & McIlwain, H. (1969) The effect of electrical stimulation upon the accumulation of adenosine 3′,5′-phosphate in isolated cerebral tissue. *J. Neurochem. 16*, 485–491.

Keynes, R. D. & Martin-Ferreira (1953) Membrane potentials in the electroplates of the electric eel. *J. Physiol. (Lond.) 119*, 315–351.

Klingenberg, M. (1970) Mitochondria metabolite transport. *FEBS Letters 6*, 145–154.

Klingenberg, M., Slenckka, W. & Ritt, E. (1959) Vergleichende Biochemie der Pyridinnucleotid-Systeme in Mitochondrien verschiedener Organe. *Biochem. Z. 322*, 47–66.

Krebs, E. G., DeLange, R. J., Kemp, R. G. & Riley, W. D. (1966) Activation of skeletal muscle phosphorylase. *Pharmacol. Rev. 18*, 163–171.

Kuo, J. F. & Greengard, P. (1969) An adenosine 3′,5′-monophosphate-dependent protein kinase from *Escherichia coli*. *J. biol. Chem. 244*, 3417–3419.

Langan, T. A. (1968) Histone phosphorylation: stimulation by adenosine 3',5'-monophosphate. *Science 162*, 579–580.

LaNoue, K., Nicklas, W. J. & Williamson, J. R. (1970) Control of citric acid cycle activity in rat heart mitochondria. *J. biol. Chem. 245*, 102–111.

Lehninger, A. L., Sudduth, H. C. & Wise, J. R. (1960) D-β-Hydroxybutyric dehydrogenase of mitochondria. *J. biol. Chem. 235*, 2450–2455.

Lowry, O. H. & Passonneau, J. V. (1964) The relationships between substrates and enzymes of glycolysis in brain. *J. biol. Chem. 239*, 31–42.

Lowry, O. H., Passonneau, J. V., Hasselberger, F. X. & Schulz, D. W. (1964) Effect of ischemia on known substrates and cofactors of the glycolytic pathway in brain. *J. biol. Chem. 239*, 18–30.

Maitra, P. K., Ghosh, A., Schoener, B. & Chance, B. (1964) Transients in glycolytic metabolism following electrical activity in *Electrophorus*. *Biochim. biophys. Acta 88*, 112–119.

Miyamoto, E., Kuo, J. F. & Greengard, P. (1969) Adenosine 3',5'-monophosphate-dependent protein kinase from brain. *Science 165*, 63–65.

Morgan, H. E. & Parmeggiani, A. (1964) Regulation of glyogenolysis in muscle. II. Control of glycogen phosphorylase reaction in isolated perfused heart. *J. biol. Chem. 239*, 2440–2445.

Namm, D. H. & Mayer, S. E. (1968) Effects of epinephrine on cardiac cyclic 3',5'-AMP, phosporylase kinase, and phosporylase. *Molec. Pharmacol. 4*, 61–69.

Namm, D. H., Mayer, S. E. & Maltbie, M. (1968) The role of potassium and calcium ions in the effect of epinephrine on cardiac cyclic adenosine 3',5'-monophosphate, phosphorylase kinase, and phosphorylase. *Molec. Pharmacol. 4*, 522–530.

Nicklas, W. J., Clark, J. B. & Williamson, J. R. (1970) Studies on K+-stimulated respiration of rat brain mitochondria. In preparation.

Papa, S., Tager, J. M., Quagliariello, E. & Slater, E. C. (eds.) (1969) *The Energy Level and Metabolic Control in Mitochondria*. Adriatica Editrice, Bari.

Posner, J. B., Stern, R. & Krebs, E. G. (1965) Effects of electrical stimulation and epinephrine on muscle phosphorylase, phosphorylase *b* kinase, and adenosine 3',5'-phosphate. *J. biol. Chem. 240*, 982–985.

Prusiner, S., Williamson, J. R., Chance, B. & Paddle, B. M. (1968a) Metabolic control in brown fat: pyridine nucleotide changes during thermogenesis in brown fat tissue *in vivo*. *Arch. biochem. Biophys. 123*, 368–377.

Prusiner, S. B., Cannon, B. & Lindberg, O. (1968b) Oxidative metabolism in cells isolated from brown adipose tissue. 1. Catecholamine and fatty acid stimulation of respiration. *Europ. J. Biochem. 6*, 15–22.

Rall, T. W. & Kakiuchi, S. (1966) The influence of certain neurohormones and drugs on the accumulation of cyclic 3',5'-AMP in brain tissue. In *Molecular Basis of Some Aspects of Mental Activity*, ed. Walaas, O., Vol. 1, pp. 417–430. Academic Press, London.

Rasmussen, H. & Tenenhouse, A. (1968) Cyclic adenosine monophosphate, Ca++, and membranes. *Proc. nat. Acad. Sci. (Wash.) 59*, 1364–1370.

Reed, L. J. (1969) Pyruvate dehydrogenase complex. In *Current Topics in Cellular Regulation*, ed. Horecker, B. L. & Stadtman, E. R., Vol. 1, pp. 233–251. Academic Press, New York.

Roberts, E., Wein, J. & Simonsen, D. G. (1964) γ-Aminobutyric acid (γABA), vitamin B$_6$, and neuronal function – a speculative synthesis. *Vitam. and Horm. 22*, 503–559.

Robison, G. A., Butcher, R. W., Øye, I., Morgan, H. E. & Sutherland, E. W. (1965) The effect of epinephrine on adenosine-3′,5′-phosphate levels in the isolated perfused rat heart. *Molec. Pharmacol. 1*, 168–177.

Robison, G. A., Butcher, R. W. & Sutherland, E. W. (1968) Cyclic AMP. *Ann. Rev. Biochem. 37*, 149–174.

Rose, I. A. & Rose, Z. B. (1969) Glycolysis: regulation and mechanisms of the enzymes. In *Comprehensive Biochemistry*, ed. Florkin, M. & Stotz, E. H., Vol. 17, pp. 93–161. Elsevier Publishing Co., New York.

Safer, B. & Hoffmann, P. (1970) Changes in flavoprotein and pyridine nucleotide redox states in rat heart. *Fed. Proc. 29*, 923 Abs.

Sattin, A. & Rall, T. W. (1967) The effect of brain extracts on the accumulation of cyclic 3′-5′-AMP (CA) in slices of guinea pig (GP) cerebral cortex. *Fed. Proc. 26*, 707.

Scheuer, J. & Berry, M. N. (1967) Effect of alkalosis on glycolysis in the isolated rat heart. *Amer. J. Physiol. 213*, 1143–1148.

Scholz, R., Thurman, R. G., Williamson, J. R., Chance, B. & Bücher, Th. (1969) Flavin and pyridine nucleotide oxidation-reduction changes in perfused rat liver. I. Anoxia and subcellular localization of fluorescent flavoproteins. *J. biol. Chem. 244*, 2317–2324.

Walsh, D. A., Perkins, J. P. & Krebs, E. G. (1968) An adenosine 3′,5′-monophosphate-dependent protein kinase from rabbit skeletal muscle. *J. biol Chem. 243*, 3763–3765.

Wieland, O. & Siess, E. (1970) Interconversion of phospho- and dephosphoforms of pig heart pyruvate dehydrogenase. *Proc. nat. Acad. Sci. (Wash.) 65*, 947–954.

Wieland, O., Van Jagow-Westermann, B. & Stukowski, B. (1969) Kinetic and regulatory properties of heart meuscle pyruvate dehydrogenase. *Hoppe-Seylers Z. physiol. Chem. 350*, 329–334.

Williamson, J. R. (1962) Effects of insulin and diet on the metabolism of L(+)-lactate and glucose by the perfused rat heart. *Biochem. J. 83*, 377–383.

Williamson, J. R. (1965) Glycolytic control mechanisms. I. Inhibition of glycolysis by acetate and pyruvate in the isoated, perfused rat heart. *J. biol. Chem. 240*, 2308–2321.

Williamson, J. R. 1966a) Metabolic effects of epinephrine in the perfused rat heart. II. Control steps of glucose and glycogen metabolism. *Molec. Pharmacol. 2*, 206–220.

Williamson, J. R. (1966b) Glycolytic control mechanisms. II. Kinetics of intermediate changes during the aerobic-anoxic transition in perfused rat heart. *J. biol. Chem. 241*, 5026–5036.

Williamson, J. R. (1970a) Control of energy metabolism in hamster brown adipose tissue. *J. biol. Chem. 245*, 2043–2050.

Williamson, J. R. (1970b) General features of metabolic control as applied to the erythrocyte. In *Red Cell Metabolism and Function*, ed. Brewer, G., pp. 117–136. Plenum Press, New York.

Williamson, J. R. & Jamieson, D. (1965) Dissociation of the inotropic from the glycogenolytic effect of epinephrine in the isolated rat heart. *Nature 206*, 364–367.

Williamson, J. R. & Jamieson, D. (1966) Metabolic effects of epinephrine in the perfused rat heart. I. Comparison of the intracellular redox states, tissue pO$_2$ and force of contraction. *Molec. Pharmacol. 2*, 191–205.

Williamson, J. R., Cheung, W. Y., Coles, H. S. & Herczeg, B. E. (1967a) Glycolytic control mechanisms. IV. Kinetics of glycolytic intermediate changes during electrical discharge and recovery in the main organ of *Electrophorus Electricus*. *J. biol. Chem.* *242*, 5112–5118.

Williamson, J. R., Herczeg, B. E., Coles, H. S. & Cheung, W. Y. (1967b) Glycolytic control mechanisms. V. Kinetics of high energy phosphate intermediate changes during electrical discharge and recovery in the main organ of *Electrophorus Electricus*. *J. biol. Chem.* *242*, 5119–5124.

Williamson, J. R., Prusiner, S., Olson, M. S. & Fukami, M. (1970) Control of metabolism in brown adipose tissue. *Lipids 5*, 1–14.

DISCUSSION

SEVERINGHAUS

Can the brain burn up the lactate which is produced during anaerobic glycolysis or must the lactate be excreted? This will make a significant difference in the time of recovery from a period of anaerobiosis.

WILLIAMSON

All the information I have is that the brain does not directly oxidize lactate to an appreciable extent.

PLUM

What happened to substrate during the one minute period of stimulation? What is the substrate for the eel's brain under physiological circumstances?

WILLIAMSON

Even a 1 minute stimulation is only sufficient to deplete creatinephosphate reserves by about 80 per cent. So the primary answer to your question is that the substrate is of course stored high energy phosphate. The back up substrate must be glucose and glycogen.

PLUM

You are working on a closed system?

WILLIAMSON

This is an isolated piece of tissue, so that endogenous energy stores serve as sole substrate. This is mainly glycogen. The glycogen content of the electric organ would have to be maintained *in vivo* by glyconeogenesis in the liver.

PLUM

Then this is very different from what happens under normal circumstances of a continuous supply of substrate, is it not?

WILLIAMSON

Probably not in the transient phase of greatly increased metabolic activity, but in the steady state glucose may replace glycogen.

Dr. Severinghaus, in relation to your question about lactate utilization, I should mention that adipose tissue, for instance, cannot oxidize lactate, because it doesn't have a very active shuttle to transport NADH from the cytoplasm to the mitochondria. It is very low in mitochondrial glutarate oxalacetate transaminase. The brain doesn't suffer from this; certainly isolated superior ganglion will use and oxidize lactate and pyruvate. Theoretically there is no reason why the tissue should not adequately use lactate. The fact that it doesn't is presumably due to the blood-brain barrier for lactate.

LOESCHCKE

I might give a partial answer to Dr. Severinghaus' question and it is a pleasure for me to mention the paper of Dr. Gertrud Loeschcke (Loeschcke & Loeschcke 1948), who measured a-v difference of brain in normal state and in hypoxia. The a-v difference of lactate in dogs was slightly negative in normal brain perfusion and in light hypoxia and it became positive in severe hypoxia.

SIESJÖ

In your scheme where you pointed out the control steps of glycolysis you mentioned ADP, AMP, and phosphate potential. You didn't mention the hydrogen ion or hydroxyl ion concentrations. Would you consider these to be important regulators of the rate of glycolysis? I am asking because so many have reported an increased lactate production when pH is increased. Another question: We have often tried to evaluate the redox state of cytoplasm from lactate/pyruvate ratios, and from the intracellular pH, which should give us some kind of cytoplasmatic NADH/NAD$^+$ ratio (Kaasik et al. 1970a, b, Siesjö & Zwetnow 1970a, b). Is this useful information?

Loeschcke, G. & Loeschcke, H. H. (1948) Über den Milchsäureaustausch zwischen arteriellem Blut und Gehirngewebe und seine Veränderungen im Sauerstoffmangel. Pflügers Arch. ges. Physiol. 249, 521–538.

Kaasik, A. E., Nilsson, L. & Siesjö, B. K. (1970a) The effect of asphyxia upon the lactate, pyruvate and bicarbonate concentrations of brain tissue and cisternal CSF, and upon the tissue concentrations of phosphocreatine and adenine nucleotides in anesthetized rats. Acta physiol. scand. 78, 433–447.

Kaasik, A. E., Nilsson, L. & Siesjö B. K. (1970b) The effect of arterial hypotension upon the lactate, pyruvate and bicarbonate concentrations of brain tissue and cisternal CSF, and upon the tissue concentrations of phosphocreatine and adenine nucleotides in anesthetized rats. Acta physiol. scand. 78, 448–458.

WILLIAMSON

The lactate/pyruvate ratio is thought to provide a measure of the cytoplasmic $NADH/NAD^+$ ratio, if near equilibrium conditions are maintained. This potential is normally about -250 to -260 mV in most cells. On the other hand, the oxidation-reduction state of the mitochondrial NAD system is 40 to 50 mV more negative than the cytoplasm under aerobic conditions. In liver, the mitochondrial NAD system appears to be in equilibrium with the β-hydroxybutyrate/acetoacetate couple, and this ratio can be used to estimate the redox state of the mitochondrial NAD pool. Unfortunately, this couple is of less use for other tissues which contain lower concentrations of β-hydroxybutyrate dehydrogenase. However, we have found that the fluorescence changes of flavoproteins can also provide an estimate of relative changes of the redox state of the mitochondrial NAD system, although this method suffers from the disadvantage of not providing absolute numbers (Scholz et al. 1969). A number of studies have shown that the redox state of the cytoplasmic and mitochondrial NAD pools need not change in the same direction. Addition of aminooxyacetic acid is a case in point, since the cytoplasmic NAD becomes more reduced but the mitochondrial NAD more oxidized. During hypoxia, however, the two systems always change towards a more reduced state. Whether there is a physiological counterpart for the type of effects seen after aminooxyacetic acid addition remains to be determined. Harris & Berent (1969) have observed an increased permeability of the mitochondria to citrate with a fall of pH, and if other anion permeases are also sensitive to pH, it is possible that the activity of the malate-aspartate H-shuttle would be pH sensitive. Thus, it is possible, although not proven, that pH changes can affect the aerobic rate of lactate formation from glucose (and the lactate/pyruvate ratio) by a control of the rate of transport of NADH from cytoplasm to mitochondria. In other words, it may be incorrect to interpret high lactate/pyruvate ratios in terms of tissue

Siesjö, B. K. & Zwetnow, N. N. (1970a). The effect of hypovolemic hypotension on extra- and intracellular acid-base parameters and energy metabolites in the rat brain. Acta physiol. scand. 79, 114–124.

Siesjö, B. K. & Zwetnow, N. N. (1970b). Effects of increased cerebrospinal fluid pressure upon adenine nucleotides and upon lactate and pyruvate in rat brain tissue. Acta neurol. scand. 46, 187–202.

Scholz, R., Thurman, R. G., Williamson, J. R., Chance, B. & Bücher, Th. (1969) Flavin and pyridine nucleotide oxidation-reduction changes in perfused rat liver. J. biol. Chem. 244, 2317–2324.

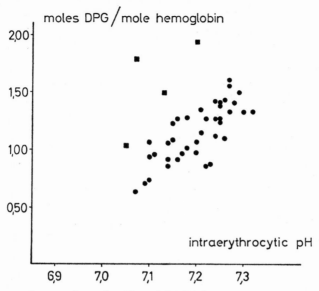

Relation between intraerythrocytic pH and 2,3-DPG in patients with metabolic acid-base disorders. The squares signify patients with inorganic serum phosphate higher than 10 mg per cent.

hypoxia, unless one could be sure that the mitochondrial NAD system also changed towards a more reduced state.

ASTRUP

I would like to stress the importance of the relationship between blood pH changes and the metabolism of organic phosphoric compounds in cells. We have during the last couple of years been interested in problems concerning red cell function and red cell metabolism and we have found that even very small pH changes of blood are able to influence the concentration of organic compounds inside the erythrocytes.

We found that the 2,3-DPG concentration in erythrocytes increased 25 per cent after ascent to 3500 m altitude (Jungfraujoch, Switzerland) and T_{50} (Po_2 at 50 per cent saturation of hemoglobin) increased from 27 to 31 mm Hg. During the first day of stay the excretion of inorganic phosphate in urine decreases by approximately 50 per cent and inorganic phosphate in serum by

Harris, E. J. & Berent, C. (1969) Calcium ion-induced uptakes and transformations of substrates in liver mitochondria. *Biochem. J. 115*, 645–652.

25 per cent. This retention of inorganic phosphate corresponds to the increase in intracellular organic phosphoric compounds. The figure shows the relationship between 2,3-DPG concentration inside the red cells and the red cell pH. It is quite clear that there is a good relationship. The data come from patients with acid-base disturbances. The four points outside the general pattern come from patients with very high inorganic phosphate values, around 10 mg per cent. We could calculate that a change of plasma pH or red cell pH of 0.01 changes the 2,3-DPG concentration approximately 5 per cent, which is enough to change the T_{50} values at 7.40 approximately 1 mm. In our opinion the small blood pH increase of 0.03–0.04 at Jungfraujoch can explain the demonstrated increase in 2,3-DPG and the retention of inorganic phosphate. This fine regulation caused by pH might also influence the organic phosphorus compounds in the brain cells, which we are discussing at this symposium.

Energy Metabolism of the Human Brain

Peter J. Cohen

This paper will consider methodology, and then turn to an examination of cerebral energy production under normal conditions. It will then examine the situation when oxygen supply is decreased, and finally discuss cerebral metabolism when oxygen supply is adequate but metabolic requirements diminished, i. e., during general anesthesia.

METHODS

Data collected in the laboratories of the Department of Anesthesia of the University of Pennsylvania have been obtained by measurement of whole brain blood flow and the analysis of constituents of arterial and jugular bulb blood. The methods of sampling, chemical analyses, expression of data, and a critique of this approach have been discussed in a previous paper (Cohen et al. 1967). In brief, cerebral blood flow (CBF) was measured by use of 85 Kr inhalation (Lassen & Munck 1955) with intermittent sampling of arterial and venous blood, extrapolation of the venous curve to infinite time, and without correction for mean transit time in the brain. Concentration of oxygen in arterial and venous blood was determined manometrically (Van Slyke & Neill 1924), while the concentrations of lactate, pyruvate, and glucose were measured enzymatically (Bergmeyer 1963). Cerebral metabolic rates for oxygen (CMR_{O_2}), glucose ($CMR_{glucose}$), and lactate ($CMR_{lactate}$) were calculated as the products of CBF and the appropriate arterial-venous content difference. Since glucose is the sole substrate for human energy metabolism (except in the starved state), analysis of brain

This work was supported in part by U.S.P.H.S. Grant 1-PO1-GM-15430-03 from the National Institutes of General Medical Sciences, National Institutes of Health.

University of Colorado Medical Center, 4200 East Ninth Avenue, Denver, Colorado 80220, U.S.A.

oxygen and glucose consumption and lactate production permitted calculation of the fraction of glucose anaerobically cleaved to lactate (lactate/glucose index or LGI) and the proportion of glucose completely oxidized (oxygen/glucose index or OGI).

NORMAL CEREBRAL METABOLISM

Values for normal human cerebral metabolism are given in Table 1A. A positive venous-arterial difference in lactate concentration was consistently found, representing a low rate of lactate production by the brain. Approximately 5 per cent of the glucose consumed by the brain appeared to undergo glycolysis but not oxidation. This may indicate that small areas of the brain are normally hypoxic and contribute a small but definite supply of lactate to both cerebral spinal fluid and venous blood under normal circumstances. However, it may also derive from the fact that cerebral tissue shows an incomplete Pasteur effect, i.e., glycolysis is not always completely inhibited by a normal oxygen supply.

CEREBRAL METABOLISM DURING HYPOXIA

We have studied man breathing 6.9–7.5% oxygen in nitrogen while sufficient CO_2 was added to the inspired gas to maintain $PaCO_2$ normal (Cohen et al. 1967). We have found, as have others (Kety & Schmidt 1948, Turner et al. 1957) that this degree of hypoxia does not alter the rate of cerebral oxygen utilization (Table 1B), which is not a sensitive index of hypoxia. CMR_{O_2} represents over-all cerebral oxygen consumption, and subtle changes or minor regional variations may not be observed. However, since there is a 19-fold difference in energy production (i.e., ATP synthesis) between the anaerobic and aerobic metabolism of glucose, analysis of carbohydrate metabolism might uncover measurable changes in glucose uptake and lactate production at a time when changes in CMR_{O_2} are too small to detect. Examination of Table 1B indicates that this is indeed the case. Although no changes in CMR_{O_2} were observed during mild hypoxia, there was a 28 per cent augmentation of glucose uptake. In addition, the OGI decreased while the LGI was greatly elevated above normal. Finally, $CMR_{latcate}$ was considerably enhanced. Thus, in the presence of a moderate decrease of oxygen availability, brought about by inhalation of a low-oxygen gas, the brain has two means of compensation. The first involves the well-known increase in CBF which serves to increase oxygen delivery. The second consists of a higher rate of glucose utilization combined with augmented anaerobic metabolism. Using the values for $CMR_{glucose}$, OGI, and LGI, we have calculated the rate of cerebral ATP production to be 0.86 mmoles/100 gm/min during normoxia and 0.90 mmoles/100 gm/min during hypoxia (mean difference 0.04, S.E. 0.04). Thus, the circulatory and metabolic compensation of the human brain to acute mild hypoxia appeared to be successful.

We must now consider the metabolic consequences attendent upon *decreased* delivery of blood containing *normal* concentrations of oxygen. Such a phenomenon exists during normoxic hyperventilation, when oxygen delivery is impaired due to diminished CBF and a shift of the hemoglobin-dissociation curve to the left. In man, the metabolic changes observed during marked hyperventilation ($PaCO_2$ less than 20 torr) mimicked those observed during normocarbic hypoxia and consisted of increased $CMR_{glucose}$, $CMR_{lactate}$, and LGI along with decreased OGI (Alexander *et al.* 1968, Cohen *et al.* 1968). Examination of cerebral tissue of animals during hyperventilation supports the concept that the diminished blood flow accompanying hypocapnia may result in cerebral hypoxia (Granholm & Siesjö 1969, Granholm *et al.* 1969). Finally, both the metabolic (Plum *et al.* 1968) and electroencephalographic alterations (Cohen *et al.* 1966) produced by hyperventilation were reversed when hyperventilation continued but hyperbaric oxygen was administered. Thus, it would appear that the metabolic similarity of normocarbic hypoxia and normoxic hypocapnia are not fortuitous, but both represent the result of diminished oxygen delivery to cerebral tissue.

CEREBRAL METABOLISM DURING ANESTHESIA

When hypocarbia or hypoxia were not present, the anesthetics so far examined (nitrous oxide, thiopental, halothane, cyclopropane, diethyl ether, and Ēthrane) have all decreased CMR_{O_2} (see Wollman *et al.* 1968, Wollman *et al.* 1969a). It is significant that the decrease in cerebral oxygen uptake was not proportional to the depth of anesthesia. Indeed, in some cases, as anesthesia was deepened, the depressed CMR_{O_2} returned towards normal (Alexander *et al.* 1970, Wollman *et al.* 1969b). A consistent picture emerges when cerebral blood flow and oxygen utilization are compared at different

Table 1. *Cerebral metabolism of normal man and the effect of normocarbic hypoxia* (Cohen *et al.* 1967)

	A Normoxia		B Normocarbic Hypoxia	
	Mean	SEM	Mean	SEM
CMR_{O_2}, ml/100 g/min	3.02	0.15	3.13	0.21
$CMR_{glucose}$, mg/100 g/min	4.48	0.29	5.73	0.52
$CMR_{lactate}$, μmole/100 g/min	2.31	0.97	10.73	2.84
OGI, %	91.92	4.06	75.76	5.66
LGI, %	4.49	1.86	18.86	5.52

depths of anesthesia (Wollman *et al.* 1969b). In normal man, the ratio CBF/CMR_{O_2} is 15 ml blood/ml O_2. During light general anesthesia this ratio does not change. As anesthesia is deepened, CBF/CMR_{O_2} increases and, of course, cerebral venous oxygen tension rises. The mechanism for this finding is as yet unknown, but the phenomenon appears to occur with all anesthetics investigated.

While CMR_{O_2} is decreased during general anesthesia, the pathways of cerebral carbohydrate metabolism appear unaltered, with one exception. During the inhalation of 5% cyclopropane, LGI was elevated while OGI showed no statistically significant change. No alterations in cerebral carbohydrate metabolism were observed during administration of 13, 20, and 37% cyclopropane (Alexander *et al.* 1970).

Does decreased CMR_{O_2} indicate that anesthesia protects the brain from hypoxia? In order to answer this fully, it must be pointed out that cerebral oxygen consumption serves two purposes: (1) maintenance of cerebral function (i.e., consciousness or awareness); (2) maintenance of processes not directly concerned with cerebral function (e.g. the metabolic events existing in the presence of deep anesthesia). Thus, Quastel (1962) has demonstrated that while the oxygen uptake of isolated brain cortex slices is approximately half that found *in vivo,* respiration may be increased to normal by electrical or cationic stimulation. While anesthetics do not affect the basal brain slice respiration, they do prevent the increase in oxygen utilization of the stimulated tissue. One must therefore consider whether diminished oxygen uptake represents interference with both processes or only the first. Brunner & Passonneau (1970) have shown that halothane, diethyl ether, methoxyflurane, and Ēthrane all diminish the rate of ATP degradation occurring in the first 15 to 30 seconds following decapitation. On the other hand, Michenfelder & Theye (1970) have shown that anesthesia does *not* affect the rate of change in cerebral ATP and lactate when measurements begin one minute after decapitation. However, when hypothermia (30°C) reduced CMR_{O_2} to the same degree as that produced by deep anesthesia, a *decreased* rate of ATP depletion and lactate accumulation occurred after the first minute of acute anoxia (Michenfelder & Theye 1970). It is clear that examination of ATP changes in the first 30 seconds of anoxia measures *all* metabolic processes in the brain; evaluation of ATP degradation after the first minute represented an examination of metabolic events concerned only with maintenance of cerebral integrity. While anesthesia affects only the metabolism of consciousness, hypothermia diminishes the rate of both metabolic processes. There must therefore be a basic difference in the mechanisms through which hypothermia and anesthesia reduce cerebral oxygen utilization. If this data can be extrapolated to man, it would suggest that the decreased cerebral metabolism observed during anesthesia will not produce the same protective effect as a similar decrease in brain respiration occurring during hypothermia.

SUMMARY

The energy metabolism of the human brain can be determined by analysis of cerebral blood flow and measurement of oxygen, glucose, lactate and pyruvate in arterial and jugular venous blood. Values in normal man have been given. When oxygen supply is diminished, during inhalation of low oxygen gases or marked hyperventilation, increased glucose flux and anaerobic metabolism are observed. General anesthesia decreases oxygen utilization without altering pathways of cerebral carbohydrate metabolism. However, it is unlikely that this offers the same type of protection against anoxia as does hypothermia.

REFERENCES

Alexander, S. C., Smith, T. C., Strobel, G., Stephen, G. W. & Wollman, H. (1968) Cerebral carbohydrate metabolism of man during respiratory and metabolic alkalosis. *J. appl. Physiol. 24,* 66–72.

Alexander, S. C., Colton, E. T., Smith, A. L. & Wollman, H. (1970) The effects of cyclopropane on cerebral and systemic carbohydrate metabolism. *Anesthesiology 32*, 236–245.

Bergmeyer, H. U. (ed.) (1963) *Methods of Enzymatic Analysis.* Academic Press, New York.

Brunner, E. A. & Passonneau, J. V. (1970) Effects of anesthesia on brain metabolites. In *Cellular Toxicity of Anesthetics,* ed. Fink, B. R. Williams and Wilkins, Baltimore. In press.

Cohen, P. J., Reivich, M. & Greenbaum, L. J. (1966) Electroencephalographic changes induced by 100% oxygen-breathing at 3 ata in awake man. In *Proc. Third Internat. Conf. Hyperbaric Med.,* Nat. Acad. Sci., pp. 323–328.

Cohen, P. J., Alexander, S. C., Smith, T. C., Reivich, M. & Wollman, H. (1967) Effects of hypoxia and normocarbia on cerebral blood flow and metabolism in conscious man. *J. appl. Physiol. 23,* 183–189.

Cohen, P. J., Alexander, S. C. & Wollman, H. (1968) Effects of hypocarbia and of hypoxia with normocarbia on cerebral blood flow and metabolism in man. *Scand. J. clin. Lab. Invest.,* Suppl. 102, IV, A.

Granholm, L. & Siesjö, B. K. (1969) The effects of hypercapnia and hypocapnia upon the cerebrospinal fluid lactate and pyruvate concentrations and upon the lactate, pyruvate, ATP, ADP, phosphocreatine and creatine concentrations of cat brain tissue. *Acta physiol. scand. 75,* 257–266.

Granholm, L., Lukjanova, L. & Siesjö, B. K. (1969) The effect of marked hyperventilation upon tissue levels of NADH, lactate, pyruvate, phosphocreatine, and adenosine phosphates of rat brain. *Acta physiol. scand. 77,* 179–190.

Kety, S. S. & Schmidt, C. F. (1948) The effects of altered arterial tensions of carbon dioxide and oxygen on cerebral blood flow and cerebral oxygen consumption of normal young men. *J. clin. Invest. 27,* 484–492.

Lassen, N. A. & Munck, O. (1955) The cerebral blood flow in man determined by the use of radioactive krypton. *Acta physiol. scand. 33,* 30–49.

Michenfelder, J. D. & Theye, R. A. (1970) Cerebral metabolic effects of anesthesia in the dog. In *Cellular Toxicity of Anesthetics,* ed. Fink, B. R. Williams and Wilkins, Baltimore. In press.

Plum, F., Posner, J. B. & Smith, W. W. (1968) Effect of hyperbaric-hyperoxic hyperventilation on blood, brain, and CSF lactate. *Amer. J. Physiol. 215,* 1240–1244.

Quastel, J. H. (1962) Effects of anaesthetics, depressants, and tranquilizers on brain metabolism. In *Neurochemistry,* ed. Elliot, K. A. C., Page, I. H. & Quastel, J. H. Second Edition. Charles C. Thomas, Springfield, Ill.

Turner, J., Lambertsen, C. J., Owen, S. G., Wendel, H. & Chiodi, H. (1957) Effect of 0.08 and 0.8 atmospheres of inspired PO_2 on cerebral hemodynamics at a "constant" alveolar PCO_2 of 43. *Fed. Proc. 16,* 130.

Van Slyke, D. D. & Neill, J. A. (1924) The determination of gases in blood and other solutions by vacuum extraction and manometric measurement. *J. biol. Chem. 61,* 523–573.

Wollman, H., Alexander, S. C. & Cohen, P. J. (1968) Cerebral circulation and metabolism in anesthetized man. In *Clinical Anesthesia Series.* F. A. Davis, Philadelphia.

Wollman, H., Smith, A. L., Neigh, J. L. & Hoffmann, J. C. (1969a) Cerebral blood flow and oxygen consumption in man during electroencephalographic seizure patterns associated with Ēthrane anesthesia. In *Cerebral Blood Flow,* ed. Brock, M., Fieschi, C., Ingvar, D. H., Lassen, N. A. & Schurmann, K., pp. 246–248. Springer-Verlag, New York.

Wollman, H., Smith, A. L. & Alexander, S. C. (1969b) Effects of general anesthetics in man on the ratio of cerebral blood flow to cerebral oxygen consumption. In *Cerebral Blood Flow,* ed. Brock, M., Fieschi, C., Ingvar, D. H., Lassen, N. A. & Schurmann, K., pp. 239–241. Springer-Verlag, New York.

DISCUSSION

COHEN

I would like to start the discussion by asking Dr. Williamson a question: Are there any measurements which we are not making but which could be made in order to detect cerebral hypoxia in man? If not, how would you then add data from animals to see whether or not cerebral hypoxia exists?

SCHEINBERG

Your presentation today and your previous publications have suggested an uncoupling of the relationship between cerebral blood flow and cerebral metabolism which of course puzzles a simple-minded approach to the regulation of cerebral circulation. I was wondering whether or not you felt that lactate production can be considered a metabolic function in view of the fact that any of the circumstances which elevate brain lactate concentration also elevates arterial lactate concentration, therefore making it difficult to consider that a steady state obtains. I would also be curious to know whether you think it is necessary to account for the difference in the apparent stoichiometric inequality between arterio-venous glucose difference and arterio-venous oxygen difference across the brain simply on the basis of lactate production. Couldn't some of the glucose which is being utilized under normal circumstances be utilized for protein and fatty acid synthesis?

COHEN

In relation to your last question I would like to mention the works by Sacks (1965) and by Geiger (1958) who used labeled glucose as a substrate. They found that in the first minutes of perfusion with radioactive glucose, much of the substrate does not appear as "hot" CO_2. There is therefore good evidence both in man and in tissues that glucose does go into protein synthesis, and that degradation of protein and other substances produces CO_2. However, if you are in a steady state the synthesis and degradation of protein or other substances should be balanced and there should be stoichiometry between glucose consumption and oxygen consumption. We had a steady

Sacks, W. (1965) Cerebral metabolism of doubly labeled glucose in humans *in vivo*. *J. appl. Physiol. 20*, 117–130.
Geiger, A. (1958) Correlation of brain metabolism and function by the use of a brain perfusion method *in situ*. *Physiol. Rev. 38*, 1–20.

state of Pco_2 and glucose concentration in our control subjects; unless one has evidence of a steady state in arterial blood it is hazardous to make conclusions from arterio-venoues differences. All I can say in terms of the lactate production is that we find it. I would like to know whether the lactate production in the brain would fall to zero if we supplied additional oxygen.

SØRENSEN

Regarding the steady state problem, I would like to mention some results Dr. Milledge and I obtained in the Andes (Sørensen et al. 1969), because we did very much the same as Dr. Cohen did, except not as well. In these subjects who had been hypoxic for their whole life we found approximately the same degree of anaerobic metabolism in the brain as Dr. Cohen did in his acute experiments during hypoxia. We measured the arterio-venous differences for glucose and oxygen and calculated the ratio between the two, but we did not measure cerebral flow and we could therefore not calculate the absolute consumptions. We found that when we made the subjects acutely hyperoxic we turned off the anaerobic metabolism to the extent which Dr. Cohen found in his normoxic experiments. We found that between 5 and 10 per cent af the glucose consumption was anaerobic when the arterial oxygen tension was increased above the normal sea level value.

SIESJÖ

You pointed out that you are using a restricted approach. We also use a very restricted approach by measuring the lactate, pyruvate, phosphocreatine, ATP, ADP, and AMP concentrations in the tissue and the lactate and pyruvate concentrations in CSF, but our data are supplementary because for example in hyperventilation and hypoxemia, we get significant increases in the lactate concentrations in the tissue and in the CSF, and an increase in the lactate/pyruvate ratio, so we come to exactly the same conclusions. We both use a restricted approach, but when working with the intact animal's brain or, as you do, with the human subject, there are simply very few measurements that we can do.

ZWETNOW

Dr. Williamson, in clinical work it is extremely important for us to detect

Sørensen, S. C., Milledge, J. S. & Severinghaus, J. W. (1969) Cerebral anaerobic metabolism and ventilatory acclimatization to chronic hypoxia. *Fed. Proc. 28,* 33.

whether or not cerebral hypoxia is present. We have learned that the jugular venous oxygen tension is not good enough as an index of cerebral hypoxia. We therefore turned to what we thought were better indeces, namely the products of metabolism. Now you seem to have rejected these possibilities, or at least the lactate/pyruvate ratio and the concentrations of labile metabolites. Which index would you then suggest would be the best indicator of cerebral hypoxia?

WILLIAMSON

I agree that this is a difficult problem. As far as the tissue metabolites can be considered, I would think that the creatine-phosphate/creatine ratio would provide the best index for hypoxia in brain. However, this clearly cannot be used in the *in vivo* situation. As far as direct kinetic readout measurements go, there is the possibility of using micro oxygen electrodes, and for animals, surface fluorometry. However, this latter technique is difficult to handle in the presence of hemoglobin and possible changes of flow rate through the capillary bed. Cytothrome *b* absorption changes provide a sensitive index of decreased electron transport, but again this involves extensive surgery. I would like to make it clear that while tissue hypoxia is always associated with a high lactate/pyruvate ratio, it is the converse which is not necessarily true. Maybe the best way of approaching the problem is by a combination of analytical measurements in the blood and measurements of blood flow and tissue Po_2 tension. I doubt whether microelectrodes would cause brain damage, and they could be inserted through a suitably prepared hole in the skull, certainly in animals.

SCHEINBERG

Dr. Cohen, in the studies in hypoxia you didn't find a change in cerebral oxygen consumption but you tried to explain your findings by suggesting that there might have been hypoxia locally in the tissue. You must have some real belief that hypoxia in the tissue occurs because lactate is produced, and there must be some way in which the lactate production increases.

COHEN

My belief that there is hypoxia is founded on a number of observations. There was a low venous tension, the subjects acted hypoxic and it is reasonable that there is a decrease in regional oxygen utilization that we can't measure. I think that we have seen other explanations of changes in glyco-lytic rate, but we mustn't forget that one of the possibilities for increased glycolytic rate is hypoxia. I don't think that those other suggestions exclude hypoxia. They just are added as things that must be considered. Doing a physiologic study one must take the most likely cause as producing a particular effect, although data in the future may prove it is wrong. The question that still remains, is simply this: There is lactate in the CSF, there is lactate in the brain tissue. It may be capable of acting as a hydrogen ion generator. What is the lactate doing there? Is it there because it is a spill or is it there because of some closed area of vascular space that hasn't been perfused and therefore is hypoxic. This we may not answer without the definitive experiment, but I think this is a question that is very significant.

ZWETNOW

Dr. Williamson, you have rejected the lactate/pyruvate ratio as an index, but nevertheless in several experimental situations where we think that hypoxia may be present, since if they are carried further they will lead to dramatic signs of hypoxia, we see no significant changes in phosphocreatine, ATP, ADP, or AMP, but we see changes in the lactate/pyruvate ratio. We have therefore tentatively interpreted an increase in the lactate/pyruvate ratio as an early sign of hypoxia, which perhaps is not right. If the lactate/pyruvate ratio is not an index of hypoxia, would then the absence of an increase in lactate/pyruvate ratio indicate that hypoxia is not there?

WILLIAMSON

To my knowledge, every time one does have hypoxia the lactate/pyruvate ratio will increase. In other words, an increase in the lactate/pyruvate ratio always follows hypoxia, but the reverse situation doesn't necessarily hold. That was essentially my point.

The Effect of Hypoxia upon Labile Substrates and upon Acid-Base Parameters in the Brain

L. Nilsson & B. K. Siesjö

In most hypoxic situations the tissue acid-base metabolism is influenced both by respiratory and nonrespiratory mechanisms which tend to alter the intracellular pH'. Thus, in *asphyxia* caused by respiratory depression there will be an increase in the CO_2 tension, determined by the degree of hypoventilation, and an increase in the lactic acid production, which is grossly proportional to the degree of hypoxia. Further, in pure *hypoxemia* the hypoxia will usually give rise to hyperventilation so that the decrease in the blood and tissue CO_2 tensions tend to counteract the acidosis caused by lactic acid production. Finally, in states of *hypoperfusion* there will also usually be a tendency to hyperventilation, but in this case the decrease in the tissue CO_2 tension will be a complex function of the arterial CO_2 tension, and the actual tissue perfusion (Kaasik *et al.* 1970b, Siesjö & Zwetnow 1970).

We have recently studied the effects of arterial hypotension and of asphyxia upon cellular acid-base parameters and upon some labile substrates in the brain (Kaasik, Nilsson & Siesjö 1970a, b). The results obtained in these studies allow a quantitative evaluation of the factors determining the intracellular pH' under these conditions. Thus, if we limit our analysis to acute arterial hypotension and to acute asphyxia, we may as a first approximation assume that the change in pH_i' will be determined by the change in the tissue CO_2 tension, and by the net increase in the intracellular concentrations of nonvolatile acids. The relative importance of the respiratory and nonrespiratory mechanisms involved can then be evaluated by using the model system described by Siesjö & Messeter (1971). If the predicted changes in pH_i' agree reasonably well with those measured, we would then be in a

---

Research Dept. 4, University Hospital, S-220 05 Lund 5, Sweden.

favourable position to separate the respiratory and nonrespiratory influences, respectively.

The analysis of intracellular acid-base changes in hypoxia is important for a critical evaluation of the redox state of the tissue. Thus, if the redox state is evaluated from the well-known steady state relation between the lactate/-pyruvate and NADH/NAD$^+$ systems according to the equation (see Hohorst et al. 1959, Williamson et al. 1967, Granholm & Siesjö 1970),

$$\frac{NADH}{NAD^+} = \frac{Lact.}{Pyr.} \cdot \frac{K}{(H^+)}$$

it is necessary to know the intracellular pH. As an example, if the pH_i' is decreased from 7.1 to 6.8, the lactate/pyruvate ratio will shift from 16 to 28 at an unchanged NADH/NAD$^+$ ratio.

The aim of the present communication is twofold. Firstly, we will analyse the factors changing the pH_i' in the acute phases of arterial hypotension and asphyxia, respectively. Secondly, we will use the acid-base data to evaluate the cytoplasmatic redox state during both the hypoxic situations and the restitution phases. In these latter analyses we will also compare the redox state during restitution with the degree of rephosphorylation of ATP and phosphocreatine, considering the possible influence of pH_i' on the creatine phosphokinase reaction.

ARTERIAL HYPOTENSION

The parameters necessary for an evaluation of intracellular acid-base changes are given in Table 1. The values have been taken from the previous communications (Kaasik et al. 1970a, b) but the lactate, ATP and phosphocreatine concentrations have been expressed as mMoles/kg of i. c. water to allow a calculation of buffer base changes. The decrease in buffer base was calculated as

$$-\triangle BB = + \triangle la^- - \frac{(\triangle PCr - \triangle ATP)}{2}$$

This equation recognizes the fact that there will be a mole to mole relationship between increase in lactate and decrease in buffer base. There will be an additional release of acid when ATP is hydrolysed, but the breakdown of phosphocreatine will provide basic equivalents. A rough estimate of the net alkalinizing effect due to phosphocreatine hydrolysis is obtained by

Table 1. Changes in acid-base parameters and in some labile substrates of the rat brain during asphyxia, induced by respiratory standstill, and during arterial hypotension, induced by bleeding. The values given are the mean values reported by Kaasik *et al.* (1970a, b) for the intracellular water of the tissue. Number of animals are given within parentheses. The decrease in the intracellular buffer base concentration was calculated from the changes in the intracellular lactate, phosphocreatine and ATP concentrations (see text).

Exp. group	Lactate mMoles/kg i. c. w.	ATP mMoles/kg i. c. w.	PCr mMoles/kg i. c. w.	$-\triangle$ BB mEq/kg i. c. w.	PtCO$_2$ mm Hg	pH$_i'$
Control (6)	1.8	4.2	7.9	0	45	7.09
Asphyxia						
1 min (4)	5.2	3.8	4.4	1.9	64	6.91
2 min (4)	15.0	3.3	2.0	10.8	71	6.71
3 min (6)	22.7	1.9	0.9	18.6	86	6.50
Arterial hypot.						
3 min (5)	7.3	4.1	7.2	5.2	40	6.94
5 min (6)	15.5	3.7	4.9	12.5	38	6.78

dividing the difference between the phosphocreatine and ATP concentrations by 2 (see Siesjö & Messeter 1971).

From the calculated change in buffer base, and from the tissue CO_2 tension, we can now derive an expected pH$_i'$ for our model system, using an 0.05 moles/l "continuous" buffer (see Siesjö & Messeter 1971). When doing this we only have to insert our CO_2 tension into the buffer equation for this system and solve for pH at a normal buffer base concentration. At this CO_2 tension, the buffer base is then decreased by the numbers given in Table 1 and the corresponding pH values calculated. These expected pH$_i'$ values have been entered into Fig. 1 as open circles. The figure shows that there was a very good agreement between the expected pH$_i'$ values and those actually measured (closed circles).

ASPHYXIA

As can be seen from Table 1, asphyxia represents a different situation in that marked increases in the CO_2 tension occur (see Kaasik *et al.* 1970a). It is thus to be expected that the increased pCO_2 will significantly contribute to the decrease in pH$_i'$. Fig. 2 compares the pH calculated from our model system, using the actual tissue CO_2 tensions and the calculated buffer base changes, with the pH$_i'$ values obtained in the experiments. We again find very

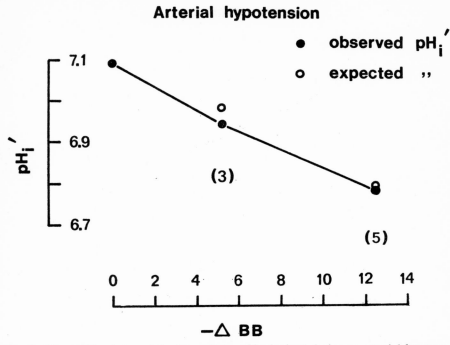

Fig. 1. The relation between the intracellular pH' obtained during an arterial hypotension of 3 and 5 min, respectively, and the pH calculated from the pCO_2 and buffer
base changes (see Table), using a model system for the intracellular space as described
elsewhere in this symposium (Siesjö & Messeter). $-\triangle$ BB denotes the decrease in the
intracellular buffer base concentration (mEq/kg of i. c. water). Note agreement between
the observed and the expected pH changes.

good agreement, suggesting that the model system adequately describes the
acute acid-base changes in the intracellular fluid, and that the calculated
buffer base changes come close to the net amounts of acid released in the
hypoxic situations.

Accepting the quantitative interpretation of the intracellular pH' changes,
we can easily use the above data to evaluate the relative importance of the
pCO_2 changes and the buffer base changes in lowering the pH_i' during
asphyxia. Fig. 3 shows the relative importance of these factors after 1, 2
and 3 min of asphyxia. It can be seen that at 1 min the influence of the
pCO_2 changes predominated, while at 3 min the buffer base changes had by
far the largest influence on pH_i'.

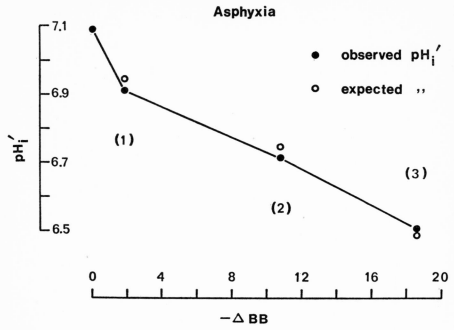

Fig. 2. The relation between the pH$_i'$ changes observed in the rat brain during 1, 2 and 3 min of asphyxia ("observed pH$_i'$") and those calculated from the pCO$_2$ and buffer base changes, using a model system to simulate the intracellular space ("expected pH$_i'$"). Note agreement between observed and expected pH changes.

REDOX STATE AND OXIDATIVE PHOSPHORYLATION

In the restitution phases after hypoxic incidences such as those caused by arterial hypotension and by asphyxia, there is a considerable lag in the normalization of some of the labile substrates. Thus, as early as 2 min after the resumption of a normal ventilation in the asphyctic animals and 2 min after the reinfusion of blood in the bled animals, the ATP, ADP and AMP concentrations were back at normal levels. However, the lactate concentrations, the lactate/pyruvate ratios, and the phosphocreatine concentrations did not normalize until considerably later. Our problem is now to reconcile those lags with the rephosphorylation of ATP. The problem seems to be easy when it comes to the lactate/pyruvate ratio. Thus, if we calculate the NADH/NAD$^+$ ratio according to the equation given previously, using a K value of 1.11 . 10^{-11} (Williamson *et al.* 1967) we find that the NADH/NAD$^+$ ratio had nor-

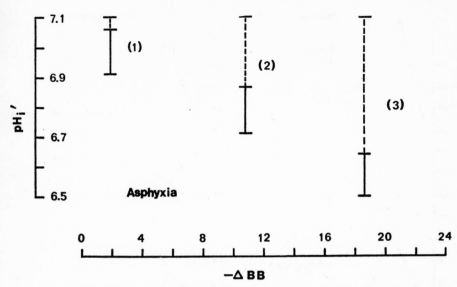

Fig. 3. A quantitative evaluation of the relative roles played by the pCO_2 and the buffer base changes in decreasing the intracellular pH of the rat brain during 1, 2 and 3 min of asphyxia. The length of the vertical bars illustrates the total decrease in pH at these times while the broken and unbroken lines show the relative importance of the buffer base and the pCO_2 changes, respectively, in decreasing the intracellular pH'.

malized at the same time as the ATP, ADP and AMP concentrations (Fig. 4). In other words, the high lactate/pyruvate ratios seen in the immediate posthypoxic periods seem to be entirely caused by the low pH_i', and should thus be unrelated to any persisting increase in the cytoplasmatic NADH/NAD$^+$ ratios.

It seems to be somewhat more difficult to explain why there is not a complete rephosphorylation of phosphocreatine in the immediate posthypoxic period, but the pH dependency of the creatine phosphokinase reaction (Kuby & Noltmann 1962) gives a hint to a solution. It is difficult to calculate the exact relations in this reaction due to the various Mg^{++}-complexes of the adenine nucleotides. However, it has been reported by Siesjö & Messeter (1971) that hypercapnia with a decrease in pH_i' from 7.1 to 6.9 gives a significant decrease in the phosphocreatine concentrations. There are thus reasons to believe that the slow rephosphorylation of phosphocreatine in the immediate posthypoxic periods may be due to the persisting intracellular acidosis.

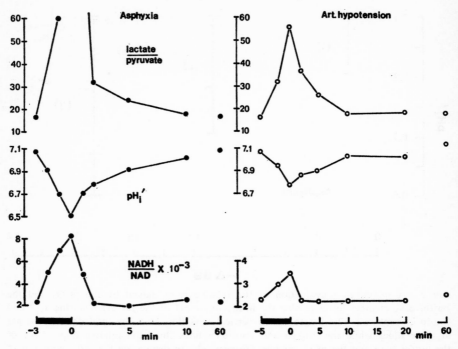

Fig. 4. The calculated intracellular lactate/pyruvate and NADH/NAD⁺ ratios, as well as the calculated pH′, in the rat brain during and after asphyxia (left part) and arterial hypotension (right part). Note the high lactate/pyruvate ratios in the immediate posthypoxic periods (2 and 5 min) but the absence of any persisting increase in the NADH/NAD⁺ ratios at these times.

SUMMARY

A discussion is given of the factors influencing the brain intracellular pH in the acute phases of arterial hypotension and of asphyxia. In *arterial hypotension* there are small changes in the CO_2 tension and the changes in the buffer base concentration predominate. In evaluating the buffer base changes, both the increases in the intracellular lactate concentrations and the changes in the phosphocreatine and ATP concentrations were taken into account. When the CO_2 tensions and the calculated buffer base changes were inserted into the equation for an acid-base model of the intracellular space, very good agreement was found between the derived pH changes and those actually found in experiments.

A corresponding analysis of *asphyxia* revealed an equally good correlation between the expected and the measured pH changes. The results allowed an evaluation of the relative importance of the pCO_2 changes and the buffer base changes, respectively, in influencing intracellular pH'. Thus, in the very first phase of asphyxia, the pCO_2 changes dominated, while later the acidifying effect of the decrease in buffer base became predominant.

The persisting decrease in the intracellular pH in the restitution phases after arterial hypotension and asphyxia, respectively, was related to the redox state of the cytoplasm and to the phosphorylation of the adenine nucleotides. It was found that the intracellular acidosis could explain the high lactate/pyruvate ratio in the early posthypoxic period, and that the cytoplasmatic NADH/NAD+ ratio normalized *pari passu* with the ATP, ADP and AMP concentrations. The long-lasting intracellular acidosis probably also explains the slow rephosphorylation of the phosphocreatine concentrations due to a pH influence on the creatine phosphokinase reaction. The results thus strongly indicate that as early as 2 min after a marked tissue hypoxia, induced by arterial bleeding or by ventilatory arrest, there is a normalization of the cytoplasmatic NADH/NAD+ ratio as well as a functionally complete rephosphorylation of the phosphocreatine and ATP concentrations.

ACKNOWLEDGMENTS

Supported by the Swedish Medical Research Council (Project B70–14X–263–06 and B70–40X–2179–02), by the Swedish Bank Tercentary Fund, by Carl-Bertel Nathhorst's Vetenskapliga Stiftelse and by PHS Research Grant No. R01 NB07838–01 from NIH.

REFERENCES

Granholm, L. & Siesjö, B. K. (1969) The effects of hypercapnia and hypocapnia upon the cerebrospinal fluid lactate and pyruvate concentrations and upon the lactate, pyruvate, ATP ADP, phosphocreatine and creatine concentrations of cat brain tissue. *Acta physiol. scand. 75*, 257–266.

Hohorst, H. J., Kreuz, F. H. & Bücher, T. (1959) Über Metabolitgehalte und Metabolit-Konzentrationen in der Leber der Ratte. *Biochem. Z. 332*, 18–46.

Kaasik, A. E., Nilsson, L. & Siesjö, B. K. (1970a) The effect of asphyxia upon the lactate, pyruvate and bicarbonate concentrations of brain tissue and cisternal CSF, and upon the tissue concentrations of phosphocreatine and adenine nucleotides in anesthetized rats. *Acta physiol. scand. 78*, 433–448.

Kaasik, A. E., Nilsson, L. & Siesjö, B. K. (1970b) The effect of arterial hypotension upon the lactate pyruvate and bicarbonate concentrations of brain tissue and cisternal CSF, and upon the tissue concentrations of phosphocreatine and adenine nucleotides in anesthetized rats. *Acta physiol. scand. 78,* 44–55.

Kuby, S. A. & Noltmann, E. A. (1962) ATP-creatine transphosphorylase. *The Enzymes 6,* 515–596.

Siesjö, B. K. & Zwetnow, N. N. (1970) The effect of hypovolemic hypotension on extra- and intracellular acid-base parameters and energy metabolites in the rat brain. *Acta physiol. scand. 79,* 114–124.

Siesjö, B. K. & Messeter, K. (1971) Factors determining intracellular pH. *Ion Homeostasis of the Brain,* ed. Siesjö, B. K. & Sørensen, S. C. Munksgaard, Copenhagen.

DISCUSSION

BROWN

I have the impression that phosphocreatine breaks down intracellularly as you drive the cell toward the acidiotic state, and that this might conceivably account for an actual increase in buffer base within the cell and an increase in the apparent buffer capacity. It seemed to me that on the figure that we just saw the phosphocreatine was going the other way.

SIESJÖ

We do find that if you induce respiratory acidosis without hypoxia, there is a decrease in the phosphocreatine concentration (Siesjö & Messeter, this symposium). This could be interpreted as being due to a shift in the creatine-phosphokinase reaction, because this as we have heard is pH dependent. The problem is that we can't find a complete rephosphorylation of phosphocreatine at the time when the intracellular pH has returned to normal, so there might be a slight influence of the CO_2 tension, as we also find with the other metabolites.

KJÄLLQUIST

Were the intracellular concentrations of lactate calculated by assuming extracellular fluid concentrations?

SIESJÖ

The extracellular fluid concentrations were measured and taken into account.

KJÄLLQUIST

Could there be any differences between the concentrations in the interstitial space and in the bulk fluid which you have measured? If so, could the fact that you calculate from bulk CSF concentrations have any influence on the results?

SIESJÖ

There is only a small influence if you take the groups at 2 or 3 minutes of hypoxia because the intracellular changes are so large, so it will make very little difference in the calculated intracellular concentrations (Kaasik *et al.* 1970 a and b).

Kaasik, A. E., Nilsson, L. & Siesjö, B. K. (1970a). The effect of asphyxia upon the lactate, pyruvate and bicarbonate concentrations of brain tissue and cisternal CSF, and upon the tissue concentrations of phosphocreatine and adenine nucleotides in anesthetized rats. *Acta physiol. scand. 78,* 433–447.

Kaasik, A. E., Nilsson, L. & Siesjö, B. K. (1970b) The effect of arterial hypotension upon lactate, pyruvate and bicarbonate concentrations of brain tissue and cisternal CSF, and upon the tissue concentrations of phosphocreatine and adenine nucleotides in anesthetized rats. *Acta physiol. scand. 78,* 448–458.

The Effect of Epileptic Seizures and Comatose States on the Oxidative Metabolism of the Brain

Fred Plum

CEREBRAL METABOLISM IN EPILEPSY

The title is a slight misnomer, because there is little new to say about cerebral oxidative metabolism in the comatose states. In these conditions it has been known for several years now that the rate of cerebral oxidative metabolism parallels fairly well the patient's state of consciousness, although the absolute correlation between the two often depends on how rapidly the abnormal cerebral state develops. At the time of Lassen's review (1959), many studies had made it abundantly clear that wide awake patients with diseases chronically affecting the brain, such as mental retardation, chronic dementia or active neurosyphilis, had levels of over-all cerebral oxidative activity which were as much as 30–40 per cent below normal; similar reductions occurring under circumstances of acute disease were observed only in patients in coma. Despite its potential importance in providing clues to protect the brain against injury, this inconsistency between behavior and cerebral metabolism in acute and chronic states has never received satisfactory explanation or even any great attention.

Except for the obvious examples of hypoglycemia and anoxia, little evidence incriminates a failure of oxidative metabolism as the primary defect in comatose states. Indeed, in most examples of metabolic coma only fragmentary and unconfirmed evidence even hints at where the primary chemical error may be or which group of neurones are most affected. Since one can give little more than speculations, it may be rewarding to turn to the area of experimental seizures which has produced considerable recent information.

Department of Neurology, The New York Hospital – Cornell Medical Center, New York, N. Y. Aided by USPHS Grants NS 04928–06 and NB 03346–09.

EPILEPTIC SEIZURES

The most fundamental questions about the epileptic seizure, i. e., why does it start, why does it stop, and what is responsible for adverse postictal aftermaths, are almost entirely unanswered in chemical terms. Up to about 1967 it was widely believed, on the basis of early experimental work, that brain metabolism increased so greatly during seizures that it outstripped its oxygen supply, resulting in relative cerebral hypoxia. This inference was suggested by several studies that described during experimental seizures a fall in cerebral tissue or venous oxygen tension or a rise in cerebral lactic acid content (Stone et al. 1945, Gurdjian et al. 1947, Olsen & Klein 1947, Bain & Pollack 1945a, b, King et al. 1967, Meyer et al. 1966). One inference from these early studies was that seizures stopped because cerebral oxidative energy reserves became so depleted that they could no longer sustain the necessary neuronal membrane potentials; only a few such as Efron (1961) seriously challenged the speculation that cerebral anoxia was responsible for postictal paralysis. We ourselves believed these ideas, as is illustrated by the fact that we initiated our studies in experimental epilepsy in an effort to produce brain tissue metabolic acidosis, which is what the laboratory was interested in at the time. As it turned out, the results were very different from the initial prediction, and indicated that many of the early results were probably the result of the animals developing generalized motor convulsions or undergoing some other complications that led to systemic hypoxia. Thus, if we took precautions to limit the seizure discharge to the brain itself and to avoid systemic hypoxia or hypotension, neither anoxia nor lactic acidosis developed in brain during generalized cerebral seizures, yet the duration of the seizures and their cerebral aftereffects remained exactly the same in the absence of these inconstant metabolic side effects.

In our studies on experimental cerebral seizures we have induced seizures in several different species, including man. Not all the same studies have been done on all the species, but the results are consistent from one series of experiments to another, and their implications can undoubtedly be extended to the care of patients with clinical epilepsy.

Our first series of experiments was conducted on dogs and large monkeys, and we still employ variations on this model. Anesthesia was induced with sodium thiopental and the animals were intubated and thenceforth anesthetized with nitrous oxide or halothane. A heat lamp or blanket maintained the body temperature at 37° C, and estimated fluid losses were replaced with saline or blood. End tidal carbon dioxide was monitored continuously as was the arterial blood pressure (BP) and the electroencephalogram (EEG). The animals were heparinized and the cerebral blood flow (CBF) was estimated continuously by the method of Rapela & Green (1964), which in the dog consists of placing an outflow cannula in the torcular (which is in the occipital bone in this species) and then plugging off the lateral sinuses with wax so that the cerebral venous effluent passed through an extracorporeal flowmeter and returned via a cannula to the animal's external jugular vein. In some experiments, a polarographic oxygen electrode was placed in the cerebral venous effluent line to monitor the PV_{O_2}. Arterial and cerebral venous blood samples were obtained intermittently, and the blood gas and acid base values were checked *in vitro* by the Radiometer device or the Van Slyke manometric apparatus. Before initiating any experimental procedure, each animal was tested for the cerebral vascular response to inhaled CO_2 and angiotensin or phenylephrine induced hypertension (autoregulation). If either response was abnormal or if the animal became hypoxic, hypothermic or hypotensive, the experiment was discontinued. During all seizures in this series the animals were ventilated with 100 % oxygen.

To study the effects of induced seizures, the animals were paralyzed with gallamine triethiodide, and anesthesia was discontinued five to fifteen minutes (depending on whether nitrous oxide or halothane was the anesthetic) before delivering either a transcerebral electrical stimulus (150V, 100 mA, 400 msec duration) or an intravenous convulsant dose (usually 0.3–0.7 gm) of pentylene tetrazol (Metrazol).

The results of a characteristic experiment are illustrated in Fig. 1. On the left side of the figure are tracings illustrating the normal cerebral vascular response to the inhalation of CO_2 and the infusion of a pressor agent. On the right is illustrated what happened during a typical seizure. As the EEG discharge began, or even before the first EEG change was noted, CBF rose. Either concurrently or almost immediately afterwards, arterial blood pressure also rose, and the curve of the mean BP rise and CBF rise parallel each other, suggesting that the cerebral vascular bed passively transmitted the elevated pressure into increased flow. Note that in the experiment illustrated, cerebral venous oxygen tension actually rose despite the intense metabolic activity of the seizure, implying that unless arterio-venous shunting was taking place (which is anatomically unlikely in the brain), the increased

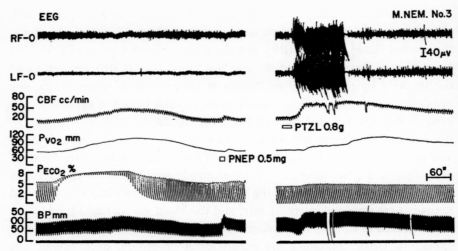

Fig. 1. Response of the CBF and Pv_{O_2} to CO_2 inhalation and phenylephrine (PNEP)-induced hypertension (left side of figure) and to a pentylenetetrazol-induced seizure (right side of figure). Graphic interruptions on the CBF and BF traces resulted when bloods were drawn. The animal was paralyzed and ventilated with oxygen during the seizure. M.NEM indicates M. nemestrina monkey.

cerebral blood flow actually supplied oxygen to the brain in excess of the greatly increased metabolic demands imposed by the seizure.

Blood pressure and cerebral blood flow during seizures were closely related. If the vasopressor response to the seizure was blocked by administering a ganglionic blocking agent or sectioning the spinal cord, CBF increased only modestly, and cerebral venous oxygen tension usually fell as the cerebral discharge reached its maximum.

The experimental results illustrated above in intact animals were typical of all those performed on paralyzed and ventilated dogs and monkeys (Plum *et al.* 1968). Fig. 2 is a summary of the data from that series: During induced seizures arterial blood pressure rose sharply, mean cerebral blood flow tripled, torcular or jugular venous carbon dioxide tension rose modestly from a mean of 46.2 to 51.4 mm Hg, and mean venous oxygen tension rose significantly from 41 to 64.3 mm Hg (P<.01). There was a slight fall in the pH of both the cerebral venous blood and the cisternal CSF, but this was fully accounted for by the modest rise in CO_2 tension. No significant change in lactate concentration occurred either in blood or CSF, nor were any significant changes found in concentrations of serum sodium or potassium.

CEREBRAL BLOOD FLOW AND GASES
DURING SEIZURES

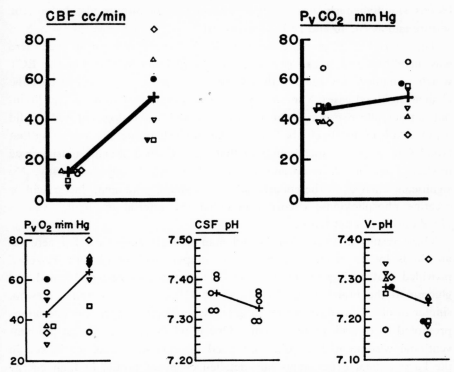

Fig. 2. Cerebral blood blow and venous blood gases during control states (left side of each figure) and seizures (right side of each). Each symbol is a separate experimental dog or monkey. The solid lines connect the means of each set of points.

Studies in humans receiving electroconvulsive therapy (ECT) have provided results consistent with the above findings in large dogs and monkeys, although fewer functions could be analyzed in the clinical setting (Posner *et al.* 1969). We examined eight patients ranging in age from 18 to 56 years who were receiving ECT for depression. As is the modern mode of treating such patients, they were lightly anesthetized with thiopental sodium or halothane, paralyzed with succinylcholine and artificially ventilated with oxygen to maintain an end-tidal P_{CO_2} as close as possible to 35–45 mm Hg. A 150 V, 100 m A stimulus delivered through bitemporal electrodes for 0.5 sec was used for ECT and was sufficient to induce a brief tonic movement of the toes or, occasionally, the face. We placed cannulas in the femoral artery and internal jugular veins of the patients and drew arterial and internal jugular venous bloods simultaneously into syringes attached to manifolds just before the seizure and at 20, 40 and 180 sec afterwards.

The arterial blood pressure was recorded in five patients and in each there was an abrupt rise (mean rise 49/37 mm Hg) immediately after the ECT which remained elevated for the observation period. Fig. 3 illustrates the changes in blood gases. Venous oxygen tension in man, with his bigger brain, did not actually rise during the seizure as it had in the dog, but neither did it fall, and it promptly climbed above control levels postictally, reflecting that blood flow exceeded metabolism at that time. Carbon dioxide tension rose modestly but the A-V difference for CO_2 widened only transiently. No significant changes in the concentration of sodium, potassium, lactic acid or creatine phosphokinase occurred in either the arterial or jugular venous blood during or after the seizure.

These results in large animals and man strongly suggested that cerebral anoxia is by no means a necessary accompaniment of cerebral seizures, provided that a vigorous blood supply delivers well-oxygenated blood and glucose to the brain. Also, Aizawa et al. (1965) had reported somewhat similar results using different techniques. Nevertheless, several considerations prompted us to seek more evidence. One is reluctant to challenge the conventional wisdom without well-buttressed information. Also, we lacked in the large animal experiments any detailed chemical profile of high energy changes during seizures. Perhaps most important was that King et al. (1967) in Lowry's laboratory had reported a substantial depletion in cerebral high energy metabolites and an accumulation of lactate during electrically induced seizures in lightly anesthetized mice and had concluded that the seizure *per se* and not systemic anoxia was at fault. However, the St. Louis group employed unventilated animals (pre-treated with light anesthesia or anticonvulsants). Accordingly we repeated the brain metabolism in, respectively, animals undergoing a full muscular convulsion, animals paralyzed and ventilated with room air, and animals paralyzed and ventilated with oxygen (Collins et al. 1970). Arterial Po_2 during the seizure averaged 85 mm Hg in the paralyzed room air animals and over 500 mm Hg in the paralyzed oxygen mice. Judging from our studies in large animals, arterial blood during tonic convulsions falls to profoundly anoxemic levels, but technical problems kept us from obtaining similar samples in convulsing mice.

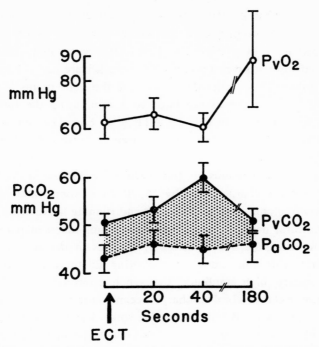

Fig. 3. Arterial and jugular venous blood gases during induced seizures in man. Because subjects were breathing oxygen the Pao_2, not pictured, was higher than 100 mm Hg.

To induce seizures, each group of mice received a 1 second electroshock stimulus (ES) applied to the base of the ears of 150 V, 150/sec, 1 msec pulse duration. At specific times following the ES the animals were rapidly submerged in liquid freon which had been chilled to $-150°$ C with liquid nitrogen. The brains were dissected frozen, and samples were prepared by methods developed by Lowry *et al.* (1964) for the enzymatic analysis of ATP (adenosine triphosphate), ADP (adenosine diphosphate), PCr (phosphocreatine), Cr (creatine), Glu (glucose) and Lac (lactate). Three to nine brain samples were analyzed to calculate each point. As indicated elsewhere (Collins *et al.* 1970), total energy balance was defined as the total high energy phosphate in the brain at each point, and energy use rates were estimated by the decapitation method of Lowry *et al.* (1964) which assumes that for a short time a decapitated animal's brain continues to metabolize at the same rate as just before decapitation. Since after decapitation the brain is a closed system with no substrate input, the rate of depletion of high-energy compounds reflects the energy use. To calculate the energy use rate, the change in concentration of PCr, ATP and lactate was compared between brains frozen immediately at several points during the seizure and the postical state and others frozen 15 sec after decapitation at the same points in the experiment. The 15 sec results extrapolated to 1 min, using the formula: $\sim$ P mmoles/kg per min $= \triangle$ PCr $+ 2\triangle$ ATP $+ \triangle$ Lac. The contribution from the breakdown of both glucose and glycogen is expressed by the elevation of lactate.

The electroshock stimulus in paralyzed mice evoked a fairly uniform behavioral response characterized by 15–20 sec of tonic extension followed by 30–45 sec of clonic jerking, posturing and running movements and 10–15 min of behavioral depression. Electrocorticograms taken in paralyzed mice (Fig. 4) after ES underwent a series of changes in rhythm and amplitude very similar to this time sequence: Following ES there were up to 20 sec of high frequency, high amplitude, dys–synchronous spike discharges. Over the next minute the cerebral discharge became slower, greater in amplitude and more synchronous. By 60–90 sec the spike discharge was complete and the amplitude of the tracing fell to less than one-half of the pre-stimulus level from which it slowly recovered over the next 15 mins.

Cerebral energy use rates during the seizure were calculated for the ictal period using paralyzed oxygen mice and for the postictal period using unparalyzed mice. These two groups were chosen because the substrate values measured for each during these times reflected a relatively steady state. In i single set of calculations in an unparalyzed animal, the energy use rate rose to 105 mmoles of $\sim$ P per min or over three times the energy use rate for normal mice of about 30 mmoles $\sim$ P/kg per min. The energy use rate calculated by the decapitation method in paralyzed oxygenated animals was lower than this figure probably because at a Pa_{O_2} of $>$ 500 mm Hg the small amount of extra oxygen dissolved in the blood in the decapitated brain provided a larger aerobic energy production. As measured in the paralyzed oxygenated animals (Fig. 5), the energy use rate after ES nearly doubled from its control of 18.9 mmoles/kg per min and remained increased for 60 seconds. Postictally, the energy use rate fell to 60–70 of control values and remained low at 8 and 16 minutes postictally. During this period of postictal depression, ATP, PCr and glucose concentrations were elevated above normal.

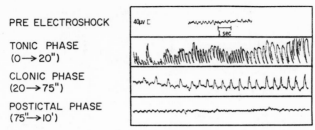

PRE ELECTROSHOCK

TONIC PHASE
(0→20")

CLONIC PHASE
(20→75")

POSTICTAL PHASE
(75"→10')

Fig. 4. EEG of mouse during an ES-induced cerebral seizure.

When one examined the cerebral metabolic response to seizures, significant differences took place in high energy metabolites, depending on whether or not the animal was paralyzed and ventilated (Fig. 6). Following ES in unparalyzed mice, PCr, ATP and Glu fell to less than 50 per cent of normal by 10 seconds and lactate rose 225 per cent by 25 seconds. After 25 seconds, as ventilation resumed, all values began to return toward normal, but lactate concentration in brain did not regain control levels for a full 8 minutes. Following ES, both groups of paralyzed ventilated mice maintained high energy phosphate levels better than did the control convulsing animals; this was particularly noteworthy in the paralyzed oxygen animals where there was no significant change from control in levels of PCr, ATP or glucose,

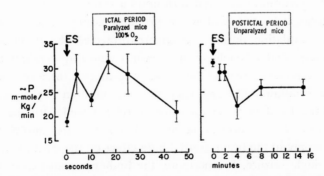

Fig. 5. Energy use rate during and after seizures. The comparatively low apparent energy use rate in the animals receiving oxygen most likely is due to additional aerobic energy production not calculated for by the decapitated method (see Collins *et al.* 1970). Note that postically, energy utilization falls despite an abundance of available substrate.

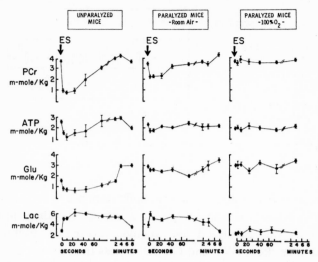

Fig. 6. Values of cerebral substrates during experimental seizures. Each point is a mean of at least 7 animals ± SEM. Control values are taken just before electric shock.

nor did brain lactate significantly rise in the oxygenated animals within 4 seconds to 4 minutes following electroshock.

These results in mice confirm that cerebral oxidative metabolism undergoes a three to four-fold increase during seizures and demonstrate that when a muscular convulsion interfered with normal ventilation, the brain incurred a large energy debt and acid waste products accumulated rapidly. Maintenance of ventilation during the seizure protected the brain against the metabolic debt, and physiologic mechanisms adjusting cerebral blood flow and oxidative metabolism had the capacity to meet a three to four-fold rise in energy expenditure. The characteristics and duration of the electrical discharge on the EEG in room air mice correlated well with the behavioral manifestations of the seizures in unparalyzed animals, implying that the metabolic supply to the brain exerted little effect on the duration and character of the single seizure. Furthermore, the findings of an excess availability of glucose and phosphocreatine combined with decreased energy utilization in the postical period indicate that the postictal depression is a primary manifestation of a seizure rather than being secondary to metabolic exhaustion of neurones or glial cells.

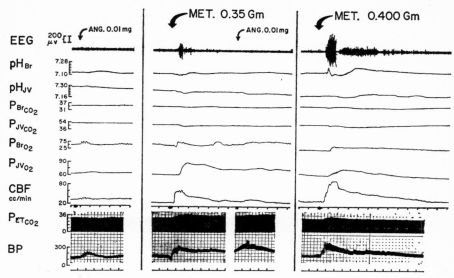

Fig. 7. The pH and respiratory gas tension of brain surface and torcular venous blood in a dog during convulsions induced by pentylenetetrazol (Met). The animal was paralyzed and ventilated on 50% oxygen. The CBF increases substantially during the seizure, but not during the angiotensin induced hypertension. During seizures the pH and Pco_2 on the brain surface change relatively little and not in the direction of sustained acidosis. As noted in Figs. 1 and 2, brain oxygen tension actually rises. In the second, larger seizure depicted on the extreme right, the abrupt rise in pH as the seizure began was an inconsistent finding, possibly artifactual. Note that BP and end-tidal CO_2 are recorded with a slightly slower time base. All pressure values are recorded in mm Hg.

THE pH OF THE BRAIN DURING SEIZURES AND ITS RELATION TO CHANGES IN BLOOD FLOW

These studies indicate that the increased oxidative demand by the brain during seizures is met by a combination of systemic hypertension and decreased cerebral vascular resistance. These vascular responses are remarkably effective in preserving oxidative metabolism so long as muscular convulsions and apnea do not result in anoxemia. Cerebral vascular autoregulation is reduced or absent postictally, even though the vessels retain their ability to dilate or constrict in response to changes in arterial carbon dioxide tensions (Brennan & Plum 1970). Presently, it is unknown what factors induce cerebral vasodilatation during the epileptic seizure. We have recently investigated this problem using the dog model described earlier

BRAIN pH AND CBF DURING SEIZURES

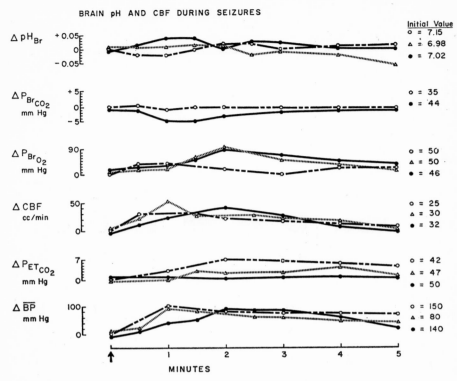

Fig. 8. Data points from three separate experiments in dogs illustrating acid-base changes on the brain surface during and immediately after seizures induced with pentylenetetrazol. A substantial rise in CBF occurs with every seizure but little change can be observed in brain acid-base balance.

in this paper, but with the additional step of placing electrodes sensitive to pH, Pco_2 and Po_2 on the surface of the cerebral cortex and in the torcular venous blood outflow line so as to record these functions continuously.

Respiratory gases and pH on the brain surface and in the cerebral venous outflow have been correlated with changes in the cerebral blood flow in 4 dogs during and after seizures induced with pentylenetetrazol. The results are consistent with one another, and excerpts from the tracing of a typical experiment are illustrated in Fig. 7. The legend gives the details for the rather complicated tracings, but one can observe that during the seizure cerebral cortical pH fell only very transiently, a matter of less than 0.02 pH units, and then rose above its control level within 2 minutes at a time that CBF

Table 1. *Effect of Ventilation on Mortality from Seizures.*
Stimulus: ES 150V, 100 mA, 1 sec every 30 sec

Animals	Condition	$\neq$ ES	Results
8 rats	convulsed	19–30 (mean 25)	all died
8 rats	paralyzed and ventilated	30	all survived and recovered consciousness
5 cats	paralyzed and ventilated	30	4/5 recovered to normal

still greatly exceeded control. The results from 3 experiments are diagrammed in Fig. 8. During seizures the mean of brain surface pH measurements neither rose nor fell significantly, although cerebral blood flow increased to as much as four times resting levels. Brain surface and outflow P_{CO_2} remained similary near control levels while brain and cerebral venous P_{O_2} actually increased. The results illustrate the remarkably precise adjustment of metabolic supply and demand in brain tissue, but the nature of the specific stimulus which regulates the contraction of the arteriolar smooth muscle during seizures remains elusive.

THE CLINICAL RISK OF STATUS EPILEPTICUS

An important and gratifying implication of the experiments on experimental epilepsy is that they promise to improve the treatment of recurrent convulsions in man. Status epilepticus carries a high mortality rate (Hunter 1960) and an even higher incidence of postepileptic brain damage. During untreated generalized convulsions profound hypoxemia occurs in arterial blood, and brain venous oxygen tension falls to below levels that will support fully cerebral aerobic metabolism (Meyer *et al.* 1966). By contrast, the present studies indicate that although generalized cerebral convulsions induce a rapid and profound increase in cerebral metabolism, adequate ventilation producing oxygenation of the arterial blood entirely prevents brain hypoxia.

This suggested that paralysis and artificial respiration might ameliorate the mortality and morbidity of status epilepticus. C. G. Wasterlain (unpublished) has recently approached this problem in our laboratory. Table 1 presents our early results in rats and cats. Recurrent generalized convulsions induced by ES were fatal for all rats at 30 seizures or less, while all of 8 paralyzed and ventilated but similarly stimulated animals survived. Four of five paralyzed

452 FRED PLUM

and ventilated cats not only survived but recovered normal behavior after status epilepticus involving 30 seizures. The results imply that systemic hypoxia and secondary cerebral hypoxia may be largely responsible for the high mortality and postictal morbidity of status epilepticus, and that both can be prevented by effective artifical ventilation.

SUMMARY

During generalized seizures, brain oxidative metabolism increases 300–400 per cent but CBF normally rises to an equal or greater degree. If increased muscle metabolism is prevented and artificial ventilation oxygenates the blood, oxidative supply meets demand and completely prevents brain hypoxia or energy depletion. During and immediately after the seizure cerebral surface pH shifts slightly (< 0.03 u) acid, then alkaline. Vascular autoregulation to pressure is impaired or lost, but vascular response to $\triangle PaCO_2$ is retained. Preventing systemic and cerebral hypoxia significantly reduces mortality in experimental status epilepticus.

REFERENCES

Aizawa, T., et al. (1965) Cerebral circulation, metabolism and electrical activity during convulsion induced by Megimide. Jap. Circulat. J. (Ni.) 29, 449–454.
Bain, J. A. & Pollock, G. H. (1949a) Normal and seizure levels of lactate, pyruvate and acid-soluble phosphates in the cerebellum and cerebrum. Proc. Soc. exp. Biol. (N. Y.) 71, 495–497.
Bain, J. A. & Pollock, G. H. (1949b) Lactate, pyruvate and acid-soluble phosphates in monkey brains treated with CO_2 and electric shock. Proc. Soc. exp. Biol. (N. Y.) 71, 497–498.
Brennan, R. B. & Plum, F. (1970) Dissociation of autoregulation and chemical regulation in cerebral circulation following seizures. Trans Amer. neurol. Ass. In press.
Collins, R. C., et al. (1970) Cerebral energy metabolism during electroshock seizures in mice. Amer. J. Physiol. 218, 943–950.
Efron, R. (1961) Post-epileptic paralysis: Theoretical critique and report of a case. Brain 84, 381–394.
Gurdjian, E. S., et al. (1947) Cerebral metabolism in Metrazol convulsions in the dog. Res. Publ. Ass. nerv. ment. Dis. 26, 184–204.
Hunter, R. A. (1960) Status epilepticus. History, incidence, problems. Epilepsia 1, 162–186.
King, L. J., et al. (1967) Effects of convulsants on energy reserves in the cerebral cortex. J. Neurochem. 14, 599–611.

Lassen, N. A. (1959) Cerebral blood flow and oxygen consumption in man. *Physiol. Rev. 39*, 183–238.

Lowry, O. H., *et al.* (1964) Effect of ischemia on known substrates and cofactors of the glycolytic pathway in brain. *J. biol. Chem. 239*, 18–30.

Meyer, J. S., *et al.* (1966) Cerebral metabolism during epileptic seizures in man. *Electroenceph. clin. Neurophysiol. 21*, 10–22.

Olsen, N. S. & Klein, J. R. (1947) Effect of convulsive activity of brain upon its carbohydrate metabolism. *Res. Publ. Ass. nerv. ment. Dis. 26*, 118–130.

Plum, F., *et al.* (1968) Cerebral metabolic and circulatory responses to induced convulsion in animals. *Arch. Neurol. 18*, 1–13.

Posner, J. B., *et al.* (1969) Cerebral metabolism during electrically induced seizures in man. *Arch. Neurol. 20*, 388–395.

Rapela, C. E. & Green, H. D. (1964) Autoregulation of cerebral blood flow. *Circulat. Res. 15*, I-205-I-211.

Stone, W. E., *et al.* (1945) Chemical changes in the cerebral cortex associated with convulsive activity. *J. Neurophysiol. 8*, 233–240.

DISCUSSION

SKINHØJ

When you tried to correlate the pH on the surface of the brain with cerebral blood flow, were you then sure that the surface pH within that short period of time measured the pH within the brain?

The other question is whether it is possible that the abolishment of autoregulation can simply be an effect of the electrical stimulus which you use to induce the seizure?

PLUM

What Fig. 7 illustrates is a metrazol-induced seizure and not an electrical seizure. However, changes in brain pH were similar in either case. Regarding measurements on the brain surface, it is certainly true that the minute one exposes the brain and puts things on it we damage it, so that most such data have to be looked upon with skepticism. However, in other experiments we also calculated the pH on the basis of changes in high energy metabolites in mouse brain during seizures and didn't find a change in the calculated pH of the brain. Therefore both physiological recordings and direct chemical analysis suggest that there are no pH changes, despite the presence of a pressure passive bed, which permit a very great increase in flow in the post-seizure state. Also, the loss of autoregulation is not a transient effect of the electrical or chemical stimulus, because it gradually recovers over about a half-hour period. During that period one can observe that the Pco_2 response is retained, and yet the pressure regulating response only slowly returns (Brennan & Plum 1970).

Thus, I think the pH findings are physiological and not artifactual.

INGVAR

We should be grateful to Dr. Plum for demonstrating so elegently the importance of keeping the ventilation normal during the seizures. However, if you spinalize animals the situation is compelety different, because then the brain gets into circulatory trouble, even if you ventilate it, because there is not a systemic circulatory response. The brain becomes hypoxic, as measured

Brennan, R. B. & Plum, F. (1970) Dissociation of autoregulation and chemical regulation in cerebral circulation following seizures. *Trans. Amer. neurol. Ass.* In press.

with a surface Po$_2$ electrode. Several years ago it was demonstrated by Ruf (1961) that when you increased the oxygenation of the animal and increased the blood pressure, it was possible to have the epilectic seizure go on for hours. This really points to the importance of the oxygenation of the brain as well as of the systemic circulation for the maintenance of epilectic activity.

PLUM

I know these experiments but neither I. H. Wagman, at the University of California, Davis (personal communication), nor we ourselves have been able to repeat them. As a matter of fact the better the oxygenation the more self-limited the seizure discharge was in our hands. So there are conflicting data on that particular point.

COHEN

What was the cause of death in the rats that were not ventilated and died?

PLUM

I don't altogether know. At least two died from cardiac arrest.

COHEN

The evidence that you have is excellent, that an epilectic seizure need not put the brain in a position where it outstrips its metabolic supply, but there is another question: How far can the brain outstrip its metabolic supply without getting into trouble? We are of course frequently confronted with the convulsing patients, and it is far more frequent in my experience that what might be the cause of death would be an immediate cardiac arrest, secondary to the hypoxia, rather than the cerebral damage.

LOESCHCKE

Your data applied to the total brain. Do you think they can be interpreted as indicating that at the discharging cell there is no lack of oxygen and not much change in hydrogen ion concentration?

Ruf, H. (1961) Experimentelle Untersuchungen über Krampverlüngerung durch Sauerstoff und Adrenalin Dauerkrämpfe nach einmaliger elektrischer Reizung oder Cardiazolgabe. *Arch. Psychiat. Nervenkr. 187,* 97–127.

PLUM

In epileptic convulsions one has pretty close to maximum discharge of surface neuronal populations, and that was really the reason for going to the final experiment with surface pH measurements. It was to try to answer whether we were missing a local pH change by doing whole brain analysis. I should also mention that the vascular changes are readily visible underneath a dissecting microscope. These vessels become bright red, as Dr. Penfield noted many years ago (Penfield 1937). During the course of the seizure they widen out and oxygen tension in them rises in the zone of the epileptic discharge. So I think we were in the area of maximal neuronal activity.

LASSEN

Your experiments support the concept of the well-known fact that changes in cerebral blood flow follow metabolism, but here you have disputed the dogma that it is the production of acid which is so important to make this link. I agree that your arguments are very strong, that the production of acid seemed to be at least very small, if not absent, but I should call attention to the fact that even on your oxygen breathing animals you find a rise of 1 mEq/L in lactate concentration and that corresponds very closely to the small rise in lactate that the group here in Lund (Siesjö & Zwetnow 1970) has found under moderate hypotension. The question is therefore still an open question: whether there are some pH changes at the local sites. I think we must accept the data as a great challenge to the pH theory and look for other mechanisms but not forget that you found a 1 mEq/l rise in lactate concentration which when placed in the proper place is perhaps not so insignificant.

PLUM

Your point is well made except that we continued to demonstrate an increase in the blood flow while hyperventilating these animals so as to lower venous P_{CO_2} below its original level. And as Fig. 7 shows, tissue pH as we best could estimate it, was above its initial level at a time when flow was considerably in excess of control.

Penfield, W. (1937). The circulation of the epilectic brain. *Ass. Res. nerv. Dis. Proc. 18*, 605–637.

Siesjö, B. K. & Zwetnow, N. N. (1970) The effect of hypovolemic hypotension on extra- and intracellular acid-base parameters and energy metabolites in the rat brain. *Acta physiol. scand. 79*, 114–124.

Quantification of "Buffering" *in vivo*

B. K. Siesjö & S. C. Sørensen

Discussion Participants: P. Astrup, E. B. Brown, W. J. Waddell,
& J. W. Woodbury

Introduction

Several times during the meeting, it was discussed how "buffering" of acid or base added to the body fluids can best be expressed quantitatively. The suggestions ranged from application of specific "buffer values" or "buffer capacities", which have previously been used to describe the physico-chemical buffering of an *in vitro* system, to the puristic approach where only the measured values are described. Because of the disagreement during the meeting, we felt that it would be desirable to try to reach some kind of an agreement on the terminology to be used. With this purpose we assembled an *ad hoc* committee after the meeting with the naive hope of reaching an agreement, although previous attempts have failed (*Ann. N.Y. Acad. Sci.* 1966). We submitted our suggestions by mail to several of the participants and asked for their opinion. After we had received the answers, it became apparent that it would not be possible to synthetize the opinions in a way which would be agreeable to the various contributors. We therefore decided to make this a written discussion where each person expresses his own opinion. We have taken advantage of the editors' prerogative to introduce and finish the discussion.

Background

The term *buffer capacity* has been used extensively in the literature to express the efficiency of a system to resist changes in pH when acid or base is added. It is implicit in the expression that the buffer capacity is due to the presence of buffers. v. Slyke (1922) defined buffers as "substances which by their presence in solution increase the amount of acid or base needed to give a unit change in pH", and this definition is generally accepted. v. Slyke expressed the buffer capacity of a solution as a numerical ratio – the buffer value

$$ß = \frac{\triangle\ B}{\triangle\ pH}$$

where $\triangle$ B is the amount of acid or base added to the system (inserted with negative sign when acid is added). The buffer value thus expresses the change in pH for a given addition of acid or base. In v. Slyke's original paper (1922) the buffer capacity was related only to the chemical properties of buffering solutions, $i.\ e.$ the concentrations of buffer acids and their pK_{Ha} values.

If the buffer value is applied to solutions containing HCO_3^- the value must be defined at a particular Pco_2. When nonvolatile acids or bases accumulate $in\ vivo,$ we have to use a respirator to keep the Pco_2 constant because the CO_2 tension is apt to vary, and the change in pH for a given change in buffer base will be influenced by the ventilatory changes. In respiratory acid-base changes, metabolic alterations (e. g. variations in the production of lactic acid) or physiological adjustments (e. g. renal excretion of acids or bases) may modify the initial pH changes.

In order to apply the buffer value term to $in\ vivo$ situations, we have to extend it to include all mechanisms which affect the pH change when acid or base is added. We may calculate an apparent "buffer value" or "buffer capacity" in a particular tissue but problems will be encountered. If the pH changes are modified by mechanisms outside the system under study, $e.\ g.$ if a pH change in brain or muscle tissue is modified by renal or ventilatory adjustments, the "buffer capacity" will not express the "buffer capacity" of the particular tissue, but rather an ability of the organism to modify pH in its various tissues.

We may however want to retain a numerical expression for the relation between the amount of acid or base added to a system and the resulting pH change, even if the use of the term under particular conditions must be qualified. If the acids or bases added are nonvolatile, it appears logical to retain the original v. Slyke expression, but if the acid is carbonic acid, another expression is desirable, because when the CO_2 tension is varied the most important buffers are not bicarbonate. Furthermore, there is a fundamental difference between buffering of strong acids or bases and of carbonic acid. When e. g. a strong acid has been added to a solution the acid no longer exists as such, but when the Pco_2 is changed the concentration of carbonic acid changes from one given value to another.

Two expressions have been used to quantitate the changes in pH for a given change in Pco_2, the $\triangle HCO_3^-/\triangle pH$ (the v. Slyke – Woodbury ratio), and the $\triangle \log Pco_2/\triangle pH$ ratio.

The $\triangle HCO_3^-/\triangle pH$ ratio is given by the slope of the HCO_3^-/pH line in the "Davenport" diagram. The ratio illustrates that H_2CO_3 is buffered by nonbicarbonate buffers. The main disadvantage of the $\triangle HCO_3^-/\triangle pH$ ratio is that it does not include a term for the CO_2 tension, the variation of which is the primary cause of the acid-base change. It also seems awkward that the ratio expresses the relation between the pH change and the amount of bicarbonate formed as a *result* of the buffering.

The $\triangle \log Pco_2/\triangle pH$ ratio is given by the slope of the (log) Pco_2/pH line in the widely used diagram of Astrup & Siggaard Andersen. The ratio includes a term for the CO_2 tension but it may be a disadvantage that another logarithmic expression is introduced. Another disadvantage is that the ratio varies with Pco_2. Therefore, if different tissues are compared the Pco_2 must be defined.

Question

When nonvolatile acids or bases are added to a body compartment or when the CO_2 tension is changed, the pH change is only instantaneously determined by the presence of buffers. Other physiological mechanisms soon affect the pH change, thus making it difficult to apply an expression for the "buffer capacity" of the particular compartment. We may try to decide if a numerical expression for the "buffer capacity" is needed. If this is the case, it is desirable to modify the expression "buffer capacity" in such a way that it will not be confused with the expression for physico-chemical buffering in *in vitro* systems. If we want to retain a numerical expression for the degree of "buffering", we may either choose between the previously used terms, i. e. the $\triangle HCO_3^-/\triangle pH$ ratio and the $\triangle \log Pco_2/\triangle pH$ ratio, or we may suggest a new expression, e. g. the Pco_2/pH ratio. It should be pointed our that such numerical expressions can be applied without being called "buffer capacity".

DISCUSSION

P. ASTRUP

I agree that it is difficult to apply the term buffer capacity to *in vivo* situations which are always accompanied by physiological compensations. For theoretical reasons I think, though, that the term should be retained, since it is of considerable physiological interest to know how the pH changes when the concentrations of carbonic acid or nonvolatile acids or bases change. Since there is a principal difference in the buffer effect after a change in Pco_2, and after a change in the concentration of a nonvolatile acid or base, I think we should make a distinction between the two situations. This can be accomplished *in vitro* by carrying out the experiments at constant Pco_2 and at constant buffer base concentration, respectively.

The buffer capacity, after changes in the carbonic acid concentration, is obtained by using the slope of the line in the Siggaard-Andersen nomogram, i. e. the $\triangle \log Pco_2 / \triangle pH$ ratio. This expression is in agreement with v. Slyke's original definition of buffer capacity.

After changes in the concentrations of nonvolatile acids or bases, the buffer capacity is obtained by carrying out the experiment at a constant CO_2 tension, e. g. at 40 mm Hg. This buffer capacity is larger than the previous one, since bicarbonate will not buffer carbonic acid although it will buffer all other acids. We can express this buffer capacity as $\triangle$ Base Excess $(mEq/L)/\triangle pH$ (at a Pco_2 of 40 mm Hg).

Both buffer capacities will vary somewhat with pH because the buffer value of proteins varies with pH. However, this is probably of minor importance, considering that we deal with relatively small variations under physiological conditions. We should note that the expression $\triangle$ Base Excess$/\triangle pH$ is in accordance with v. Slyke's original definition of buffer value. This is, however, not the case with the expression $\triangle [HCO_3^-]/\triangle pH$ which therefore should not be used. At any rate, the expression should not be called a buffer capacity, since it is not related to the buffer capacity and since it has nothing to do with the pH changes occurring after a change in the carbonic acid concentration.

The above-mentioned two expressions for the buffer capacity ($\triangle \log Pco_2/\triangle pH$ and $\triangle BE/\triangle pH$) are in accordance with physicochemical buffering in *in vitro* systems and can thus be accepted on theoretical grounds. It should be mentioned, though, that you can raise objections against the last expression, since the system has a fixed CO_2 tension. This means that the carbonic acid is released from or retained in the system in *a controlled way* by adding nonvolatile acid or base respectively. This is not the case, when we deal with non-bicarbonate systems. Therefore, if we for instance were to compare the buffer capacity stricte sensu of phosphate buffers with bicarbonate buffers, we should be sure that the carbon dioxide which is released after addition of a nonvolatile acid remains in the system. However, this would not be very sensible, and actually we have largely to ascribe the buffer capacity of bicarbonate buffers to the very fact that the carbonic acid can disappear.

E. B. BROWN

I think the problem has been concisely stated in the introduction. I think that a more clear distinction should be drawn between the added efficiency of CO_2 buffering in an open system compared with a closed system, which is a purely physical difference and which can be present in either an *in vitro* or *in vivo* system, and in physiological adaptations (such as hyperventilation to decrease the CO_2 tension) which would not be present in an *in vitro* system. An illustration of this difference might be the increase in bicarbonate provided by renal action to buffer increased CO_2, as contrasted with the situation *in vitro* in which the amount of buffer present initially does not change. Regarding the quantification of the buffering during changes in P_{CO_2}, I will also mention that the concentration of H_2CO_3 is a linear function of P_{CO_2} and has a constant value at any constant P_{CO_2}, but when the P_{CO_2} is altered, hydrogen ions are added or removed from the solution and the best measure (at least as a first approximation) of the amount of hydrogen ions added is the initial change in bicarbonate concentration, not the difference in concentrations of H_2CO_3.

I am comfortable with either the $\triangle HCO_3^-/\triangle pH$ or $\triangle \log P_{CO_2}/\triangle pH$ ratios, and I would be happy to have these expressions used in any given situation with a clear delineation of the time at which the values were obtained. If we are already committed to the concept of buffer capacity because of usage, then this term should be clearly modified by the addition of the adjective "apparent" or "effective" when applied to tissue buffering.

May I suggest that, in addition to the differences pointed out between the *in vivo* and *in vitro* situation in buffering, the additional factor of time should be mentioned clearly. With *in vitro* buffering time is not involved. With *in vivo* apparent or effective buffering is clearly a function of time after addition of acid or base.

W. J. Waddell

My manuscript to the symposium expresses the way I feel about tissue "buffer capacity". I would prefer that the term not be used as such because it implies a reproducible, predictable change such as that which occurs with the addition of acid or base to a solution of defineable composition *in vitro*. The extent of our knowledge, at the present time, of the mechanisms of regulation of intracellular pH are too meager to justify a term containing "buffer capacity". If I were to suggest a term it might be "intracellular pH response" or "adjustment" as a result of the change in Pco_2 or extracellular pH or some other condition. All the parameters of the experiment which are known should be clearly stated, such as metabolic status of the animal, duration of exposure to the experimental variable, etc. Then the final results should be plotted as $\triangle pHi/\triangle pHe$ and should of course include the information that would also allow plotting $\triangle \log Pco_2/\triangle pH$. To me, $\triangle \log Pco_2/\triangle pH$ is far more useful than the other terms such as $\triangle Pco_2/\triangle pH$ or $\triangle HCO_3^-/\triangle pH$.

J. W. Woodbury

As far as I can tell from thumbing through v. Slyke's paper (*J. biol. Chem. 52*, 525–570, 1922), he does not use the phrase "buffer capacity". Although he does not explicitly define $\beta = dB / dpH$ as "buffer value" in the text, his use of this phrase in section headings (cf. Contents at start of paper), as the ordinate in Figs. 3, 7, and 8, and as a specific statement beside his equations (11) – (14), p. 538, indicates that in his mind "buffer value" is defined by β. I know not where the phrase "buffer capacity" came from, but I think it should be dropped; the word "capacity" implies to me the maximum value of ß (at pH = pK), not a variable whose value depends on pH. Hence, I conclude that we should stick with v. Slyke's original usage and define $\beta = dB / dpH$ as buffer value not buffer capacity. (This decision is, of course, uninfluenced by the "disvovery" that I followed v. Slyke and used "buffer value" in Chapter 46 of Ruch-Patton's *Physiology and Biophysics,* 1965.)

Unfortunately, we don't have the written wisdom of v. Slyke to help us out much *in vivo*. There are, however, several obvious extensions of the concept of buffer value to the intact organism:

(1) Despite the utility of Astrup's diagram in analyzing data, I regard it as more confusing than useful to adopt $\triangle\log pCO_2/\triangle pH$ as a measure of resistance to pH change. I also believe that whatever measure is adopted, it should have the same units as v. Slyke's β.

(2) I agree that the term "buffer" should be restricted to chemical buffering and should be avoided in referring to physiological regulatory activities.

(3) Physiological regulatory activities should be separated from buffering, but the problem is not just one of how the degree of regulation is to be measured, but also of specifying other important parameters. Two examples illustrate this point: (a) the rates of completion of the various regulatory processes vary from a few minutes to months or years. Hence, the time since the onset of the disturbance, or more precisely the whole past history of acid-base loading, must be specified; (b) as you point out, in studying a tissue, there are external as well as internal contributions to the regulation.

(4) Even if the time course is specified, two problems arise in specifying the degree of regulation: (a) what term(s) are used to distinguish regulation from buffering? (b) how is the magnitude of the regulation specified?

(a) Physiological regulatory processes are slower than buffering so they could be called "*slow* *b*uffering" or "slob" for short. However, this term is unlikely to win wide acceptance. Possibly more acceptable acronyms are "prop" for *p*hysiological (or *p*H) *r*egulatory *p*rocesses, "buffer" for physiological *buffer,* "proph" for *pro*tection of *pH. A*lthough a bit strained, I rather like "prop" because it describes the process: propping up pH. There are various kinds of props: respiratory prop: propre or resprop; renal prop: renprop. Transmembrane H^+ movement regulation would be transprop, etc.

(b) The problem of quantifying the degree of propping is resolvable, I think, to everybody's satisfaction by using the ratio of total regulation at a given time to the chemical buffering value: In the pH-HCO_3^- system, where $\beta = \triangle[HCO_3^-]/\triangle pH$, the prop ratio (PR) would be simply the total apparent buffer slope due to buffering and physiological regulatory processes (in slykes) divided by the expected physico-chemical buffer value (in slykes):

$$\text{Prop ratio} = \frac{\text{physiological regulation slope}}{\text{buffer slope}}$$

This is a dimensionless quantity.

The situation is somewhat more complicated in the log pCO_2 – pH system

but is easily resolved to sufficient accuracy. The relationship between the
two systems is approximately

$$\frac{\triangle \log pCO_2}{\triangle pH} = -1 - \frac{\triangle [HCO_3^-]}{2.3 \, [HCO_3^-]} \cdot \frac{1}{\triangle pH}$$

$$= -1 - \frac{\beta}{2.3 \, [HCO_3^-]}$$

Hence the prop ratio is given by

$$PR = \frac{\left(\dfrac{\triangle \log pCO_2}{\triangle pH}\right)_{total} + 1}{\left(\dfrac{\triangle \log pCO_2}{\triangle pH}\right)_{buffer} + 1} = \frac{\beta \, total}{\beta \, buffer}$$

(Remember that $\triangle \log pCO_2/\triangle pH$ is a negative number of absolute value
greater than 1 and that $\triangle \log pCO_2/\triangle pH = -1$ when $\beta = 0$.)

This maneuver avoids the ambiguous and probably unsolvable problem
of which system is best or most useful, β or $\triangle \log pCO_2/\triangle pH$. Both are
useful ways of handling data.

In summary: (1) buffering should be saved for physicochemical processes;
(2) physiological regulatory processes can be referred to concisely as props
with usable prefixes to indicate the types of processes involved; (3) the acid-
base regulatory behavior of a living organism or part hereof is specified by
the prop ratio, the types of regulatory responses involved, and the extent
of completion of these regulatory processes.

SIESJÖ & SØRENSEN

We may conclude by saying that it is probably futile to try to reach an
agreement on terminology at the present stage, but this discussion has
emphasized the importance of making a clear distinction between chemical
buffering and physiological regulation processes, and of the element of time
in *in vivo* situations. Regardless of the terminology we use in describing our
acid-base results and regardless of our opinion about the merits or disadvantages of the specific regulatory ratios, we should report all parameters
which are necessary for a calculation of any of these.

An Epilogue*
A Hypothetical Model for CSF Formation and Blood-Brain Barrier Function

J. W. Woodbury

I would like to expand on the model of CSF secretion proposed after my talk. I believe this model accounts for most of the pertinent facts that have been presented here. This model is not very different than those discussed by others (cf. Held, Fencl & Pappenheimer 1964) but is considerably more detailed and attempts to account for most of the major characteristics of CSF secretion. There are some deficiencies but the model is by and large internally consistent and detailed enough to suggest possibly fruitful experiments. Indeed, in order to be useful, a model must have "corroborative detail, intended to give artistic verisimilitude to an otherwise bald and unconvincing narrative" to use the immortal words of Pooh-Bah in Gilbert and Sullivan's "The Mikado" as he defended his detailed lies to the Mikado about the supposed beheading of the Mikado's son, Nanki-Poo. The inevitable comparison that I am sticking my neck out and may be beheaded is acknowledged.

Fig. 1 is a diagram of the model. The major assumptions used in this model are:

1. Secretion of CSF is due to the activity of a Na^+-for-K^+ exchange pump in the membrane of choroid plexus cells facing the CSF (left hand vertical line labelled pump membrane). This membrane has near zero Na^+ permeability. There may be some secondary secretory process, e. g., filtration.

2. In most circumstances, the maximum rate of secretion is determined by the blood flow to the choroid rather than the maximum rate of the pump.

---

* This is an expanded version of a contribution which was presented at the end of the symposium at an informal gathering around the blackboard. It was therefore not followed by any formal discussion.

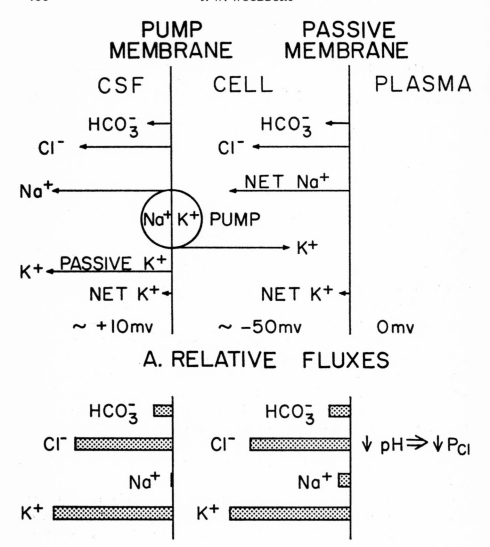

Fig. 1. Model of CSF secretion. *A.* Lengths of arrows indicate relative sizes of ion fluxes through membranes. Water flux is too large to show. Net K+ flux arrow is exaggerated in length. *B.* Relative ion permeabilities. Na+ permeability of pump membrane is near zero. Water permeability is too large to show.

3. The blood facing (passive) membrane has no (or slow) pump and non-zero permeabilities to Na^+, K^+, Cl^-, and HCO_3^- ions, and water.

4. This model attempts to account for the major monovalent ion concentrations: Na^+, K^+, Cl^- and HCO_3^-, and the CSF-blood potential. Other substances are ignored.

SECRETION AND COMPOSITION OF THE CSF

The Pump Membrane

The pump membrane transports Na^+ from cells to CSF. In the steady state, an equal amount of Na^+ enters from the plasma. Na^+ flux through the cell must be balanced by an equivalent flux of anions, mostly Cl^- and HCO_3^-. Since the CSF is somewhat higher in $[Cl^-]$ and lower in $[HCO_3^-]$ than the plasma, it is deduced that both membranes are slightly more permeable to Cl^- than to HCO_3^- (Fig. 1B) because the concentrations in the secreted fluid depend on the relative permeabilities and internal concentrations. In the steady secretory state, the net flux of a substance is proportional to its permeability and a direct function of the electrochemical potential difference. If the membrane permeabilities of Cl^- and HCO_3^- were the same, then their fluxes would be in the ratio of their concentrations in the cells and in plasma and their concentrations in CSF would be in the same proportions as in plasma.

The active Na^+ transport into CSF "drags" Cl^- and HCO_3^- fluxes along and this solute movement in turn "drags" a flux of water through the cell such that the secreted fluid is about isotonic. This pumping process may remove up to 25 per cent of the plasma water and the resulting increases in plasma osmotic pressure and ion concentrations probably limit the maximum secretion rate (and may account for the potential).

The explanation of K^+ distribution is a little more complicated. In general, the lower $[K^+]$ of fresh CSF (if it is lower, cf. Ames, Sakanoue & Endo 1964) follows from the postulate of a coupled Na^+–K^+ exchange pump. The pumping of K^+ from CSF to cell against the secretory flow reduces the K^+ concentration in the CSF: the $[K^+]_{CSF}$ is proportional to the difference between the inward active flux and the outward passive flux (Fig. 1A).

If the pump is one-for-one then the active K^+ influx equals active Na^+ efflux. However, the net flux of K^+ into CSF is only $[K^+]_{CSF}/[Na^+]_{CSF}$ $\simeq 2.6/150 \simeq 0.017$ of the net Na^+ flux. Thus the passive flux of K^+ into

CSF must be 1.017 times Na^+ flux to give the net flux of 0.017. The driving force is the concentration gradient of K^+ from plasma to CSF. Since the gradient is small, the permeability of the membrane to K^+ must be large, as is typical of cell membranes.

The Passive Membrane

The foregoing shows that the CSF can be produced by a pump and unexceptional permeability properties of the pump membrane. The relative permeabilities of the passive membranes to ions are much the same except that the permeability to Na^+ must be relatively higher to allow a sufficient influx of Na^+. The secretion rate of CSF depends on P_{Na}. However, P_{Na} is probably much less than P_K, e. g., $P_{Na} \simeq 0.1 \ P_K$; a modest P_{Na} and the large electrochemical gradient on Na^+ suffice to generate the necessary flux. On the other hand, the passive P_{Na} of the pump membrane is probably as low as possible to prevent wastage of energy.

The permeabilities for Cl^- and HCO_3^- of the passive membrane are in the same ratio as in the pump membrane; Cl^- and HCO_3^- simply flow through the cell down an electrochemical gradient. The passive membrane's permeability to K^+ is about the same as the pump membrane. In summary, the main difference between the pump and passive membranes is that the pump membrane has a "hot" Na^+–K^+ pump and low P_{Na} while the passive membrane has a higher P_{Na} and no pump.

THE CSF-PLASMA POTENTIAL

Origin of the Potential

The pump is the ultimate source of all driving forces on ions. When the Na^+ pump starts there is an accumulation of excess Na^+ charges in the CSF; these build up until the voltage is high enough to produce an equal flux of anions. On this basis the potential is directly proportional to the pumping rate and hence to the secretory rate. Since both the membranes are assumed to be highly permeable to chloride, the generated potential need not be larger than a few millivolts.

The potential is affected by changes in CSF $[K^+]$ and not by changes in plasma $[K^+]$ (Held, Fencl & Pappenheimer 1964) or only slightly (Cameron, this Symposium). This rather puzzling result is a consequence of the high P_{Na} of the passive membrane; in the range of attainable plasma

[K$^+$]'s, the potential vs [K$^+$] curve is nearly flat when P$_{Na}$ is relatively large. On the other hand, the pump membrane has a low P$_{Na}$ and hence the potential is much more affected by a similar range of changes in CSF [K$^+$].

The Effects of pH on the Potential

The increase in the CSF-plasma potential produced by a fall in plasma pH but not by CSF pH requires the postulation of a special mechanism. Two possibilities are that a fall in pH increases P$_{Na}$ and/or decreases P$_{Cl}$ of the passive membrane. The choice is made on the basis of whether the increase in CSF production produced by acidosis is by a direct stimulation of pump rate or an increase in blood flow (see below). An increase in P$_{Na}$ would cause an increase in flow by raising [Na$^+$]$_i$ and stimulating the pump, thereby increasing the potential; a decrease in P$_{Cl}$ would have little effect on flow rate (perhaps a slight decrease) but would increase the potential by increasing the drag on Cl$^-$, necessitating an increase in the driving force.

Some distinction can be made between the two possibilities by assuming that one of the main functions of the mechanism producing CSF is to regulate closely its pH. On this basis, the decrease in P$_{Cl}$ is somewhat preferred because this decrease would increase the relative amount of HCO$_3^-$ in the CSF and thus compensate for the acidosis. In respiratory acidosis there would be another effect, the increase in Pco$_2$ would increase [HCO$_3^-$] in the cells as well as in the plasma and thereby produce an additional increment in the [HCO$_3^-$] of CSF. This proposed effect of pH on P$_{Cl}$ is also attractive because such an effect is found in frog skeletal muscle (Hutter & Warner 1967); a decrease in pH decreases P$_{Cl}$.

REGULATION AND EFFECTS OF INHIBITORS

Effects of Acid-Base Changes on the Secretion Rate

There is considerable disagreement in the literature about the effects of acid-base changes on the rate of secretion. Some investigations find little effect, particularly of acidosis (Held, Fencl & Pappenheimer 1964) while others (Oppelt, this Symposium) find quite a large effect. The simplest explanation is the one attributed to Pappenheimer by Ames, Highashi & Nesbett (1965) that the secretion rate is limited by blood flow to the choroid plexus and the effects of acid-base changes are attributable to their effects on blood flow.

If a pH decrease does increase flow rate directly, then it is attractive to suppose that a fall in pH increases P_{Na} and/or P_K.

Effects of Ouabain and Acetazolamide

The effect of ouabain in decreasing secretion rate and the slope of the potential/pH curve (Held, Fencl & Pappenheimer 1964) is certainly expected from any secretory model utilizing the Na-K pump. It is not clear why the secretory rate is not reduced to zero by concentrations of ouabain that probably stop the pump. Possibilities are that part of the secretion is due to a Cl^- $.HCO_3^-$ pump or that part of the secretion is due to pressure gradient filtration as in the kidney. I don't care much for either possibility.

The mechanism of inhibition of secretion by acetazolamide is not obvious. The simplest way out is to assume that the cellular alkalosis due to carbonic anhydrase inhibition causes a cerebral vasoconstriction and thus decreased flow. Alternatively, the type of scheme put forth by Maren (1967) in his review can be made to work. In this scheme all secreted HCO_3^- comes from CO_2; hence there must be a H^+ pump in the passive membrane to create a net HCO_3^- flux (an influx of CO_2 and an outflux of H^+ = an influx of HCO_3^-). This scheme appears to require more complicated control mechanisms. There is little doubt that such a system is needed in "hotter" secretory organs such as kidney and pancreas but the CSF is so similar to plasma in composition that elaborate mechanisms do not appear to be needed. Phylogenetically speaking, the more complicated system may be simpler, however.

I haven't found any data in the literature on the effect of acetazolamide on the CSF-plasma potential. This permits a prediction: In my picture, there should be a slight fall in potential associated with the decreased secretion rate, whereas there should be an increase similar to that in acidosis if Maren's picture is correct.

In summary this model postulates that:

1. Secretion of CSF is due to a Na-K exchange pump in the CSF facing membranes of choroid plexus cells. This membrane is highly permeable to K^+, Cl^- and HCO_3^- and impermeable to Na^+. The other membrane has no pump and high permeabilities to K^+, Cl^-, HCO_3^- and a lesser but quite large permeability to Na^+.

2. The reduced $[HCO_3^-]$ of CSF is due to both membranes having a slightly lower permeability to HCO_3^- than to Cl^-. The low $[K^+]$ is due to the active influx of K^+.

3. The CSF-plasma potential builds up due to pumping of Na⁺ into CSF. Excess Na⁺ builds up in the CSF until the potential is high enough to drag a flux of anions equal to the Na⁺ flux. K⁺ diffuse passively from plasma to CSF because of the low [K⁺] in CSF.

4. The increase in potential caused by a decrease in plasma pH is ascribed to a decrease in the Cl⁻ permeability of the passive membrane. The variable effects of pH changes on the secretion rate are ascribed to changes in blood flow to the choroid plexus on the basis that blood flow limits the rate of secretion. The differential effects of plasma and CSF [K⁺] on the potential are ascribable to the different Na⁺ permeabilities of the two membranes.

5. The effects of ouabain and acetazolamide on secretion rate follow from the above postulates.

REFERENCES

Ames, A., III, Higashi, K. & Nesbett, F. B. (1965) Effects of P_{CO_2}, acetazolamide and ouabain on volume and composition of choroid plexus fluid. *J. Physiol. (Lond.) 181*, 516–524.

Ames, A., III, Sakanoue, M. & Endo, S. (1964) Na, K, Ca, Mg and Cl concentrations in choroid plexus fluid and cisternal fluid compared with plasma ultrafiltrate. *J. Neurophysiol. 27*, 672–681.

Held, D., Fencl, V. & Pappenheimer, J. R. (1964) Electrical potential of cerebrospinal fluid. *J. Neurophysiol. 27*, 942–959.

Hutter, O. F. & Warner, A. E. (1967) The pH sensitivity of the chloride conductance of frog skeletal muscle. *J. Physiol. (Lond.) 189*, 403–425.

Maren, T. H. (1967) Carbonic anhydrase: chemistry, physiology, and inhibition. *Physiol. Rev. 47*, 595–781.

ALPHABETICAL AUTHOR INDEX

Italics denote the mainpapers.

LIST OF PARTICIPANTS

A. AMES
Neurosurgical Service
Massachusetts General Hospital
Fruit Street
Boston, Massachusetts 02114, USA.

P. ASTRUP
Department of Clinical Chemistry
Rigshospitalet
9 Blegdamsvej
DK-2100 Copenhagen Ø, Denmark.

J. M. BESSON
Laboratoire de Physiologie des Centres
Nerveux,Faculté de Sciences
Université de Paris
4 Avenue Gordon-Bennet
F-75-Paris XVI, France.

M. W. B. BRADBURY
Sherrington School of Physiology
St. Thomas's Hospital Medical School
London, S. E. 1., England.

E. B. BROWN
Department of Physiology
University of Kansas Medical Center
Rainbow Boulevard at 39th Street
Kansas City, Kansas 66103, USA.

I. R. CAMERON
Department of Clinical Physiology
St. Thomas's Hospital Medical School
London S. E. 1., England.

P. J. COHEN
Department of Anesthesia
University of Colorado
4675 East Sixth Avenue
Denver, Colorado 80220, USA.

C. CRONE
Institute of Medical Physiology A
University of Copenhagen
28 Juliane Mariesvej
DK-2100 Copenhagen Ø, Denmark.

H. DAVSON
University College
Gower Street
London W. C. 1., England.

V. FENCL
Department of Physiology
Harvard Medical School
25 Shattuck Street
Boston, Massachusetts 02115, USA.

L. GRANHOLM
Neurosurgical Service A
University Hospital
S-220 05 Lund, Sweden.

J. HESS-THAYSEN
Department of Medicine P
University of Copenhagen
Rigshospitalet
9 Blegdamsvej
DK-2100 Copenhagen Ø, Denmark.

B. HINDFELDT
Department of Neurology
University Hospital
S-220 05 Lund, Sweden.

T. F. HORNBEIN
Department of Anesthesiology
University of Washington
School of Medicine
Seattle, Washington 98105, USA.

D. INGVAR
Neurofysiologisk Laboratorium
E – blocket
University Hospital
S-220 05 Lund, Sweden.

P. W. KRUHØFFER
Institute of Medical Physiology B
University of Copenhagen
30 Juliane Mariesvej
DK-2100 Copenhagen Ø, Denmark.

N. A. LASSEN
Department of Clinical Physiology
Bispebjerg Hospital
23 Bispebjerg Bakke
DK-2400 Copenhagen NV, Denmark.

H. H. LOESCHCKE
Institut für Physiologie
Ruhr-Universität Bochum
11 Friederikastrasse
D-463 Bochum, Germany.

N. LUNDBERG
Neurokirurgiska Kliniken
University Hospital
S-220 05 Lund, Sweden.

T. H. MAREN
Department of Pharmacology
College of Medicine
The J. Hillis Miller Health Center
University of Florida
Gainesville, Florida 32601, USA.

K. MESSETER
Department of Surgery
University Hospital
S-220 05 Lund, Sweden.

A. H. MINES
Department of Physiology
University of California
San Francisco Medical Center
San Francisco, California 94122, USA.

L. NILSSON
Department of Anesthesiology
University Hospital
S-220 05 Lund, Sweden.

W. W. OPPELT
Department of Pharmacology and
Therapeutics College of Medicine
The J. Hillis Miller Health Center
University of Florida
Gainesville, Florida 32601, USA.

R. ORKAND
Department of Zoology
University of California
Los Angeles, California 90024, USA.

F. PLUM
Department of Neurology
The New York Hospital
Cornell Medical Center
525 East 68th Street
New York, N. Y. 10021, USA.

U. PONTÉN
Department of Neurology
School of Medicine
P. O. Box 875, Biscayne Annex
University of Miami
Miami, Florida 33152, USA.

D. P. RALL
National Cancer Institute
National Institutes of Health
Bethesda, Maryland 20014, USA.

P. SCHEINBERG
Department of Neurology
University of Miami
Miami, Florida 33152, USA.

N. SEGAL
Department of Physiology
St. Thomas's Hospital Medical School
London, S. E. 1., England.

476

J. W. Severinghaus
Cardiovascular Research Institute
University of California Medical Center
San Francisco, California 94122, USA.

B. K. Siesjö
Research Department 4
E – blocket
University Hospital
S-220 05 Lund, Sweden.

E. Skinhøj
Department of Neurology
Bispebjerg Hospital
23 Bispebjerg Bakke
DK-2400 Copenhagen NV, Denmark.

O. Sten-Knudsen
Institute of Biophysics
University of Copenhagen
28 Juliane Mariesvej
DK-2100 Copenhagen Ø, Denmark.

S. C. Sørensen
Institute of Medical Physiology B
University of Copenhagen
30 Juliane Mariesvej
DK-2100 Copenhagen Ø, Denmark.

H. H. Ussing
Institute of Biological Chemistry
University of Copenhagen
2 Øster Farimagsgade
DK-1353 Copenhagen K, Denmark.

W. J. Waddel
Dental Research Center
University of North Carolina
Chapel Hill, North Carolina 27514, USA.

K. Welch
Department of Physiology
University of Colorado
4200 East 9th Avenue
Denver, Colorado 80220, USA.

J. Weyne
Laboratorium voor Normale en
Pathologische Fysiologie
Rijksuniversiteit
De Pintelaan 115
Gent, Belgium.

J. R. Williamson
Department of Biophysics and
Physical Biochemistry
The School of Medicine
Johnson Research Foundation
University of Pennsylvania
Philadelphia, Pa. 19104, USA.

C. D. Withrow
Department of Pharmacology
College of Medicine
University of Utah
Salt Lake City, Utah 84112, USA.

D. M. Woodbury
Department of Pharmacology
College of Medicine
University of Utah
Salt Lake City, Utah 84112, USA.

J. W. Woodbury
Department of Physiology
University of Washington
School of Medicine
Seattle, Washington 98105, USA.

N. N. Zwetnow
Department of Neurosurgery
University of Gothenburg
Sahlgrenska Sjukhuset
S-413 35 Göteborg, Sweden.

Subject Index

For entries with multiple page references, the main discussion is indicated by the use of italic-face number.